ALGEBRAIC THEORY OF PARTICLE PHYSICS

Frontiers in Physics

DAVID PINES, Editor

P. W. Anderson — **CONCEPTS IN SOLIDS:** *Lectures on the Theory of Solids*

N. Bloembergen — **NONLINEAR OPTICS:** *A Lecture Note and Reprint Volume*

N. Bloembergen — **NUCLEAR MAGNETIC RELAXATION:** *A Reprint Volume*

R. Brout — **PHASE TRANSITIONS**

G. F. Chew — **S-MATRIX THEORY OF STRONG INTERACTIONS:** *A Lecture Note and Reprint Volume*

P. G. de Gennes and Philip A. Pincus (Trans.) — **SUPERCONDUCTIVITY OF METALS AND ALLOYS**

R. P. Feynman — **QUANTUM ELECTRODYNAMICS:** *A Lecture Note and Reprint Volume*

R. P. Feynman — **THE THEORY OF FUNDAMENTAL PROCESSES:** *A Lecture Note Volume*

H. L. Frisch and J. L. Lebowitz — **THE EQUILIBRIUM THEORY OF CLASSICAL FLUIDS:** *A Lecture Note and Reprint Volume*

H. Frauenfelder — **THE MOSSBAUER EFFECT:** *A Review—With a Collection of Reprints*

S. C. Frautschi — **REGGE POLES AND S-MATRIX THEORY**

M. Gell-Mann and Y. Ne'eman — **THE EIGHTFOLD WAY:** *A Review—With a Collection of Reprints*

W. A. Harrison — **PSEUDOPOTENTIALS IN THE THEORY OF METALS**

R. Hofstadter — **ELECTRON SCATTERING AND NUCLEAR AND NUCLEON STRUCTURE:** *A Collection of Reprints with an Introduction*

M. Jacob and G. F. Chew — **STRONG-INTERACTION PHYSICS:** *A Lecture Note Volume*

L. P. Kadanoff and G. Baym — **QUANTUM STATISTICAL MECHANICS:** *Green's Function Methods in Equilibrium and Nonequilibrium Problems*

I. M. Khalatnikov and Pierre C. Hohenberg (Trans.)
AN INTRODUCTION TO THE THEORY OF SUPERFLUIDITY

T. L. Loucks — **AUGMENTED PLANE WAVE METHOD:** *A Lecture Note and Reprint Volume*

A. M. Lane — **NUCLEAR THEORY:** *Pairing Force Correlations to Collective Motion*

Y. Ne'eman — **ALGEBRAIC THEORY OF PARTICLE PHYSICS**

P. Nozières — **THEORY OF INTERACTING FERMI SYSTEMS**

R. Omnès and M. Froissart
MANDELSTAM THEORY AND REGGE POLES: *An Introduction for Experimentalists*

G. E. Pake — **PARAMAGNETIC RESONANCE:** *An Introductory Monograph*

D. Pines — **THE MANY-BODY PROBLEM:** *A Lecture Note and Reprint Volume*

J. R. Schrieffer — **THEORY OF SUPERCONDUCTIVITY**

E. J. Squires — **COMPLEX ANGULAR MOMENTA AND PARTICLE PHYSICS:** *A Lecture Note and Reprint Volume*

L. Van Hove, N. M. Hugenholz, and L. P. Howland
PROBLEMS IN QUANTUM THEORY OF MANY-PARTICLE SYSTEMS: *A Lecture Note and Reprint Volume*

ALGEBRAIC THEORY OF PARTICLE PHYSICS

HADRON DYNAMICS IN TERMS OF UNITARY SPIN CURRENTS

YUVAL NE'EMAN

Tel-Aviv University

This manuscript was prepared while the author was at the Southwest Center for Advanced Studies, Dallas.

W. A. BENJAMIN, INC.

1967 New York Amsterdam

ALGEBRAIC THEORY OF PARTICLE PHYSICS

Library of Congress Catalog Card Number 67-18116
Manufactured in the United States of America

W. A. BENJAMIN, INC.
New York, New York 10016

EDITOR'S FOREWORD

The problem of communicating in a coherent fashion the recent developments in the most exciting and active fields of physics seems particularly pressing today. The enormous growth in the number of physicists has tended to make the familiar channels of communication considerably less effective. It has become increasingly difficult for experts in a given field to keep up with the current literature; the novice can only be confused. What is needed is both a consistent account of a field and the presentation of a definite "point of view" concerning it. Formal monographs cannot meet such a need in a rapidly developing field, and, perhaps more important, the review article seems to have fallen into disfavor. Indeed, it would seem that the people most actively engaged in developing a given field are the people least likely to write at length about it.

"Frontiers in Physics" has been conceived in an effort to improve the situation in several ways. First, to take advantage of the fact that the leading physicists today frequently give a series of lectures, a graduate seminar, or a graduate course in their special fields of interest. Such lectures serve to summarize the present status of a rapidly developing field and may well constitute the only coherent account available at the time. Often, notes on lectures exist (prepared by the lecturer himself, by graduate students, or by postdoctoral fellows) and have been distributed in mimeographed form on a limited basis. One of the principal purposes of the "Frontiers in Physics" series is to make such notes available to a wider audience of physicists.

It should be emphasized that lecture notes are necessarily rough and informal, both in style and content, and those in the series will prove no exception. This is as it should be. The point of the series is to offer new, rapid, more informal, and, it is hoped, more effective ways for physicists to teach one another. The point is lost if only elegant notes qualify.

A second way to improve communication in very active fields of physics is by the publication of collections of reprints of recent articles. Such collections are themselves useful to people working in the field. The value of the reprints would, however, seem much enhanced if the collection would be accompanied by an introduction of moderate length, which would serve to tie the collection together and, necessarily, constitute a brief survey of the present status of the field. Again, it is appropriate that such an introduction be informal, in keeping with the active character of the field.

A third possibility for the series might be called an informal monograph, to connote the fact that it represents an intermediate step between lecture notes and formal monographs. It would offer the author an opportunity to present his views of a field that has developed to the point at which a summation might prove extraordinarily fruitful, but for which a formal monograph might not be feasible or desirable.

Fourth, there are the contemporary classics—papers or lectures which constitute a particularly valuable approach to the teaching and learning of physics today. Here one thinks of fields that lie at the heart of much of present-day research, but whose essentials are by now well understood, such as quantum electrodynamics or magnetic resonance. In such fields some of the best pedagogical material is not readily available, either because it consists of papers long out of print or lectures that have never been published.

"Frontiers in Physics" is designed to be flexible in editorial format. Authors are encouraged to use as many of the foregoing approaches as seem desirable for the project at hand. The publishing format for the series is in keeping with its intentions. In most cases, both paperbound and clothbound editions of each book are available.

Finally, suggestions from interested readers as to format, contributors, and contributions will be most welcome.

DAVID PINES

Urbana, Illinois
August 1964

PREFACE

"When the theory of atomic structure was just beginning to be developed, Arnold Sommerfeld's famous 'Atombau und Spektrallinien' appeared. It summarized in a clear and concise way all that was worth knowing up to the time of its publication. It was of tremendous help to research workers, even beginners, and it stimulated an enormous amount of further development and discoveries in atomic structure, experimental as well as theoretical. Such a book should not be confused with an advanced textbook, which covers a subject after and not before it is fully understood." (S. Goudsmit, in *Physics Today* **19**, no. 9 p. 54.)

I have little hope that "Algebraic Theory of Particle Physics" will do for the "hadronists" what Sommerfeld's book did for the atomicists; the only point of similarity may perhaps be found in the last sentence—this is certainly no textbook and we are treating a subject before it is fully understood. However, this book does attempt to summarize the "great-leap-forward" in particle physics during the years 1961-1966. The important original papers in this development have been collected and commented upon in three Benjamin books,

The Eightfold Way—Gell-Mann and Ne'eman
Symmetry Groups—Dyson
Current Algebras—Adler and Dashen

Following a course I gave at Caltech early in 1965 and lectures given at the Universities of Illinois and Texas and at the Southwest Center for Advanced Studies (Dallas), I was led to write a first set of lecture notes, which were published in the proceedings of two 1965 summer schools, the Pacific (Honolulu, to be published by Gordon and Breach) and Tokyo (see "High Energy Physics," W. A. Benjamin, Inc., New York, 1966) Summer Institutes. These were the first extended descriptions which went beyond the symmetry concept and used the more recent methods of the algebra of the currents. The symmetry itself has since been described in several books and monographs such as Lipkin's "Lie Groups for Pedestrians" (North Holland), Park's "Introduction to Strong Interactions" (Benjamin), and Carruthers' "Introduction to Unitary Symmetry" (Interscience). I know of no such attempts to cover the more advanced material, other than the proceedings of the 1966 summer schools which will probably all contain series on currents.

In 1965-66 I taught a course at Tel-Aviv University in which I tried to sort out and systematize the various approaches in using physical algebras, and emphasize the main dynamical ideas; this was followed by a summer course which I gave in Geneva at the invitation of the C.I.C.P. (an inter-university organization including Geneva, Lausanne and Neuchatel). Having written up these lectures, I thought it would be worthwhile to add more recent developments, fill in some gaps, edit the material and publish this book, which is thus somewhere between a lecture-note volume and a monograph. This was done in the creative atmosphere of the Southwest Center for Advanced Studies, where I stayed during the late summer of 1966. I would like to thank President G. K. Johnson, Prof. L. Berkner, and Prof. I. Robinson for this opportunity.

Chapters 1 and 11 are devoted to a general sketch and review of the subject. Chapter 2 and the appendixes supply the needed mathematical result out of group and representation theory. I have assumed knowledge of the rotation group, and do not give proofs. Chapter 3 introduces the various roles an algebra can fulfill in quantum mechanics, mainly through a study of the hydrogen atom spectrum in terms of its algebraic structure; this is a "return to fundamentals" we initiated, I think, at the Second Coral Gables Conference.

Chapter 4 reviews the results of Unitary Symmetry; in Chapter 5 we reuse SU(3), this time as an algebra constructed out of the weak and electromagnetic currents, without any commitment to symmtery. Chapter 6 applies SU(3) to the evaluation of weak and electromagnetic transitions.

Having viewed the SU(3) algebra in terms of currents in Chapter 5, we extend in Chapter 7 the algebraic structure to $SU(3) \times SU(3)_{\gamma_5}$, the chiral algebra (rather than a chiral symmetry, although we compare the results with the latter) of vector and axial vector currents. This chapter contains the most interesting results derived from the algebra using dispersion relations; the methods are explained in Chapters 5 and 7. Chapter 8 extends the approach to larger subalgebras of U(12) and discusses those subgroups which happen to produce "accidental" symmetries (at rest, for collinear motion, etc.). This covers the main applications of SU(6), $SU(6)_W$ and related topics.

Having gone from a symmetry in Chapter 4 to a transition-operator algebra (the algebra of the currents) in Chapters 5 to 8, we devote Chapter 10 to another kind of algebraic systematics, the spectrum-generating-algebra. This is still a highly speculative attempt, based upon the application of unitary infinite dimensional representations of noncompact groups to the description of the hadron spectrum. No clear result has been achieved to date, but the subject seems to me to bear much promise, and I have therefore included it.

Thinking of the ways in which further research may develop, I have discussed three other extremely recent suggestions. At the end of Chapter 8 I have presented a summary of Gell-Man's initial ideas for a local algebra taken between states at infinite momentum, and of the approach based upon superconvergence suggested by Fubini and collaborators. I have devoted Chapter 9 to the idea of an algebra of factorized Regge residues, which was put forward in recent publications by Cabibbo, Horwitz, Kokkedee, and myself. Like the use of noncompact groups as spectrum generating algebras, these three subjects are highly speculative, though I am biased enough to believe that the subject-matter of Chapter 9 is here to stay. I hope that its further development will explain among other things the connection between Chapters 4 and 5: why do the weak currents also generate a symmetry of the S-matrix?

In writing these notes I have perhaps often given my own intepretation of the formalism rather than a generally accepted one, and ask forgiveness of my colleagues if they should find some of their ideas completely deformed. I have tried to supply a detailed bibliography for each subject, so as to enable the reader to get to the sources and check for himself, whenever my text does not provide the necessary clarity.

There is another aspect where I have followed a personal whim. I like new physical concepts to carry specific names rather than some phrase which may be a good description but can also be misunderstood.

I believe that some of the difficulties we find in acquainting the lay public with our results originate in the fact that we speak of "strong" and "weak" interactions. These are not names, and most of our contemporaries have not realized that physics contains forces other than electromagnetism and gravitation. I have used Okun's "hadron" for a "strongly-interacting particle," and have introduced the term "atonous" for the weak interaction. "Endosymmetry" and "endoalgebras" relate to "internal degrees of freedom" without thereby implying a mechanical model for the "internal" structure.

I would like to thank Dr. Joel Yellin who read the proofs and improved my English, besides making many valuable comments.

Finally, I would like to thank Gillian Curtis in Tel-Aviv and Gwen Vaughan in Dallas, in addition to an anonymous typist in Lausanne who typed the various chapters. This book is thus the fruit of an international collaboration in more than one sense.

YUVAL NE'EMAN

Tel Aviv, Israel
April 1967

CONTENTS

1

INTRODUCTION

ANALYTICAL AND ALGEBRAIC METHODS IN HADRON PHYSICS

Our understanding of the behaviour of strongly interacting matter is based upon the application of two methods, the one analytical and the other algebraic. We do not treat here the techniques of the analytical branch, known as "dispersion relations"; these consist in a thorough exploitation of the mathematics of analytical continuation, as applied to the conventional dynamical observables (total energy, momentum transfer squared, angular momentum, etc.) of a scattering problem. We shall however make use of these techniques in some cases where they either allow more insight into the algebraic methods or supplement them usefully. Indeed, some of the nicest recent physical results have been derived through such a combination of the two "cultures"; and the ideas we shall discuss in the second part of this treatise may yet develop into a comprehensive theory of hadron matter.

Dispersion relations apply the principles of unitarity (the conservation of probability), Poincaré invariance and some postulates with respect to the analyticity of the S-matrix. It has been conjectured in recent years that these principles in themselves may be sufficient for a complete description of the strong interactions; the actual treatment would then be based upon sets of coupled equations describing the bootstrap, a self-interacting system of hadron states in which each is solved in terms of the others. Whether or not hadron matter should in principle be regarded as such a system, with no fundamental building blocks, is still an open question. However, even if this were the correct structural theory-present observations certainly seem to imply that all known stable and meta-stable hadrons are composite—there is no indication that it would ever supply anything but an a posteriori "in principle" interpretation of the basic notions developed by the algebraic approach: the existence of an internal symmetry (it doesn't look as if it could point to a specific group) and its realization in a particular set of multiplets. Note that it could also happen that an alternative interpretation should prove the more useful of the two—for instance in terms of some set of fundamental fields, if and when the mathematical structure of interacting quantum fields is clarified through the development of axiomatic quantum field theory. In either case, the main body of dispersion theory will certainly be included in the final formulation of hadron physics.

The algebraic approach is a development of the methods of matrix mechanics introduced at the outset of quantum theory and modern quantum field theory. Mostly, it exploits the phenomonological discovery of unitary spin, a ninefold dynamical observable, the components of which are each somewhat akin to electric charge in that they fix the strength of the forces: exactly for the weak-nuclear and electromagnetic hadron interactions; roughly, and perhaps even exactly (in a more evolved formulation) for the strong nuclear force. They represent a quasi-conserved system of charge-currents, roughly the sources of these forces. They also supply the basis for a spectroscopic ordering of hadrons, a classification scheme. In this treatise, we are mostly concerned with the extraction of physical predictions from our knowledge of the unitary spin carried by given hadrons.

CONCEPTUAL EVOLUTION OF THE ALGEBRAIC METHOD

The application of algebraic methods to the description of hadron matter has recently undergone a rapid evolution, as a result of which several novel and powerful formal tools have emerged. The following conceptual stages can be distinguished in this development:

a. The identification of a charge-like quantum number B particular to hadrons (in addition to electric charge and local Lorentz invariance), common to all interactions and ensuring the separate conservation of half-odd-integer spin hadrons (presumably with Fermi statistics), i.e. baryons. The latter correspondence

$$(-1)^{2J} = (-1)^{3B} \tag{1.1}$$

defines a group-extension of the Lorentz group.

b. The definition of some additional so called "internal" symmetries of the system of hadron states. These are approximate in the physical world, but become exact when the electromagnetic, weak and gravitational interactions are "turned off." The conceptual picture then corresponds to an approximate rendering of reality, with the weakness of these excluded interactions restricting the distorting effects due to their omission. Iso-spin **I** and strangeness S (or hypercharge Y = B + S), the new quantum numbers, represent transformations corresponding to the Lie groups SU(2) and U(1) respectively. To these we should adjoin the discrete PCT transformations, a combination of an internal and two external reflections.

c. The generalization of the idea of an approximate symmetry to states whose energy levels are separated by intervals of up to 400 MeV; this separation appears due to interactions of strength greater than that which is involved in electromagnetic splittings. The new ASA (approximate symmetry algebra) generates the group U(3) and contains the previously defined internal symmetries. The lowest lying multiplets are generally identified with unmixed irreducible representations of that group – or, at times with some well-defined specific mixtures. It is assumed that in some ideal sense the strong interactions can be considered invariant under the group, but the mass splittings indicate of course the existence of a part of the hadron Hamiltonian which breaks U(3). This symmetry breaking has very definite transformation properties; other effects of this contribution are to be expected in the study of reaction amplitudes etc. The purity of low-lying baryon representations is an important factor in the usefulness of the concept of Unitary Spin.

d. The hadrons participate in electromagnetic and weak interactions; the dynamics of these interactions are described through a perturbation treatment in which the source term for the non-hadron field is exactly represented by some component of a hadron unitary spin charge-current density —as far as parity-conserving reactions go. It is possible that this system of current densities in fact defines U(3) the matrix elements of the generators of this group being represented by the contributions of the space-integrals of the vector charges; the fact that the strong-interaction Hamiltonian is approximately a scalar under U(3) would then be somewhat circumstantial. Note however that the weak and electromagnetic currents in themselves can only really generate U(3) if we adjoin a further semi-strong "fifth" interaction causing the mass splitting inside U(3) multiplets.

e. Generalizing to vector and axial vector current densities, we can construct the system of space-integrals of the two sets of charges. The universality of the weak interaction then requires the algebraic system to close on two octets plus the U(3)-scalar parts) and the algebra generates the "chiral" $[U(3) \times U(3)]_{\gamma_5}$. This algebra acquires its simplest representation in terms of U(3)−triplet (quark) fields; any larger multiplet requires the imposition of additional conditions, such as a local gauge and universally coupled fundamental vector-meson fields.

f. Whether or not the algebraic structure thus defined represents a very approximate symmetry of hadron matter, it can be used as a well-defined TOA (algebra of transition operators). Equal-time commutation relations between the charges' space-integrals are given by the structure-constants of $[U(3) \times U(3)]_{\gamma_5}$. Other such algebraic systems i.e. commutations relations, can be defined for the densities themselves, the generators and the densities, various moments, some parts of the non-strong Hamiltonian with the generators etc...; the system can also be generalized to other than the time-components of the densities. Such TOA have been used to derive numerous useful sum-rules; comparison with experiment shows that the most complete system of space-integrals of all components of hadron densities closes on $[U(6) \times U(6)]_{\gamma_5}$. If one assumes the physical existence of tensor-type densities the system closes on the algebra of U(12).

g. Various sub-algebras of the U(12) currents TOA appear to generate very approximate hadron symmetries. At rest, there is a $[U(6) \times U(6)]_\beta$ ASA; for collinear motion this yields $U(6)_W$ etc. These kinematical symmetries can be physical only if there exists some mechanism suppressing many-particle intermediate states, collinearity being otherwise violated. Because of baryon conservation, the redundant particles can only be pairs of mesons—local or non local (the non-local sets vanish in a commutator). The appearance of such states would in fact wreck the applications of these ASA in general, as one would be faced with divergent matrix elements; in other words, the usefulness of an ASA depends upon the assumption that the matrix elements are saturated by the main identified low-lying representations. Superflous besons represent a multitude of higher many-particle states with no guaranteed cut-off. These difficulties are obviated either by using commutators in a TOA sense or by working between states at $v/c \to 1$, where one can apparently construct $U(6)_{\alpha_Z \alpha_X}$, $U(6)_W$ or $U(3) \times U(3)$ subgroups of these groups as an ASA without conceptual errors.

h. Returning to the strong interactions, one is confronted with a picture of highly symmetric situations corresponding roughly to the pattern that would have emerged had the hadrons been composed "naively" of weakly-bound light quarks (330 MeV each) moving at non-relativistic velocities. This picture is however highly paradoxical since one then wonders at the stability of qqq and $q\bar{q}$ structures. There are indeed chances that actual free quarks may exist—but the experimental evidence seems to put a lower limit of several BeV on their masses, in which case it is again hard to understand the connection between these states and the nucleon's light components.

i. The recent suggestions of a further algebraic extension may settle these paradoxes. It consists in an extension of the current-structure to strong interactions, through the identification of an algebraic $[U(3) \times U(3)]_\beta$ structure in the system of factorized vertex-strengths making up the residues coupled to Regge trajectories. The strengths in forward-scattering are identified with the densities of the algebra generators; trajectories are thus universally coupled to this system of vector and scalar "charges."

j. It has been conjectured that one may apply to the classification of hadrons the type of algebraic structures appearing in ordinary quantum-mechanical systems and fixing the composition of the space of solutions. These spectrum-generating algebras (SGA) do not commute with the Hamiltonian; however, they contain the ASA in box-diagonal form—either at rest or perhaps rather at $v/c \to 1$.

Mathematically, they may operate in spaces larger than the Hilbert space itself. In most soluble cases, the SGA are represented by non-compact algebras with infinite-dimensional unitary representations. For the hadrons, this picture may be an idealization; however, it should provide a description of the sequence of hadron excitations with either parity. It remains to be seen whether such excitations will occur both in angular-momentum and unitary-spin or whether they will be confined to the first domain only. Note that they should reproduce the rotational excitations predicted by the Regge-pole bootstrap conjecture.

OUTLINE

In the following text, we just review the most relevant parts of the theory of Lie algebras and groups and their representations, mainly emphasizing the applications to Unitary groups in general and U(3) in particular. The discussion avoids mathematical proof and deals with results only, sometimes replacing proofs by rough intuitive arguments. The aim is only to provide that working knowledge which is essential for the understanding of the physical theory.

After the mathematical chapters, we try to gain some algebraic insight through the analysis of a familiar problem in quantum mechanics—the hydrogen atom. We then turn to the hadrons and study the consequences of unitary symmetry in the strong interactions, and the application of unitary spin considerations to the mass-splitting interaction, to electromagnetism and to the weak interactions.

We study the TOA of chiral charges and discuss the methods which have been used to apply it, mainly drawing upon dispersion theory. We then review the entire system of generators derived from space-integrals of charge-current components and its possible applications. This leads us to the study of its candidate ASA subalgebras. We then look at the suggested algebras of factorized residues—"strong" currents, in fact. Finally we touch upon the various possible SGA capable of describing the entire system of hadrons.

2

THE ABSTRACT ALGEBRA OF UNITARY SPIN

DEFINING MATRICES AND QUANTUM NUMBERS; QUARKS

The generators of Unitary Spin[1,2]—a set of quantum observables—form a Lie algebra; this is isomorphic to an abstract algebra whose simplest—defining—representation is given by the set of hermitian 3×3 matrices. Gell-Mann's[2] normalization of matrices and structure constants has become traditional, with

$$\mathrm{Tr}\,(\lambda_i \lambda_j) = 2\delta_{ij} \tag{2.1}$$

$$[\lambda_i, \lambda_j] = 2if_{ijk}\lambda_k \tag{2.2}$$

$$\{\lambda_i, \lambda_j\} = 2d_{ijk}\lambda_k + \tfrac{4}{3}\delta_{ij} \tag{2.3}$$

$$\begin{aligned} \mathrm{Tr}\,\lambda_k[\lambda_i, \lambda_j] &= 4if_{ijk} \\ \mathrm{Tr}\,\lambda_k\{\lambda_i, \lambda_j\} &= 4d_{ijk} \end{aligned} \tag{2.4}$$

Of course, Eq. (2.2) characterizes the algebra itself; the other equations are true for the 3-dimensional case only.

Our nine matrices reduce under commutation into the bases of two Lie algebras; an Abelian one built on λ_0, and the traceless algebra A_2 (in Cartan's classification) spanned by λ_1 to λ_8. The latter is the simplest extension in 3 dimensions of the system of 2×2 Pauli spin matrices (Cartan's A_1). Exponentiating A_2 with unrestricted real parameters generates SU(3), the group of unitary unimodular 3×3 matrices; with all nine λ_i, we get U(3), the group of unitary 3×3 matrices.

$$\lambda_0 = \sqrt{\tfrac{2}{3}} \begin{vmatrix} 1 & \cdot & \cdot \\ \cdot & 1 & \cdot \\ \cdot & \cdot & 1 \end{vmatrix}$$

$$\lambda_1 = \begin{vmatrix} \cdot & 1 & \cdot \\ 1 & \cdot & \cdot \\ \cdot & \cdot & \cdot \end{vmatrix} \quad \lambda_2 = \begin{vmatrix} \cdot & -i & \cdot \\ i & \cdot & \cdot \\ \cdot & \cdot & \cdot \end{vmatrix} \quad \lambda_3 = \begin{vmatrix} 1 & \cdot & \cdot \\ \cdot & -1 & \cdot \\ \cdot & \cdot & \cdot \end{vmatrix}$$

$$\lambda_4 = \begin{vmatrix} \cdot & \cdot & 1 \\ \cdot & \cdot & \cdot \\ 1 & \cdot & \cdot \end{vmatrix} \quad \lambda_6 = \begin{vmatrix} \cdot & \cdot & \cdot \\ \cdot & \cdot & 1 \\ \cdot & 1 & \cdot \end{vmatrix}$$

$$\lambda_5 = \begin{vmatrix} \cdot & \cdot & -i \\ \cdot & \cdot & \cdot \\ i & \cdot & \cdot \end{vmatrix} \quad \lambda_7 = \begin{vmatrix} \cdot & \cdot & \cdot \\ \cdot & \cdot & -i \\ \cdot & i & \cdot \end{vmatrix}$$

$$\lambda_8 = \sqrt{\tfrac{1}{3}} \begin{vmatrix} 1 & \cdot & \cdot \\ \cdot & 1 & \cdot \\ \cdot & \cdot & -2 \end{vmatrix} \qquad (2.5)$$

The correspondence with the usual quantum numbers is (e is the proton charge)

$$B = (\tfrac{1}{6})^{1/2}\lambda_0, \qquad I_x = \tfrac{1}{2}\lambda_i, \quad I_y = \tfrac{1}{2}\lambda_2,$$

$$I_z = \tfrac{1}{2}\lambda_3, \qquad Y = (\tfrac{1}{3})^{1/2}\lambda_8 \qquad (2.6)$$

$$Q = \tfrac{1}{2}e(\lambda_3 + (\tfrac{1}{3})^{1/2}\lambda_8)$$

We note that this "basic" representation describes a multiplet with $B = \frac{1}{3}$, splitting into an isodoublet and an isosinglet and with Q/e, i.e., the electric charges $(\frac{2}{3}, -\frac{1}{3}, -\frac{1}{3})$. The use of this multiplet as a mathematical building block for the entire system of hadrons was first suggested[3] by Goldberg and Ne'eman. Gell-Mann,[4] and independently Zweig[5] later applied it extensively and raised the possibility that an actual particle (a "quark" or an "ace") might exist with these quantum numbers and in some sense be considered as the fundamental hadron. We shall see further on how a quark-field triplet does provide the simplest model which reproduces the algebraic properties of hadron matter. However, if quark states exist as free particles, they are apparently of very high mass (>5 BeV) and have not yet been seen.

The space x^m upon which the λ_i act (quark-space, for instance) is a complex 3-dimensional one. We may now go over to another 3-dimensional space y_n, contravariant with respect to the x^m. For example, we may go over to $(x^m)^\dagger$, the complex conjugate row vector, though it needn't be just this one. By requiring invariance of the scalar product $\delta^n_m x^m y_n$ we find that the generators λ'_i operating on y_n should be represented by

$$\lambda'_i = -(\lambda_i)^\sim = -(\lambda_i)^*$$

and we can check that the new λ'_i indeed fulfill the same commutation relations, with the structure constants f_{ijk} of Eq. (22). The f_{ijk} and d_{ijk} coefficients are given in Appendix 1. Had we done this with the Pauli spin algebra, we would still have gotten an equivalent representation only. The new matrices

$$-\sigma_x, \ \sigma_y, \ -\sigma_z$$

define two states with the same quantum numbers (σ^2, σ_z) as the σ_x, σ_y, σ_z except that we have to invert the spinor on which they act, putting the spin-up state down and vice versa. This means that the new space may be reached by a unitary transformation, since the operation of raising and lowering the σ_Z eigenvalue exists within the group. Of course, had we adjoined the σ_0 identity 2×2 generator (equivalent to λ^0 in SU(3)) we would have reached an inequivalent representation: both new states would have negative σ_0 eigenvalues, and no such state existed in the 2-space to start with. The SU(2) operations closed upon the original states, and therefore cannot lead to these new ones. We thus have a new space altogether and the new matrices cannot be reached from the old ones by a unitary transformation.

For SU(3), the new **3*** representation (we use the dimensionality of the basis as a shortened notation for the representation, and write * for the conjugate representation) is not equivalent to the **3**. We can easily see that the lowest state has $I = 0$, $Y = -\frac{2}{3}$; in the **3*** representation, it will correspond to a $I = 0$, $Y = +\frac{2}{3}$ state; there is no such state in the space defined by the λ_i and therefore no unitary transformation can transform the two into each other. Quarks and antiquarks thus span inequivalent representations **3** and **3*** of SU(3) or U(3).

In the construction of the λ_i set, we have been guided by hermiticity, the normalization (2.1), the identification of the upper left hand 2×2 sub-matrix with the 2×2 representation of the SU(2) matrices of I-spin; we also show explicitly two other such SU(2) sub-groups nowadays known as U-spin (the lower right hand set of submatrices, including λ_6 and λ_7) and V-spin (the 3-1 and 1-3 subset, including λ_4 and λ_5). However, I_Z, U_Z and V_Z are linearly dependent, and we replace U_Z and V_Z by a combination λ_8 which is defined by the requirement that it should commute with the three I-spin matrices $(\lambda_1, \lambda_2, \lambda_3)$. This is necessary if we wish to identify λ_8 with a good quantum number, i.e., with a multiple of hypercharge, which can be measured at the same time as the I-spin.

It is worth rewriting the A_2 matrices in a real basis, i.e., defining

$$\omega_{I^+} = \frac{\sqrt{2}}{2}\begin{vmatrix} \cdot & 1 & \cdot \\ \cdot & \cdot & \cdot \\ \cdot & \cdot & \cdot \end{vmatrix} \qquad \omega_{I^-} = \frac{\sqrt{2}}{2}\begin{vmatrix} \cdot & \cdot & \cdot \\ 1 & \cdot & \cdot \\ \cdot & \cdot & \cdot \end{vmatrix}$$

$$\omega_{U^+} = \frac{\sqrt{2}}{2}\begin{vmatrix} \cdot & \cdot & \cdot \\ \cdot & \cdot & 1 \\ \cdot & \cdot & \cdot \end{vmatrix} \qquad \omega_{U^-} = \frac{\sqrt{2}}{2}\begin{vmatrix} \cdot & \cdot & \cdot \\ \cdot & \cdot & \cdot \\ \cdot & 1 & \cdot \end{vmatrix} \qquad (2.7)$$

$$\omega_{V^+} = \frac{\sqrt{2}}{2}\begin{vmatrix} \cdot & \cdot & \cdot \\ \cdot & \cdot & \cdot \\ 1 & \cdot & \cdot \end{vmatrix} \qquad \omega_{V^-} = \frac{\sqrt{2}}{2}\begin{vmatrix} \cdot & \cdot & 1 \\ \cdot & \cdot & \cdot \\ \cdot & \cdot & \cdot \end{vmatrix}$$

with $\mathrm{Tr}\,(\omega_i)^+\omega_i = \frac{1}{2}$

$$[\omega_{I^+}, \omega_{I^-}] = \omega_{I_Z} \qquad [\omega_{U^+}, \omega_{U^-}] = \omega_{U_Z}$$

$$[\omega_{V^+}, \omega_{V^-}] = \omega_{V_Z} \qquad (2.8)$$

$$\omega_{U_Z} \equiv U_Z = -\frac{1}{4}\lambda_3 + \frac{\sqrt{3}}{4}\lambda_8$$

$$\omega_{V_Z} \equiv V_Z = -\frac{1}{4}\lambda_3 - \frac{\sqrt{3}}{4}\lambda_8 \qquad \omega_8 = \frac{1}{2}\lambda_8 \qquad (2.9)$$

$$I_Z + U_Z + V_Z = 0 \qquad Y = \tfrac{2}{3}(U_Z - V_Z) \qquad (2.10)$$

ROOT AND WEIGHT DIAGRAMS

The generators λ_3 and λ_8, or alternatively ω_{I_Z} and ω_8 constitute the Cartan sub-algebra, i.e., the diagonal, commutative subset. An algebraic theorem states that the space spanned by the Cartan sub-algebra is isomorphic to a Euclidean space $(\vec{i}_Z, \vec{y})$, $\vec{i}_Z \equiv i_Z$, $\vec{y} \equiv y$, of the same dimensionality; this dimensionality is "r", the *rank* (r = 2 in SU(3)) of the Lie algebra. It represents the number of good linear quantum numbers contained in the algebra. We

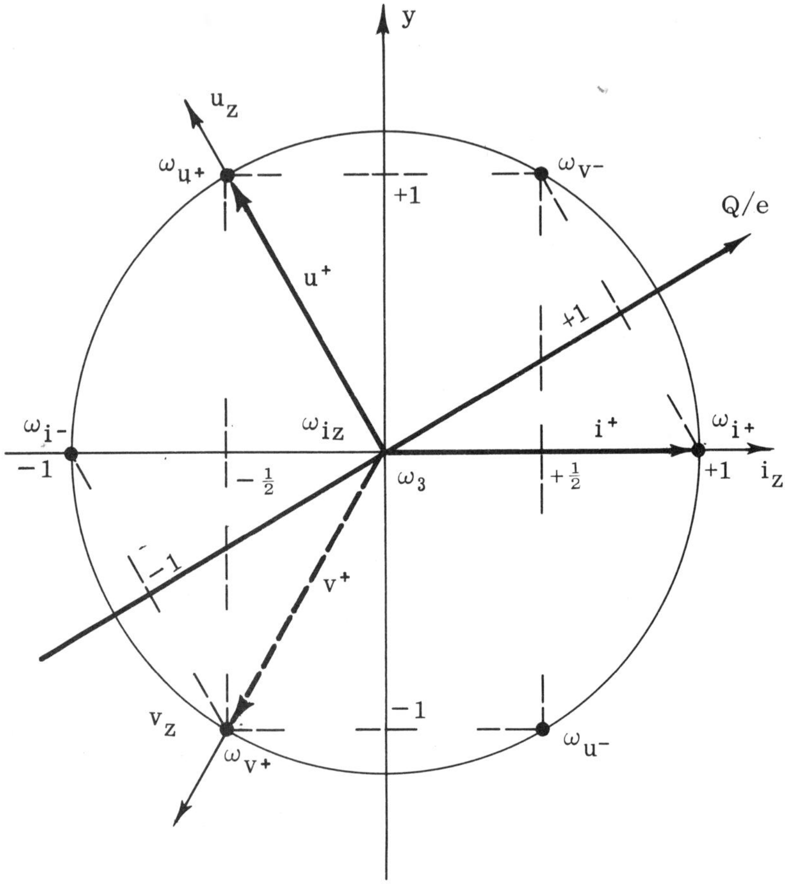

Fig. 2-1. The root diagram

can make use of this theorem and draw the algebra's *root diagram* (Fig. 2.1). We draw the orthogonal coordinate axes i_z and y, the position of all eight root-vectors $\vec{\omega}_\chi$ being given by the eigenvalues of the corresponding commutators:

$$[\omega_{i_z}, \omega_\chi] = i_z(\omega_\chi)\omega_\chi = (\vec{i}_z \cdot \vec{\omega}_\chi)\omega_\chi$$

$$[\omega_8, \omega_\chi] = \frac{\sqrt{3}}{2}\, y(\omega_\chi)\omega_\chi = \frac{\sqrt{3}}{2}(\vec{y} \cdot \vec{\omega}_\chi)\omega_\chi \tag{2.11}$$

(We have dropped the arrows in the diagram.)

We have also drawn the Q/e axis, for electric charge. This enables us now to tabulate the physical action of our root-vectors ω_χ (see Table 2.1).

Table 2-1
The Root Vectors of SU(3) and the Physical Currents

	Δi_z	Δy	$\Delta Q/e$	$\Delta\lambda$	$\Delta\mu$
ω_{I^+}	1	0	1	2	−1
ω_{I^-}	−1	0	−1	−2	1
ω_{I_z}	0	0	0	0	0
ω_{U^+}	$-\frac{1}{2}$	1	0	−1	2
ω_{U^-}	$\frac{1}{2}$	−1	0	1	−2
(ω_{U_z})	0	0	0	0	0
ω_{V^+}	$-\frac{1}{2}$	−1	−1	−1	−1
ω_{V^-}	$\frac{1}{2}$	1	+1	1	1
(ω_{V_z})	0	0	0	0	0
$\omega_{Y'}$	0	0	0	0	0

When the generators ω_χ act on a vector $|i_z, y\rangle$ in some representation, they turn it into another vector $|i'_z, y'\rangle$ such that

$$\begin{aligned} i'_z &= i_z + \Delta i_z(\chi) \\ y' &= y + \Delta y(\chi) \end{aligned} \tag{2.12}$$

This can be checked by applying χ explicitly; the new eigenvalues are

$$i'_z = \omega_{I_z} | i'_z \rangle = \omega_{I_z} \omega_\chi | i_z \rangle = \omega_\chi \omega_{I_z} | i_z \rangle$$
$$+ [\omega_{I_z}, \omega_\chi] | i_z \rangle$$
$$= i_z \omega_\chi | i_z \rangle + \Delta i_z \omega_\chi | i_z \rangle$$
$$= (i_z + \Delta i_z) | i'_z \rangle \cdots$$

Physically speaking, Table 2.1 gives us the action of SU(3) currents, which consist in transitions due to the action of the algebra generators.

We may use the same coordinates to describe any representation of the group; this is then a *weight diagram*. In fact, the root diagram itself is at the same time the weight-diagram for the *adjoint representation* of the Lie algebra. This is the representation spanned by the generators themselves: We can visualize our 8-dimensional space with unit-vectors λ_{1-8}. The algebra operates upon this space in the form of eight 8×8 matrices (the adjoint representation—also called regular—has the dimensionality of the algebra, i.e., its dimensionality is the same as the number of linearly independent parameters). The matrix elements are just the structure constants. Indeed, we can rewrite Eqs. (2.2) with $({}^j{}_k)$ denoting rows and columns

$$[\lambda_i, \lambda_j] = -2F_i{}^{(j}{}_{k)} \lambda_k \qquad (2.13)$$
$$F_i{}^{(j}{}_{k)} = -if_{ijk}$$

where we have introduced the factor 2 so as to get Gell-Mann's normalization,

$$[F_i, F_j] = if_{ijk} F_k \qquad (2.14)$$

The weight diagram of a representation is just the set of eigenvalues (i_z, y) of its basis. For the 3-dimensional basis "**3**" upon which the ω_χ of Eq. (2.11) operate we get the diagram shown in Fig. 2.2; and for **3*** we have the diagram of Fig. 2.3. The **3** representation describes the quarks, denoted $q^Q(u^{2/3}, d^{-1/3}, s^{-1/3})$ as in Gell-Mann's notation; the **3*** describes antiquarks.

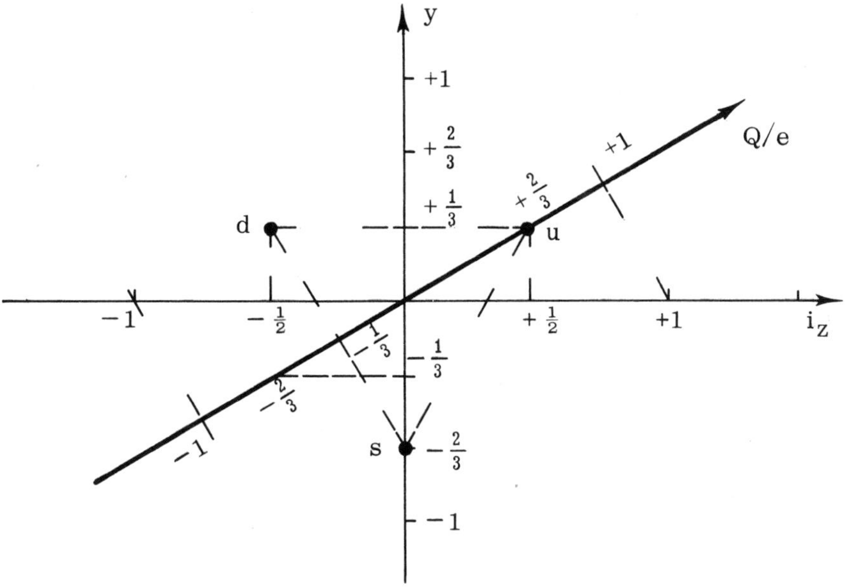

Fig. 2-2. The quark (1, 0) or (1, 0, 0)

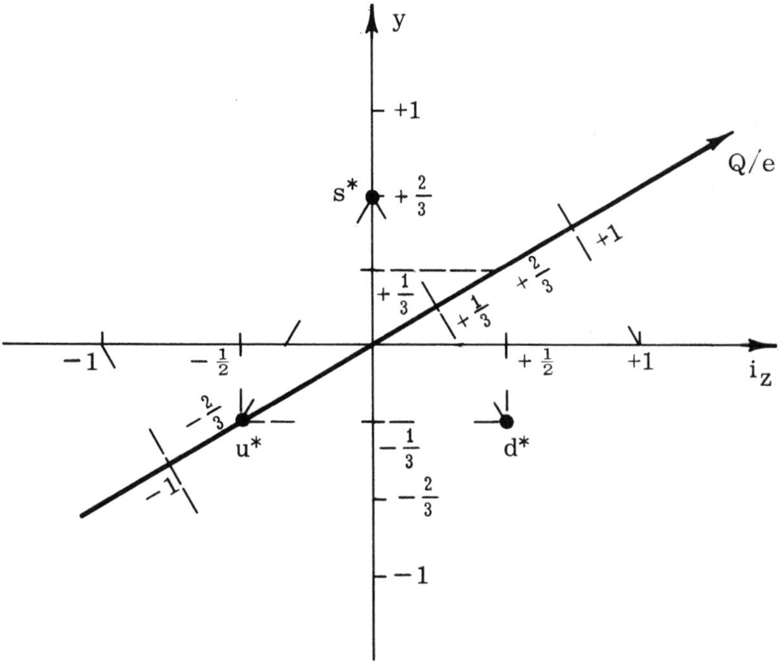

Fig. 2-3. The antiquark (0, 1) or (0, 0, −1)

HIGHEST WEIGHT AND REPRESENTATION CONSTRUCTION

The conventional way of describing a representation is based upon the location of its *highest weight*. For an algebra of rank r, we pick r linearly independent raising operators χ^+ [for SU(3), we may pick any two out of ω_{I^+}, ω_{U^+} and ω_{V^+}; in Fig. 2.1 we have marked out ω_{I^+} and ω_{U^+}]. These form a set of *simple roots*, which is an alternative basis in the Cartan subalgebra; we shall make use of the simple-roots when we list all semi-simple Lie algebras and the method of constructing their complete set of roots in Appendix 3.

The highest weight in a given representation is the weight of that vector which is annihilated by the application of the χ^+ set. For instance, the $u^{2/3}$ quark defines the highest weight of the representation in Fig. 2.2, since

$$\omega_{I^+}|u^{2/3}\rangle = 0 \qquad \omega_{U^+}|u^{2/3}\rangle = 0$$

which is graphically obvious, as the application of the corresponding root-vectors from Fig. 2.1 to $u^{2/3}$ in Fig. 2.2 does not lead to other weights. The highest weight of **3** is thus $(\frac{1}{2}, \frac{1}{3})$; however, it is more convenient—for reasons we shall soon realize—to use a different coordinate system for the description of the highest weights: we pick the coordinates (λ, μ)

$$\begin{aligned} \lambda &= 2i_z \\ \mu &= -i_z + \tfrac{3}{2}y = 2u_z \end{aligned} \qquad (2.15)$$

(see Fig. 2.4). We now have the weight (1, 0) describing the quark representation of dimensionality d = $\underline{3}$. We note that $\lambda = 0$ is orthogonal to $\vec{\omega}_{I^+}$, and $\mu = 0$ to $\vec{\omega}_{U^+}$. These new coordinates thus measure values of i_z and u_z. It can be shown that for any SU(3) representation, the dimensionality d is given by

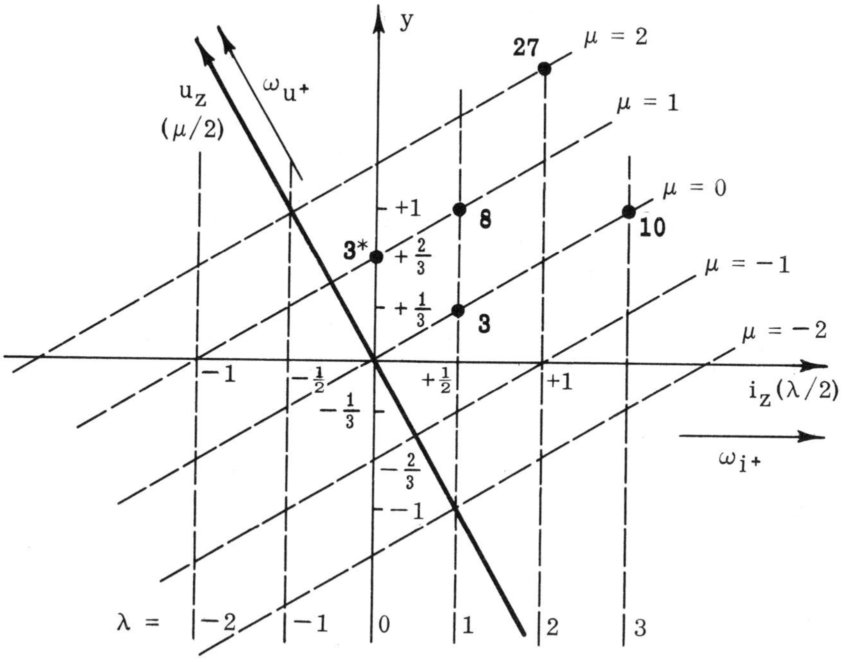

Fig. 4. The (λ, μ) lattice.

$$d = \tfrac{1}{2}(\lambda + 1)(\mu + 1)(\lambda + \mu + 2) \tag{2.16}$$

Similarly, any SU(n) has an algebra of rank $r = n - 1$ (as the diagonal has just $n - 1$ linearly independent matrix elements once we exclude the trace); its representations are defined by highest weights $(\lambda_1, \lambda_2, \ldots, \lambda_{n-1})$ and its dimensionality by

$$d = \frac{1}{2!3!\ldots(n-1)!}(\lambda_1 + 1)(\lambda_1 + \lambda_2 + 2)\cdots$$
$$\cdots(\lambda_1 + \lambda_2 + \cdots + \lambda_{n-1} + n - 1)(\lambda_2 + 1)(\lambda_2 + \lambda_3 + 2)\cdots$$
$$\cdots(\lambda_2 + \lambda_3 + \cdots + \lambda_{n-1} + n - 2)\cdots(\lambda_{n-1} + 1) \tag{2.17}$$

Given the highest weight, we can construct the entire representation by operating successively with the various $\chi^{\pm}$. For SU(3) all vectors in the (λ, μ) representation must lie on the lattice produced by consecutive subtraction of an integer from either λ or μ

$$(\lambda, \mu), (\lambda - 1, \mu), (\lambda - 2, \mu)\ldots, (\lambda, \mu - 1),$$

$$(\lambda - 1, \mu - 1), (\lambda - 2, \mu - 1)\ldots$$

On the other hand, SU(3) weight diagrams are bounded by weights forming a hexagon—except for the case where either $\lambda = 0$ or $\mu = 0$, in which they collapse to form a triangle (if both $\lambda = \mu = 0$, they collapse to a dot). The hexagon vertices are

$$(\lambda, \mu), (\lambda + \mu, -\mu), (\mu, -\lambda - \mu), (-\lambda, \lambda + \mu),$$

$$(-\lambda - \mu, \lambda), (-\mu, -\lambda)$$

Let us now draw the (1, 1) weight diagram (Fig. 2.5). If we draw it for the λ_{1-8}, or rather for their $\omega_{I^+}\ \omega_{I^-}\ \omega_{I_Z}$ $\omega_{U^+}\omega_{U^-}\omega_{V^+}\omega_{V^-}\omega_8$ linear combinations, we can use Table 2.1. We note that the (0, 0) weight occurs twice, once for ω_{I_Z} and once for ω_8. Indeed, if we apply it to the basic physical realization of SU(3) in the form of the baryon octet model, we find Σ^0 and Λ^0 with identical (zero) i_z and y. How then do we know what the multiplicity n of a weight is in an SU(3) representation? One finds for SU(3) that only hexagons (i.e., $\lambda \neq 0$, $\mu \neq 0$) have $n > 1$ occuring. Going from the periphery inwards, each successive hexagon (the most inward may be a triangle or a dot) has an increase of 1 in the multiplicity. Of course, this can also be learned directly, by successive application of the ω_χ, checking each time the *complete* set of quantum numbers for a state. We know for instance that Σ^0 has $|I| = 1$ and Λ^0 has $|I| = 0$.

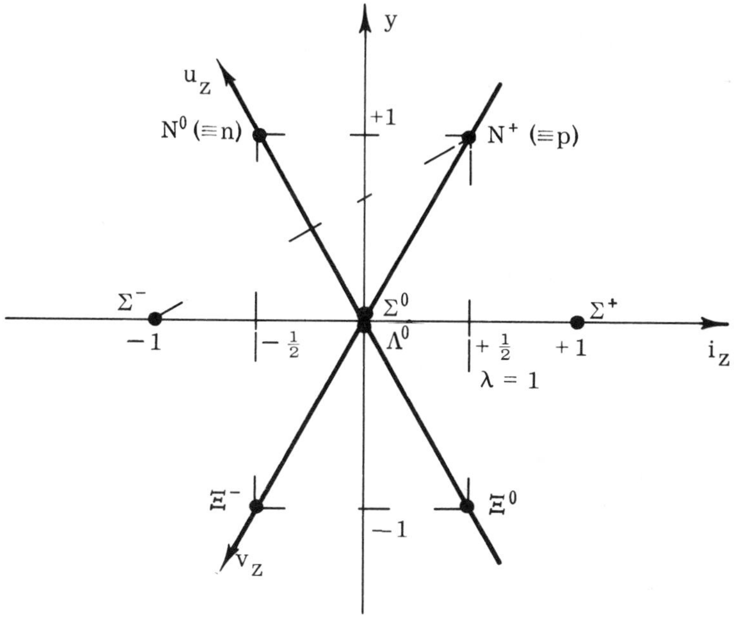

Fig. 2-5. The (1, 1) octet representation (baryons) or (2, 1, 0).

Racah's formula states that for a semi simple Lie algebra with p parameters, and rank r, one requires

$$\ell = \frac{1}{2}(p - 3r) \tag{2.18}$$

additional (nonlinear) quantum numbers to remove all degeneracies and specify each vector in the representation. In our case, $\ell = \frac{1}{2}(8 - 3 \times 2) = 1$ and we use the total I-spin accordingly. Note that in a group like SU(6), $p = 36 - 1 = 35$, $r = 5$, $\ell = 10$; the choice of these operators is one of the more complicated problems in working with physical applications.

U(3) NOTATION

SU(3) does not fix the baryon number B for a representation, as it does not include λ_0 in its algebra. The (1, 1) octet may therefore represent baryons as in Fig. 2.5

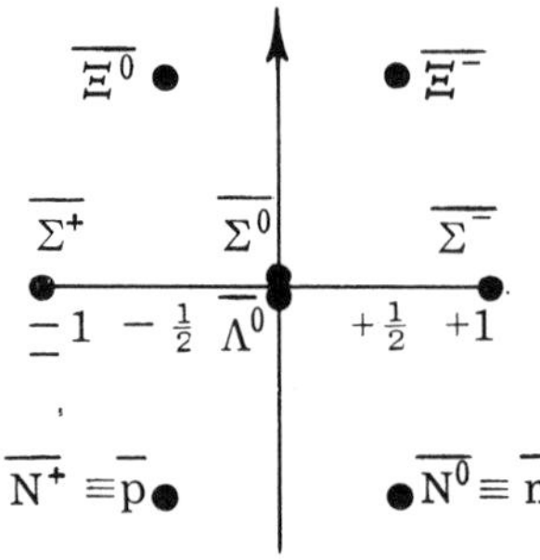

Fig. 2-6. The (1, 1) octet of antibaryons

(0, −1, −2)

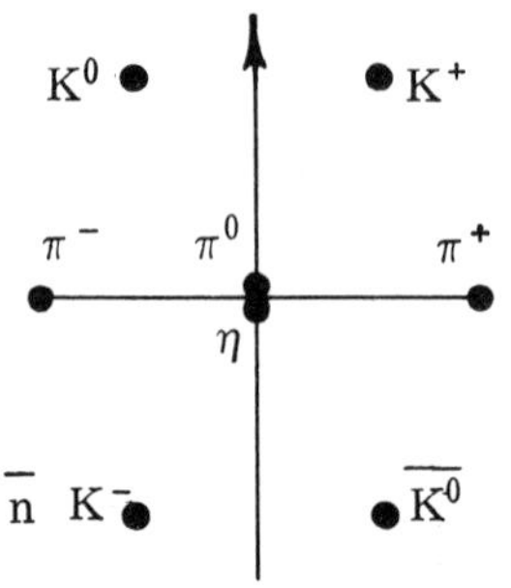

Fig. 2-7. The (1, 1) octet of mesons with $j^P = 0^-$

(1, 0, −1)

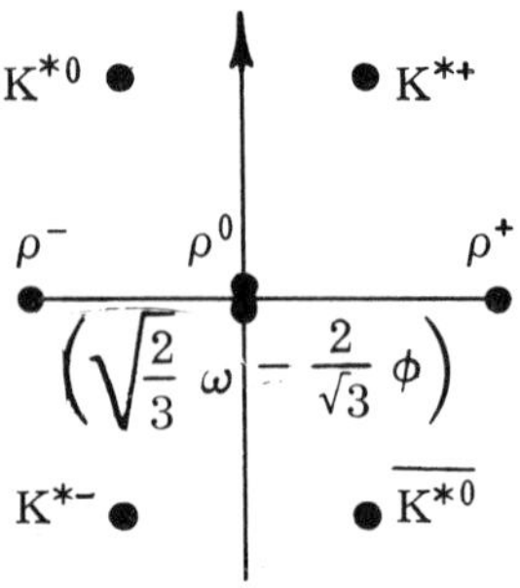

Fig. 2-8. The (1, 1) octet and (0, 0) singlet of mesons with $j^P = 1^-$

(1, 0, −1) and (0, 0, 0)

or mesons with spin-parity $j^P = 0^-$ as in Fig. 2.7, or (see p. 25) mesons with $j^P = 1^-$ as in Fig. 2.8, or antibaryons as in Fig. 2.6.

To distinguish between these, we have to go over to U(3) and use a 3-dimensional weight diagram (we may for instance put B as the third axis).

We use the Goldberg-Ne'eman highest U(3) weight notation,[3] though we redefine the generators (the matrix element $H_i{}^{(m}{}_{n)} = \delta_i{}^m \delta_{in}$ in the 3-dimensional representation)

$$H_1 = I_Z + \tfrac{1}{2}Y + B,$$

$$H_2 = -I_Z + \tfrac{1}{2}Y + B, \qquad (2.19)$$

$$H_3 = -Y + B$$

so as to represent q^Q by (1, 0, 0); the parenthesis contains the eigenvalues (h_1, h_2, h_3) of that state in a (i_Z, y) diagram from which the generators ω_{I^+} and ω_{U^+} lead nowhere. Of course, $B = \frac{1}{3}\Sigma h_i$ and is an invariant.

It can be seen that adding the same constant to all three h_i corresponds to a change in baryon number only; thus (2, 1, 0), (1, 0, −1) and (0, −1, −2) represent octets with B = 1, 0, −1 respectively; (3, 0, 0) is the **10** with B = 1 etc. On the other hand,

$$\lambda = h_1 - h_2$$
$$\mu = h_2 - h_3 \tag{2.20}$$

REDUCTION OF SOME DIRECT PRODUCTS

We examine the product $q \times q^\dagger$, or $(1, 0) \times (0, 1)$. We are dealing with a tensor

$$T^\alpha{}_\beta = Z^\alpha Z_\beta$$

in which the only available reducing operation consists in contraction,

$$T^\alpha{}_\beta = (Z^\alpha Z_\beta - \tfrac{1}{3}\delta^\alpha{}_\beta Z^\gamma Z_\gamma) + (\tfrac{1}{3}\delta^\alpha{}_\beta Z^\gamma Z_\gamma)$$
$$= T^{\dot\alpha}{}_{\dot\beta} + \tfrac{1}{3}\delta^\alpha{}_\beta |Z|^2 \tag{2.21}$$

where a dot denotes the corresponding contraction, leading to the irreducible tensor. Considering that $T^\alpha{}_\beta$ can be represented as a 3×3 matrix, we realize that its components are isomorphic to the λ_i or ω_χ sets; the reduction in Eq. (2.21) is just the separation of the identity from the SU(3) generators in U(3). We may represent Eq. (2.21) in the form of matrix multiplication of $q^\alpha \times q^\dagger_\beta$,

$$\begin{pmatrix} u \\ d \\ s \end{pmatrix} \times (u^\dagger, d^\dagger, s^\dagger)$$

$$= \begin{vmatrix} uu^\dagger & ud^\dagger & us^\dagger \\ du^\dagger & dd^\dagger & ds^\dagger \\ su^\dagger & sd^\dagger & ss^\dagger \end{vmatrix}$$

$$= \begin{vmatrix} uu^\dagger - \frac{1}{3}(uu^\dagger + dd^\dagger + ss^\dagger) & ud^\dagger & us^\dagger \\ du^\dagger & dd^\dagger - \frac{1}{3}(uu^\dagger + dd^\dagger + ss^\dagger) & ds^\dagger \\ su^\dagger & sd^\dagger & ss^\dagger - \frac{1}{3}(uu^\dagger + dd^\dagger + ss^\dagger) \end{vmatrix}$$

$$+ \frac{1}{3}(uu^\dagger + dd^\dagger + ss^\dagger) \begin{vmatrix} 1 & & \\ & 1 & \\ & & 1 \end{vmatrix}$$

Checking the quantum numbers of the matrix elements in both resulting irreducible representations shows that we have here an octet (Fig. 2-7) and a singlet χ of mesons,

$$= \begin{vmatrix} (\frac{1}{2})^{1/2}\pi^0 + (\frac{1}{6})^{1/2}\eta & \pi^+ & K^+ \\ \pi^- & -(\frac{1}{2})^{1/2}\pi^0 + (\frac{1}{6})^{1/2}\eta & K^0 \\ K^- & \overline{K}^0 & -2(\frac{1}{6})^{1/2}\eta \end{vmatrix}$$

$$+ \begin{vmatrix} \chi & & \\ & \chi & \\ & & \chi \end{vmatrix}$$

We notice that we have constituted the diagonal matrix elements so as to have in the octet an isovector π and an isosinglet η. The π^0 is given by $1/\sqrt{2}\,\pi^0\lambda_3$ and the η by $1/\sqrt{6}\,\eta\lambda_8$. The above matrix representation is in fact equivalent to writing the meson octet P^α as an eight-dimensional vector in the space of the algebra. We shall make use of this possibility when working with octets. In the same way we could have (Fig. 2-5)

$$\begin{vmatrix} (\frac{1}{2})^{1/2}\Sigma^0 + (\frac{1}{6})^{1/2}\Lambda^0 & \Sigma^+ & N^+ \\ \Sigma^- & -(\frac{1}{2})^{1/2}\Sigma^0 + (\frac{1}{6})^{1/2}\Lambda^0 & N^0 \\ \Xi^- & \Xi^0 & -2(\frac{1}{6})^{1/2}\Lambda^0 \end{vmatrix}$$

for the baryon octet B^{α}, and for the antibaryon $\overline{B}^{\alpha}$ (Fig. 2-6)

$$\left|\begin{array}{ccc} (\frac{1}{2})^{1/2}\,\overline{\Sigma^0} + (\frac{1}{6})^{1/2}\,\overline{\Lambda^0} & \overline{\Sigma^-} & \overline{\Xi^-} \\ \overline{\Sigma^+} & -(\frac{1}{2})^{1/2}\,\overline{\Sigma^0} + (\frac{1}{6})^{1/2}\,\overline{\Lambda^0} & \overline{\Xi^0} \\ \overline{N^+} & \overline{N^0} & -2(\frac{1}{6})^{1/2}\,\overline{\Lambda^0} \end{array}\right|$$

As to the vector mesons V^{α}, we shall see in Chapter 5 that the actual states in the diagonal display mixing between octet and singlet, as if λ_0 and λ_8 were replaced by $(h_1 + h_2)$ and h_3 instead (fig. 2-8).

$$\left|\begin{array}{ccc} (\frac{1}{2})^{1/2}\,\rho^0 + (\frac{1}{2})^{1/2}\,\omega^0 & \rho^+ & K^{*+} \\ \rho^- & -(\frac{1}{2})^{1/2}\,\rho^0 + (\frac{1}{2})^{1/2}\,\omega^0 & K^{*0} \\ K^{*-} & \overline{K^{*0}} & \phi^0 \end{array}\right|$$

In Eq. (2.21), the extracted tensor is the trace, a scalar, i.e., it corresponds to (0, 0); $T^{\dot{\alpha}}{}_{\dot{\beta}}$ is of course the (1, 1).

We now turn to antisymmetric products of two and three quarks. For the latter, we note that

$$\epsilon_{\alpha\beta\gamma}\, q^{\alpha}_{A}\, q^{\beta}_{B}\, q^{\gamma}_{C}$$

gives us a scalar. This is the determinant constructed from 3 quarks. We see that (0, 0) is contained in (1, 0) $\times$ (1, 0) $\times$ (1, 0) and forms its totally antisymmetric part. Comparing now with the fact that we get (0, 0) from (1, 0) $\times$ (0, 1), we note that the ansymmetric part of (1, 0) $\times$ (1, 0) should be SU(3)-equivalent to the antiquark (0, 1). This is true of any SU(n): we can always make a scalar

$$\epsilon_{\alpha_1\alpha_2\ldots\alpha_n}\, v^{\alpha_1}_{A}\, v^{\alpha_2}_{B} \ldots v^{\alpha_n}_{N}$$

and find that we get a tensor behaving like the contravariant vector v_{α_n}

$$\epsilon_{\alpha_1\alpha_2\ldots\alpha_n}\, v^{\alpha_1}_{A}\, v^{\alpha_2}_{B} \ldots v^{\alpha_{n-1}}_{M} \sim v_{\alpha_n} \quad \text{or} \quad (v^{\alpha_n})^{\dagger}$$

To visualize the direct physical implications, take the $q \times q$ product. This can also be done in matrix form $q^Q \cdot q^{Q\sim}$. We get for the antisymmetric part,

$$(u_1 d_2 - d_1 u_2) \sim s^*$$

$$(d_1 s_2 - d_2 s_1) \sim d^*$$

$$(s_1 u_2 - s_2 u_1) \sim u^*$$

in terms of isospin, we see that what we have looks like s^*, d^*, u^*; if we subtract one unit from the hypercharges, we get **3*** exactly. Considering that SU(3) itself allows such redefinitions of hypercharge (as we are only adding a scalar contribution), we have indeed found that $T^{[\alpha,\beta]}$ behaves as a (0, 1) representation (we use square brackets to indicate antisymmetrization). The symmetric part of the product $T^{[\alpha,\beta]}$ has 6 components; the highest weight will be just the sum of (1, 0) and (1, 0), i.e., it is a (2, 0) representation.

YOUNG TABLEAUX

There are various ways of performing the reduction of direct (Kronecker) products of representations of SU(n); these methods are all essentially the same, but they offer various simplifications which become important when one is dealing with more complicated situations. We shall use the method of Young tableaux.

It can be shown that to any representation $(\lambda_1, \lambda_2, \ldots \lambda_{n-1})$ of SU(n) there corresponds a Young tableau, i.e., a scheme with $\lambda_1 + \lambda_2 + \cdots + \lambda_{n-1}$ cells in the first row, $\lambda_2 + \cdots + \lambda_{n-1}$ in the second, etc. so that the highest weight $(\lambda_1, \lambda_2, \ldots \lambda_{n-1})$ can be read as the differences in the numbers of cells in the consecutive rows.

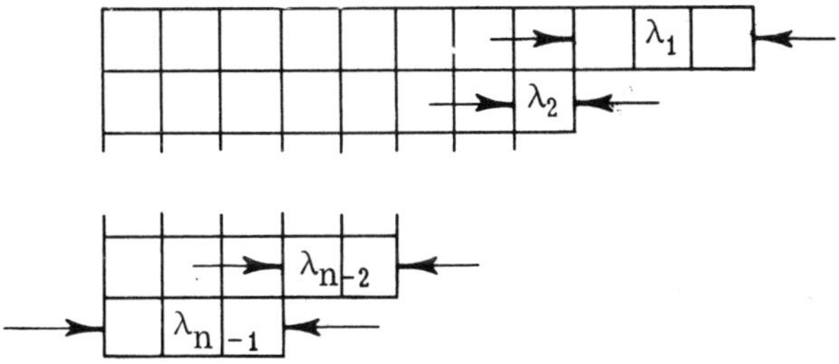

Fig. 2-9. A Young tableau

As can be seen in Fig. 2.9 the tableau itself never has a shorter row on top of a longer one, though rows may be equal if $\lambda_i = 0$.

Thus as in Fig. 2.9 a Young tableau has only n − 1 allowed rows; compare with Fig. 2.10 for SU(3).

The theory of Young symmetrizers represents the operation of symmetrization by horizontal alignments, of antisymmetrization by vertical ones. All representations of SU(n) can be reached from recurring Kronecker multiplication of the basic n-vector (1, 0, . . .) by itself; indeed we have seen that the contravariant n* or (0, . . . , 1) can be reached through the projection of the totally antisymmetric part in the product of n − 1 basic (1, 0,. . .) representations. We see this fact born out in the diagram Fig. 2.11.

We also know that further antisymmetric multiplication by one more (1, 0, . . .) leads to the scalar (0, 0, . . . 0); in

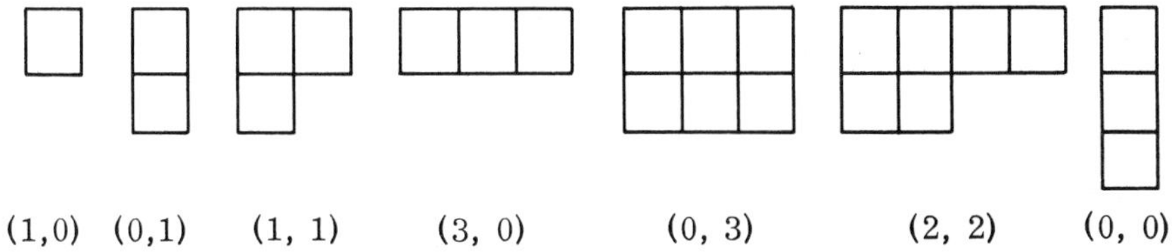

Fig. 2-10. Some SU(3) tableaux

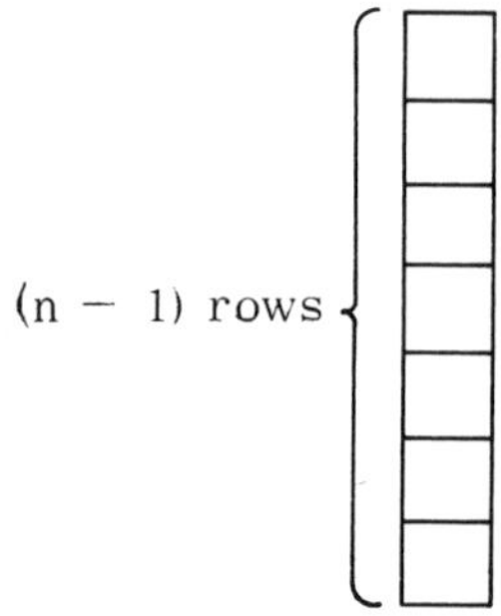

Fig. 2-11. The (0, 0, ... 1) tableau

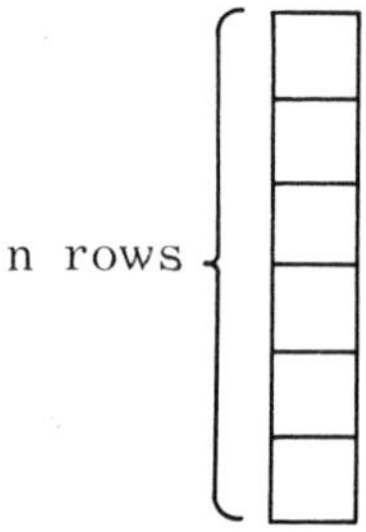

Fig. 2-12. The (0, 0, 0 ... 0) tableau

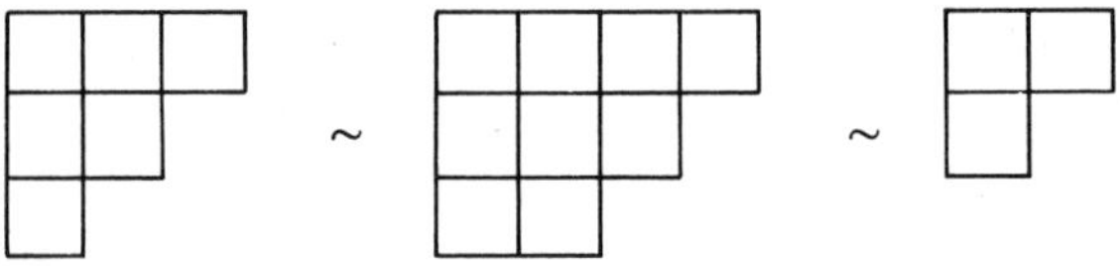

Fig. 2-13. Isomorphic SU(3) tableaux (1, 1)

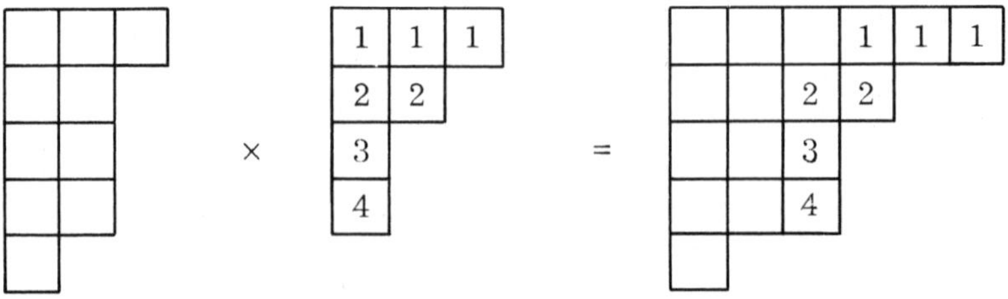

Fig. 2-14. Kronecker multiplication

tableau notation, we would get the tableau shown in Fig. 2.12 which explains why tableaux are characteristic of a representation only up to the $n - 1^{th}$ row. We may add as many columns of n cells to the left of a tableau as we wish; we are only multiplying it by a scalar; for SU(3) we have, for example, tableaux as shown in Fig. 2.13. From the tableau, we can construct the representation directly, as we read out the highest weight coordinates and can then construct the entire weight diagram as we did before by operating with the ω_χ.

We draw one tableau and adjoin to it the cells of the other tableau, after having marked them according to the row to which they belonged (Fig. 2.14). The reduced product is given by the sum of all possible relocations of the cells of the second tableau, provided that in the resulting tableaux:

1. No row should be shorter than the ones underneath it.
2. Counting in each row from the right, starting from the upper row downwards, the number n(1) of "1" cells should at any point along the path be larger or equal to n(2), the number of "2" cells up to that point etc. Thus

$$n(1) \geq n(2) \geq n(3) \geq \cdots n(\ell)$$

at any point along our path.

3. Checking each row from left to right, the markings should not diminish in their values.
4. Checking each column from top to bottom, the markings should increase in their values.

In Fig. 2.15, we draw examples of tableaux violating these rules. Such tableaux vanish in the product in Fig. 2.14.

These rules are entirely sufficient to reduce any product of SU(n) representations. When facing the problem of computing the Clebsch series and its coefficients, this provides a complete answer—except for separating equivalent representations. First, we find the content in terms of irreducible representations through the Young tableaux. We then pick out the highest amongst the "highest weights"; it

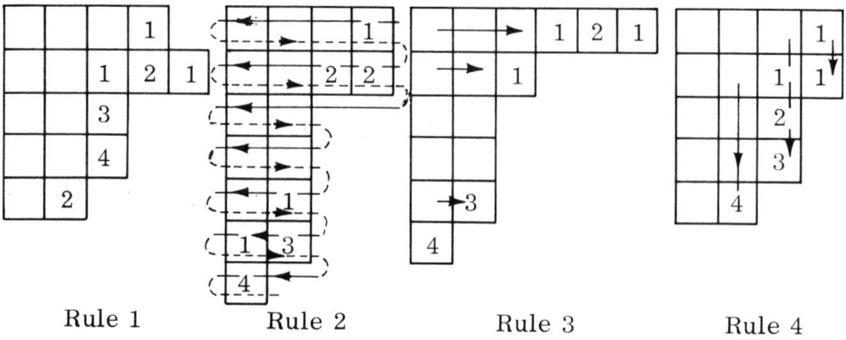

Rule 1: 1st row is shorter than 2nd row (in this case rule 3 is also violated).
Rule 2: n(1) $\ngtr$ n(2) at left-end of row 2.
Rule 3: 2 → 1 from left to right is forbidden (here in first row).
Rule 4: In last column (to the right) values do not increase downwards.

Fig. 2-15. Vanishing diagrams in Kronecker multiplication with Young tableaux

is clear that this weight exists only in one representation, the one shown in Fig. 2-14. This highest weight is the sum of the highest weights of the factors. We then use the ω_χ and map the complete representation; this included some weight which coincides with the second "highest weight" among all "highest weights" in the product. It should be the vector orthogonal to the one included in the representation we just mapped. We thus get its explicit value and can start mapping out the entire representation using the ω_χ etc.

Tables of SU(3) products have been prepared for a variety of cases.[6] Beyond our above discussion, we have only to treat the problem of several equivalent representations appearing in a product. In such cases, there are further free parameters which can be regarded as the freedom to pick our axes in a Euclidean space spanned by these representations. We have to use some further principle—

generally depending upon the physical problem. Charge conjugation, symmetry properties, etc., can be used to distinguish between the various equivalent representations.

One very important example occurs in the product

$$\mathbf{8} \times \mathbf{8} = \mathbf{1} + \mathbf{8} + \mathbf{27} + \mathbf{8} + \mathbf{10} + \mathbf{10}^* \tag{2.22}$$

The two octets are equivalent; however, looking at the product in terms of identical octet vector indices (and not in terms of the original $3 \times 3 \ldots$) we see that it splits into a symmetric $1 + 8 + 27$ and an antisymmetric $8 + 10 + 10^*$. These octet couplings are known as F (antisymmetric) and D (symmetric).

To understand the structure of these couplings, we refer to the 3×3 matrix representation of the various octets. Let us do this in terms of physical couplings; we study couplings $\bar{B}BP$ or $\bar{B}BV$, etc. We are projecting a scalar (0, 0) out of $(1, 1) \times (1, 1) \times (1, 1)$. In terms of matrices, this can only be the trace of the matrix product, as we require a linear invariant. There are two linearly independent scalars,

$$a \operatorname{Tr}(\bar{B}BP) \qquad b \operatorname{Tr}(\bar{B}PB)$$

we can replace these by commutator and anticommutator combinations,

$$f \operatorname{Tr}(\bar{B}[P, B]) \qquad d \operatorname{Tr}(\bar{B}\{P, B\})$$

and using Eqs. (2.2) and (2.3)

$$P^\alpha[\lambda_\alpha, \lambda_\beta] B^\beta = 2if_{\alpha\beta\gamma} P^\alpha B^\beta \lambda_\gamma$$

$$P^\alpha\{\lambda_\alpha, \lambda_\beta\} B^\beta = 2d_{\alpha\beta\gamma} P^\alpha B^\beta \lambda_\gamma$$

Since $\bar{B} = \bar{B}^\gamma \lambda_\gamma$ we find the couplings

$$f_{\alpha\beta\gamma} \bar{B}^\gamma P^\alpha B^\beta \qquad d_{\alpha\beta\gamma} \bar{B}^\gamma P^\alpha B^\beta$$

which are antisymmetric and symmetric in all three indices. If we differentiate these scalars by $(\partial/\partial P^{\alpha})$, for instance, we get antisymmetric and symmetric octets,

$$f_{\alpha\beta\gamma}\,\overline{B}^{\gamma}B^{\beta} \qquad d_{\alpha\beta\gamma}\,\overline{B}^{\gamma}B^{\beta}$$

We note that the $f_{\alpha\beta\gamma}$ coupling is the one we get through "universality" considerations.

We shall discuss these points in Chapter 4. In the meantime, we observe that we get from equations (2.13) and (2.14),

$$\overline{B}^{\gamma} f_{\alpha\beta\gamma} B^{\beta} = i\overline{B}^{\gamma} F^{\alpha}_{(\beta,\gamma)} B^{\beta} = i\overline{B}F^{\alpha}B \tag{2.23}$$

i.e., we have fermion bilinears $\overline{B}B$ whose arrangement corresponds to the generators of U(3), in the particular representation of the B^{β}. They will thus perform just those transitions we listed in Table 2.1; these are the *currents*. Covariantly, there is an additional Dirac γ^{μ} with a 4-vector index, so that (2.23) forms a charge-current four-vector. Alternatively, we can think of (2.23) as meson states "made of" $\overline{B}B$ current-like combinations; they then represent (with the 4-vector index) the V set of vector-mesons, which are coupled to the conserved currents of unitary spins. The coupling is just the natural number appearing in the abstract F^{α} matrix representation of the generators, which is why it is called "universal": it would be the same in

$$i\partial^{\mu}\,\overline{P}^{\gamma} F^{\alpha}_{(\beta,\gamma)} P^{\beta}$$

i.e., for mesons, etc.

In a field theory[7] we can derive universality through a local gauge principle by using the Yang-Mills method (see Chapter 4). This is because the mesons (vector mesons in this case) are coupled to conserved currents; these currents are given, according to Noether's theorem by the product canonical momentum $\times$ variation of the fields

The canonical momentum is $\bar{B}\gamma^{\mu} \equiv \bar{B}^{\gamma} \lambda_{\gamma}\gamma^{\mu}$; the variation under $\exp(ia^{\alpha}\lambda_{\alpha})$ is

$$ia^{\alpha}[\lambda_{\alpha}, \lambda_{\beta}]B^{\beta} = -2a^{\alpha} f_{\alpha\beta\gamma} B^{\beta} \lambda_{\gamma}$$

and we get

$$L = \bar{B}^{\gamma} \gamma^{\mu} f_{\gamma\alpha\beta} B^{\beta} V_{\mu}^{\alpha} + \text{h.c.} \qquad (2.24)$$

In Appendix 1 we include the f_{ijk}, d_{ijk} coefficients. The entire reduction of **8** $\times$ **8** is given in Appendix 2.

RACAH COEFFICIENTS

One is often faced with the following problem: given a reaction $\phi_1 + \phi_2 \longleftrightarrow \phi_3^* + \phi_4^*$ in the s-channel, what are the contributions of the various amplitudes $\phi_1 + \phi_3 \longleftrightarrow \phi_2^* + \phi_4^*$ in the t-channel (we have defined all particles ϕ_n with incoming momenta in the Mandelstam amplitude) to the independent s-channels? Mathematically, this is just a matter of studying the linearly independent scalars (0, 0) contained in the $\phi_1 \times \phi_2 \times \phi_3 \times \phi_4$ product. If we denote the s-amplitudes by A, B . . . and their components by $\alpha, \beta \ldots$ and the t-amplitudes by X, Y . . . with components ξ, η, we may describe s-channel and t-channel amplitudes as

$$p^{A} = \sum_{\alpha\beta} a_{ij}^{A\alpha\beta} b_{k\ell}^{A\alpha\beta} \phi_1^{i} \phi_2^{j} \phi_3^{k} \phi_4^{\ell} \qquad (2.25')$$

$$p^{X} = \sum_{\xi\eta} x_{mn}^{X\xi\eta} y_{uv}^{X\xi\eta} \phi_1^{m} \phi_2^{n} \phi_3^{u} \phi_4^{v} \qquad (2.25'')$$

and the Racah coefficient is R_X^A in

$$p^{A} = R_X^A p^X \qquad (2.25)$$

In Appendix 2, we supply some of the R_X^A.

TRIALITY

It is important to note that only representations where the number of cells in the SU(3) tableau $(h_1 + h_2 - 2h_3)$ is a multiple of 3 have been observed to date. Baird and Biedenharn[8] have introduced the notion of triality τ, where

$$\left.\begin{aligned} &\tau \equiv h_1 + h_2 - 2h_3 \pmod 3 \\ &\text{and at the same time} \\ &\tau \equiv 3B \pmod 3 \end{aligned}\right\} \qquad (2.26)$$

which therefore assigns $\tau = 1$ to a quark, $\tau = -1$ to an antiquark and $\tau = 0$ to the observed 1, 8, 10, 10*. [These denote SU(3) representations by their dimensionality, whatever the B-number; 10* is (0, 0, −3) for an antibaryon or (1, 1, −2) for a meson, (−1, −1, −4) for the physical deuteron.]

Trialities are additive modulo 3, i.e., for $D_c \subset D_a \times D_b$ we get

$$\tau_c = \tau_a + \tau_b \pmod 3 \qquad (2.27)$$

Could it be that there are no $\tau = \pm 1$ representations in nature? If quarks really exist and are the basic constituents of all hadron states, fractional electric charges would forbid $\tau \neq 0$ states to mix and certainly to decay into $\tau = 0$ states; they could decay into each other through β-decay or K-capture.

Note that the $\tau = 0$ representations are the only vector representations of a group SU(3)/Z(3), or U(1) × SU(3)/Z(3) if we adjoin B. This group is related to SU(3) in much the same way as the 3-dimensional rotation group SO(3) is related to SU(2). The unimodularity condition allows as many as 3 elements in the group center Z(3), the set of group elements which commute with the entire group. For such as element A of Z(3)

$$A = \begin{vmatrix} \alpha & & \\ & \alpha & \\ & & \alpha \end{vmatrix}$$

to fulfill Det A = 1, we have $\alpha^3 = 1$, and α therefore can be 1, exp $(2\pi i/3)$, or exp $(4\pi i/3)$; this implies a three-valuedness of the $\tau = 1, -1$ representations, which disappears whenever we deal with representations appearing in a product of a multiplication of 3n, $\tau = \pm 1$ "iso trial" representations (n = an integer). If one were to explain the inappearance of $\tau = \pm 1$ representations, one could thus look for a model whose symmetry group is SU(3)/Z(3). However, this in itself would not suffice, as the physical picture corresponds to ray representations in the Hilbert space. The way out would thus be to go beyond postulation of SU(3)/Z(3) and assume the existence of a larger group containing it, provided this larger group does not have $\tau = \pm 1$ representations when going over to the rays. Such a group[9] may be SO(8). Its 8-dimensional representation (two conjugate spinor representations and one vector representation) all contain the (1, 1) representation of SU(3). All representations of the group SO(8) can be constructed from these three, so that we always have $\tau = 0$ representations of SU(3) only. SO(8) in that decomposition contains only SU(3)/Z(3) and would be almost the only alternative to systems allowing $\tau = \pm 1$.

UNITY PARITY

Working with SU(3), it is sometimes convenient to use its extension with the charge-conjugation operator[10] C. The effect is to add an inversion around the origin, in a 3-dimensional U(3) weight diagram. The inversion allows us to introduce a phase: by convention, this is the charge parity of the 3rd and 8th components, in an octet. The entire method works of course only for representations that are eigen-representations of C (i.e., that transform into themselves). For (3, 0)—the decuplet—for instance, we have to take (3, 0) + (0, 3) and (3, 0) − (0, 3), the combinations with a definite η_c for the neutral components.

A meson octet $\phi^{\alpha}{}_{1}$ for instance, has a definite unitary parity $\eta_u = \eta_c(\phi^1, \phi^3, \phi^4, \phi^6, \phi^8) = -\eta_c(\phi^2, \phi^5, \phi^7)$ where the upper indices correspond to octet components as in the matrices (5). In coupling SU(3) representations with definite unitary parity, the total unitary parity is conserved. It is given by the product of the individual unitary parities times the parities of the coupling coefficients: (+1) for symmetric couplings, (−1) for antisymmetric ones.

The inversion around the origin in an SU(3) weight diagram is known as R-inversion. It is not a good quantum number; however, it has been suggested[11] that R may somehow be useful for mesons only; one then uses

$$\eta_A = \eta_R \cdot \eta_C \qquad (2.28)$$

known as A-parity. The **8**, $j = 0^-$ then get $\eta_A = -1$, the **8**, $j = 1^-$ would have $\eta_A = +1$ (but with the ϕ as the 8th component); $\eta_A(\omega^0) = -1$, as $\omega^0 \to 3\pi$. Some A-violating reactions have been observed.

REFERENCES

1. Y. Ne'eman, *Nucl. Phys.*, **26**, 222 (1961).*
2. M. Gell-Mann, Cal. Tech. report CTSL-20 (1961) unpublished.*
3. H. Goldberg and Y. Ne'eman, *Nuovo Cimento* **27**, 1 (1963).
4. M. Gell-Mann, *Phys. Letters* **8**, 214 (1964).*
5. G. Zweig, CERN reports 8182/TH., 401 and 8419/TH., 412 (1964) unpublished.
6. H. Goldberg, Israel AEC report IA-834 (1963); J. J. de Swart, *Rev. Mod. Phys.*, **35**, 916 (1963);* Y. Dothan and

*Reprinted in *The Eightfold Way*, M. Gell-Mann and Y. Ne'eman, W. A. Benjamin, publisher (1964).

H. Harari, Israel AEC report IA-777 (1963), also published as *Nuovo Cimento Sup.*, **3**, 48 (1965); P. McNamee and F. Chilton, *Rev. Mod. Phys.*, **36**, 1005 (1965).

7. C. N. Yang and H. Mills, *Phys. Rev.*, **96**, 192 (1954) and R. Shaw, dissertation (unpublished) 1954. See also Refs. 1 and 2.
8. G. E. Baird and L. C. Biedenharn, *Proceedings of the 1964 First Coral Gables Conference on Symmetry Principles at High Energy*, W. H. Freeman Publishers, p. 58.
9. Y. Ne'eman, *Phys. Letters* **4**, 81 (1962) and **5**, 312 (1963); see also *Phys. Rev.*, **138**, B 1474 (1965).
10. Y. Dothan, *Nuovo Cimento* **30**, 399 (1963).
11. J. B. Bronzan and F. E. Low, *Phys. Rev. Letters*, **12**, 522 (1964).

3

THE ROLE OF ALGEBRA IN QUANTUM MECHANICS; COMPACT AND NONCOMPACT GENERATORS AND GROUPS

INTRODUCTION

We shall now review the entire algebraic approach and try to derive some methodological conclusions which will enable us at a later stage to make some specific suggestions with respect to the hadrons. The actual schemes we shall use are inspired by the application of two ideas somewhat new to particle physics,[1-4] the one physical and the other mathematical. Physically, we extend the algebraic approach to include the exploitation of algebras which do not generate symmetries of the system and can be used without appealing to an idealized picture in which they leave the Hamiltonian invariant. Mathematically, we make use of noncompact algebras in various roles, ensuring the conservation of probability through the use of unitary infinite-dimensional representations. We introduce a type of such representations which seems particularly suitable for the description of ideally-infinite sequences of energy levels.

THE HYDROGEN ATOM

A simple illustration of both concepts is given by the hydrogen atom. It is well known that the Hamiltonian with a $1/r$ potential has a larger symmetry than the spatial rotation group SO(3), in that it commutes with the Laplace-Lentz-Pauli operator (in the classical Kepler problem, **A** defines the direction and eccentricity of the ellipse; the trajectory is found by multiplying $\mathbf{A} \cdot \mathbf{r}$)

$$\mathbf{A} = \frac{1}{2Ze^2m} \{\mathbf{L} \times \mathbf{p}) - (\mathbf{p} \times \mathbf{L})\} = \frac{\mathbf{r}}{r} \qquad (3.1)$$

with the orthogonality condition

$$\mathbf{A} \cdot \mathbf{L} = 0$$

The angular momentum generators **L** and the operators

$$\mathbf{M} = (-2H)^{-1/2} \mathbf{A} \qquad (3.2)$$

close on the algebra of SO(4). The representations of this SO(4) are given in terms of (j, k), with

$$J_i = \tfrac{1}{2}(L_i + M_i) \quad \text{and} \quad K_i = \tfrac{1}{2}(L_i - M_i) \qquad (3.3)$$

and a subsidiary condition $J^2 = K^2$ which follows directly from the orthogonality of A and L. The spectrum consists of the following representations,

$$(0, 0), (\tfrac{1}{2}, \tfrac{1}{2}), (1, 1), (\tfrac{3}{2}, \tfrac{3}{2}), \ldots \qquad (3.4)$$

where (0, 0) is the 1s, $(\frac{1}{2}, \frac{1}{2})$ the 2s and 2p states, (1, 1) the n = 3 states, etc. Note that

$$-\frac{1}{2H} = \mathbf{L}^2 + \mathbf{M}^2 + 1$$

It has recently been pointed out[4] that there exist four additional noncompact generators N_α which, when commuted with the L_i and M_i, close upon SO(1, 4); the N_α thus represent rotations into a mathematical fifth and time-like dimension. One *ladder representation*[3,4] of this group is then just the entire infinite sequence (0, 0), $(\frac{1}{2}, \frac{1}{2})$, (1, 1), $(\frac{3}{2}, \frac{3}{2})$, ... mentioned above.

The explicit noncompact operators have been computed[5] by H. Bacry for the classical case and by R. Musto for the quantized one. The latter operators are,

$$N^{\circ} = N^{+} + N^{-}$$

$$\mathbf{N}^{1} = [i\, N^{+}\mathbf{M}(-2H)^{-1/2} - N^{+}(\mathbf{M} \wedge \mathbf{L})]K_{+}$$
$$- [i\, N^{-}\mathbf{M}(-2H)^{-1/2} + N^{-}(\mathbf{M} \wedge \mathbf{L})]K_{-} \qquad (3.6)$$

where

$$N\pm = \pm \tfrac{1}{2} H \left(i\, r\, p_r\, D_{\pm} \pm \frac{r\, D_{\pm}}{(-2H)^{-1/2} \pm \hbar} \pm D_{\pm}(-2H)^{-1/2} \right) H^{-1} \qquad (3.7)$$

$$D_{\pm} = \sum_{k=0}^{\infty} \frac{1}{k!} \left(\frac{-i}{\hbar} \right)^{k} (\mathbf{r} \cdot \mathbf{p})^{k} [\log \{1 \pm \hbar(-2H)^{-1/2}\}]^{k} \qquad (3.8)$$

$$K_{\pm} = -\left(\frac{1}{2H} \pm \hbar(-2H)^{-1/2} + L^{2} \right)^{-1} \qquad (3.9)$$

Note that[6] one can define an additional set of such operators P, introduce an ''orthogonality-type'' condition between the N and P sets and get the generators of SO(2, 4) = SU(2, 2). Closure will introduce a compact generator $-iS = [N^{i}, P^{i}]$ whose eigenvalues will coincide with the principal quantum number n.

It has been claimed that little could be learned from the hydrogen atom because it does not supply a model for couplings, an important problem at the hadron level. It has also been claimed that the dynamical SO(4) symmetry of hydrogen does not survive when dealing with scattering situations, thus distinguishing it from hadron symmetries. We shall try to show that one can indeed carry the hydrogen example much further than that.

The analogue to hadron couplings is not two-atom scattering. It does emerge from the study of the two-electron bound-state spectrum (we leave out spin) as the product of two single-electron spectra in the same $Z = 2$ potential. To get the idealized unbroken-symmetry situation, we also leave out the Coulomb interaction between the two electrons, which we can later treat as a symmetry-breaking term. The "new" two-electron wave function is thus distinct from the product of the two sets of bound states only through the Pauli principle. This is in fact a prescription in picking the physical combined bound-state spectrum out of the reduction of this product. To simplify our example, assume some cut-off for the Z/r potential, so that each electron has the following allowed spectrum to start with (we use 3.3),

$N_{J=L}$	$(j, \mathbf{k})$	SO(4) dimensionality d
2s, 2p	$(\frac{1}{2}, \frac{1}{2})$	4
1s	$(0, 0)$	1

With a finite set of bound states, we may replace SO(1, 4) by SO(5), and the above spectrum is **5**, a 5-vector. The product of the two one-electron spectra is

$$\mathbf{5} \times \mathbf{5} = \mathbf{10} + \mathbf{14} + \mathbf{1}$$

the 10 representing the antisymmetric combinations. These are the only ones allowed by the Pauli principle. The SO(4) content is

$$(\mathbf{4} + \mathbf{1}) \times (\mathbf{4} + \mathbf{1}) = (\mathbf{4} + \mathbf{3} + \mathbf{3})_{\text{antisym}}$$

$$+ (\mathbf{9} + \mathbf{4} + \mathbf{1}) + \mathbf{1}$$

Indeed the two-electron states will respect a symmetry defined by $\mathbf{J}(e_1) + \mathbf{J}(e_2) = \mathbf{J}^{\text{Tot}}$ (the total angular momentum of the electron shells) and $M(e_1) + M(e_2) = M^{\text{Tot}}$. It is clear that when one electron is in "its own" 1s state, the other is in "its" $(\frac{1}{2}, \frac{1}{2})$ so that the "total" SO(4) is $d^{Tot} = 4$, containing $J^{Tot} = 0, 1$; that when the 1s is empty in both "original" spectra we may have one electron in its 2s and the other in any 2p situation, i.e., we are in a resulting antisymmetric $d^{Tot} = 3$ in the 4×4 product (with $J^{Tot} = 1$); and that if both are in their 2p states we again get $J^{Tot} = 1$ and are in a $d^{Tot} = 3$. We have thus created a situation in which the new spectrum 10 does indeed represent a coupling; and we observe that SO(5) classifies coupled states through a representation appearing in the product of the original discrete spectra. We also note that the dynamical origin of the SO(4) symmetry carries over to the coupled states.

We can thus abstract the following lesson: hadron couplings may be symmetric under a large group which is no symmetry of the Hamiltonian but nevertheless classifies the solutions. There is an algebra providing a symmetry of the entire Hamiltonian, but in a field theory we now see that the Interaction-Hamiltonian may obey an even larger symmetry, the symmetry of the spectrum generating algebra. This is easily realized in a strong-coupling model in which the interaction Hamiltonian may support more symmetry then the kinetic energy term, e.g., some type of spin-independence. However, we see here that such a result is much more general. Of course, the actual hydrogen problem has in addition a Coulomb repulstion between electrons, and we shall get contributions from the one-electron continua, breaking SO(4). Both SO(4) and SO(1, 4) can only be useful if their matrix elements still "saturate" mainly between the states of the discrete spectrum.

THE THOMAS-REICHE-KUHN SUM RULE

Let us now introduce an additional set of operators acting upon the above ladder representation. Take for example the dipole-moment operators

$$d_i = er_i \qquad (3.10)$$

and their time derivatives,

$$\dot{d}_i = i[H, d_i] = \frac{e}{m} P_i \tag{3.11}$$

with their commutation relations then given by

$$[\dot{d}_i, d_j] = -i \frac{e^2}{m} \delta_{ij} \tag{3.12}$$

leading to the result

$$\sum_i [\dot{d}_i, d_i] = -i \frac{3e^2}{m} \tag{3.13}$$

We now compute the matrix elements of the commutator for the 1s state, expanding the various products over all states,

$$\langle 1s | [\dot{d}_i, d_i] | 1s \rangle = 2i \sum_n (E_1 - E_n) \times |\langle 1s | d_i | n \rangle|^2$$

from which we get the well-known Thomas-Reiche-Kuhn sum rule,

$$\sum_{n,i} (E_1 - E_n) |\langle 1s | d_i | n \rangle|^2 = -\frac{3e^2}{2m} \tag{3.14}$$

This treatment provides us with examples of algebraic systems which are by definition *not* symmetries. The N_α exist for the sole purpose of connecting *different* solutions of the Schrödinger equation corresponding to different representations of the Hamiltonian's symmetry, which is SO(4). In actual physical situations, the SO(4) algebra itself is really an approximate symmetry algebra (ASA), due to the presence of fine and hyperfine structure; in hadron physics, we in fact have mostly ASA, considering that only the electric and baryon charge gauges are perfect symmetries. Note also that for SO(4) to be useful, i.e. to be imposed on couplings, we have to make sure that its generators connect one-particle states with most of the strength of their matrix elements. If they do not have such an approximate *saturation*, the continuum states will destroy the usefulness of the ASA.

The complete SO(1, 4) is not an approximate symmetry group in the usual sense; to achieve invariance, we would have to turn off the 1/r potential which distinguishes between SO(4) levels, and the fully degenerate idealization would bear only the remotest resemblance to the original problem. However, its algebra does play a physical role and fixes the complete set of solutions; had we not been given the actual Schrödinger equation for the hydrogen atom, we could still have listed all states just from the knowledge of the *spectrum generating algebra* (SGA) of the problem, here SO(1, 4). Note that this is really the situation in particle physics, where we shall indeed replace some unmanageable dynamics by the postulation of such an SGA, identified phenomenologically from the experimental spectrum of eigenstates of the Hamiltonian. Also, we observe that replacing SO(1, 4) by our SO(5) group would look at first like an ASA (the states in a **5** or **10** are not too distant in energy), but we would then be unable to use the same group to classify the rest of the spectrum.

The d_i and $\dot{d}_i$ provide us with a third type of physical operator algebra. They close upon the three-dimensional Heisenberg algebra and have matrix elements connecting any states all over the spectrum. However, we see that we can still derive some results from this *transition-operator algebra* (TOA) in the form of sum rules like (3.14), provided the summation over states can be stopped at some level which is not very distant from the state acted upon (here the 1s). Following Dashen and Gell-Mann[1], we therefore regard such systems as useful if the generators connect us mostly to states lying nearby in the energy (in our sum rule we see in fact that the matrix elements become very small for higher n values). In actual practice in hadron physics, dispersion relations provide us with methods of estimating contributions of a continuum directly from experimental quantities, assuming that the dispersion integrals converge.

We thus have come across three types of algebras of physical operators. Only the ASA can meaningfully be considered to commute with the Hamiltonian. They have roughly one irreducible representation per level, though sometimes it may be a reducible one like $8 + 1$ of SU(3) for the vector mesons on p. 25. The SGA do not generate symmetries, but they fix the spectrum through the fact that it corresponds to one or more of their irreducible representations, reducing into a direct sum of irreducible representations of the ASA contained in them. The TOA straddle the entire spectrum in a disorderly fashion but have one property making them useful still, i.e., their matrix elements converge and lead mainly to nearby states.

NONCOMPACT GENERATORS

In particle physics the internal or external generators F^a in an algebra fulfilling any of the above-mentioned roles may belong to a noncompact group. Indeed, well-known examples are provided by the Lorentz and Poincaré groups (the homogeneous and inhomogeneous transformation-symmetries of Minkowski space). The generators have to remain Hermitian, as they correspond to physical observables; the structure-constants f^{abc} are now not antisymmetric in the (b, c) indices, and the p-dimensional F^a matrices are not orthogonal, and therefore not even hermitian, because of the reality of the f^{abc}. The Killing-Cartan classification of Lie algebras and Lie groups (see Appendix 3) restricts the available algebras to the four series A_r (isomorphic to the traceless $r + 1$ dimensional matrices), B_r ($\approx$ to orthogonal $2r + 1$ dimensional matrices), C_r ($\approx$ to symplectic $2r$ dimensional matrices), D_r ($\approx$ orthogonal $2r$ dimensional matrices) and the five isolated G_2, F_4, E_6, E_7, E_8. When the defining representation generators R^a are Hermitian, we get the compact algebras,

$$[R^a, R^b] = i\, r^{ab}{}_c\, R^c \qquad (3.15)$$

representing the physical commutator,

$$[F^a, F^b] = i r^{ab}{}_c F^c \tag{3.16}$$

The noncompact generators N^d are isomorphic to anti-Hermitian matrices iR^d in the defining representation, so that

$$[N^d, N^e] = -i r^{de}{}_f R^f \tag{3.17}$$

we note the change of sign in the structure constant. The entire algebra splits into a compact sub-algebra K^a and the noncompact generators N^a, so that

$$[K^a, K^b] = i r^{ab}{}_c K^c \tag{3.18}$$

$$[K^a, N^d] = i r^{ad}{}_g N^g \tag{3.19}$$

$$[N^d, N^e] = -i r^{de}{}_f K^f \tag{3.20}$$

With the $N^d \approx iR^d$, $(R^d)^\dagger = R^d$, there is no finite-dimensional hermitian representation of the N^d. They have to be represented in an *infinite-dimensional representation*; such a representation can be constructed for example for the algebra generating the group SO(1, 2) of orthogonal transformations in a space with signature (−1, 1, 1). The generators of this algebra

$$N^1 \approx i\sigma^1, \; N^2 \approx i\sigma^2, \; K^3 \approx \sigma^3 \tag{3.21}$$

are isomorphic to the corresponding generators of SU(2), with rotations around the 3rd axis remaining real, whereas the other transformations describe rotations by imaginary angles (going between space-like and time-like directions). A Hermitian representation is given by

$$N^1 = \tfrac{1}{2}\left|\begin{array}{ccccccc} \cdot & 1 & \cdot & \cdot & \cdot & \cdot & \cdot \\ 1 & \cdot & 2 & \cdot & \cdot & \cdot & \cdot \\ \cdot & 2 & \cdot & 3 & \cdot & \cdot & \\ \cdot & \cdot & 3 & \cdot & 4 & \cdot & \\ \cdot & \cdot & \cdot & 4 & \cdot & \cdot & \\ \cdot & & & & & & \end{array}\right.$$

$$N^2 = \tfrac{1}{2}\left|\begin{array}{cccccc} \cdot & i & \cdot & \cdot & \cdot & \cdot \\ -i & \cdot & 2i & \cdot & \cdot & \cdot \\ \cdot & -2i & \cdot & 3i & \cdot & \cdot \\ \cdot & \cdot & -3i & \cdot & 4i & \cdot \\ \cdot & \cdot & \cdot & -4i & \cdot & \cdot \\ \cdot & \cdot & \cdot & \cdot & \cdot & \cdot \end{array}\right. \qquad (3.22)$$

$$K^3 = \tfrac{1}{2}\left|\begin{array}{ccccc} 1 & \cdot & \cdot & \cdot & \cdot \\ \cdot & 3 & \cdot & \cdot & \cdot \\ \cdot & \cdot & 5 & \cdot & \cdot \\ \cdot & \cdot & \cdot & \cdot & \end{array}\right.$$

Suppose we were dealing with a gauge group SO(1, 2). In that case, additive conservation-laws exist

$$\frac{d}{dt} N^1 = 0 \qquad \frac{d}{dt} N^2 = 0 \qquad \frac{d}{dt} K^3 = 0 \qquad (3.23)$$

The continuity equations also hold,

$$\partial^{\alpha} j_{\alpha}(N^1) = 0 \qquad \partial_{\alpha} j_{\alpha}(N^2) = 0$$

$$\partial_{\alpha} j_{\alpha}(K^3) = 0 \qquad (3.24)$$

but the only possible matrix representations for N^1, N^2, $j_{\alpha}(N^1)$ and $j_{\alpha}(N^2)$ are infinite-dimensional (note that as in (2.24) $j^{\alpha a} = i\pi^{\alpha r} S^a \phi_r$, and here $S^a \sim N^a$). Writing such $j_{\alpha}(N^i)$ as a fermion bilinear, for instance, would require infinite-dimensional multiplets ϕ_r, $r = 1 \cdots \infty$. Moreover, the 3-dimensional adjoint representation itself being non-unitary (i.e., with non-Hermitian generators), we cannot have the SO(1, 2) group as a local-gauge requiring a Yang-Mills interaction. Indeed, any $\phi_{\alpha a}$ vector-mesons would also have infinite multiplicities as they would also have to contribute to the $j_\alpha(N^i)$.

In Chapter **10**, we describe a method for the construction of ladder representations.[3,7]

REFERENCES

1. R. Dashen and M. Gell-Mann, *Phys. Letters* **17**, 142 (1965).* The basic assumption in this paper has however to be refined as suggested by S. Coleman; all statements should apply to matrix elements of commutators. We shall discuss this problem in Chapter 8. See also Ref. 20 in Chapter 8.
2. R. Dashen and M. Gell-Mann, *Phys. Letters* **17**, 145 (1965).*
3. Y. Dothan, M. Gell-Mann and Y. Ne'eman, *Phys. Letters* **17**, 148 (1965).*
4. Y. Dothan and Y. Ne'eman, *Proc. of the 1965 Athens (Ohio) Conf. on Resonant Particles*, p. 17.* See also A. O. Barut, P. Budini and C. Fronsdal, *Proc. Roy. Soc.* **A291**, 106 (1966); for representations of SO(1, 4), see L. H. Thomas, *Ann. Math.* **42**, 113 (1941).
5. H. Bacry, *Nuovo Cimento* **41**, A222 (1966); R. Musto, *Phys. Rev.* **148**, 1274 (1966).

*Reprinted in *Symmetry Groups*, F. J. Dyson, W. A. Benjamin, publisher (1966).

6. Y. Ne'eman, "Comptes-Rendus du Colloque (1966) du C.R.N.S. sur les Extensions du Groupe de Poincaré aux Symetries internes des Particules Elementaires," to be published. See also I. A. Malkin and V. A. Manko, *JETP Letters* **2**, 146 (1965).
7. I. M. Gelfand and M. A. Naimark, "Unitary Representations of the Classical Groups," Germ. transl. Akademie-Verlag, Berlin (East) 1957.

4

UNITARY SYMMETRY

ASSIGNMENTS

The known hadron spectrum[1,2] contains several well defined U(3) multiplets and many unclassified states; the latter seem to yield to the classification at the rate of about one new multiplet per year.

The baryon multiplets consist of,

(a) $j = \frac{1}{2}^+$, $d = 8$ (the defining representation[3,4]). This will be completely settled when the parity of $\Xi(1314)$ is measured in the present polarized target experiments.

(b) $j = \frac{3}{2}^+$, $d = 10$. The assignment[5] will be completely settled when the spin and parity of $\Omega(1674)$ are measured.[6]

(c) $j = \frac{5}{2}^+$, $d = 8$, consisting[7] of $N(1688, \frac{5}{2}^+)$, $\Lambda(1820, \frac{5}{2}^+)$, $\Sigma(1910, \frac{5}{2}^+ ?)$, $\Xi(1930, \frac{5}{2}^+ ?)$.

(d) $j = \frac{7}{2}^+$, $d = 10$, consisting[7] of $\Delta(1920, \frac{7}{2}^+)$, $\Sigma(2035, \frac{7}{2}^+)$, and the as yet undiscovered $\Xi(\sim 2100)$ and $\Omega(2200\text{-}2300)$.

(e) $j = \frac{1}{2}^-$, $d = 1$, the[7] $\Lambda(1405, \frac{1}{2}^-) \rightarrow \Sigma + \pi$.

Other multiplets are very problematic:

(f) $j = \frac{3}{2}^-$, $d = 8$ or $d = 8 + 1$. We have[2,7] $N(1518, \frac{3}{2}^-)$, $\Lambda(1700, ?)$, $\Sigma(1600, \frac{3}{2}^- ?)$, $\Xi(1820, ?)$ and $\Lambda(1520, \frac{3}{2}^-)$.

(g) $j = \frac{5}{2}^-$, $d = 8$ or 10^*, based upon the conjectured $N(1688, \frac{5}{2}^-)$, $\Sigma(1765, \frac{5}{2}^-)$.

(h) $j = \frac{1}{2}^+$, $d = 8?$, if indeed the phase-shift analysis studies should be considered[2] as a proof of the existence of $N(1400, \frac{1}{2}^+)$.

(i) $j = \frac{1}{2}^-$; there are some hypothetical states[2] corresponding to d = 10, 8 or 27.

For the mesons, we have four "good" nonets d = 1 + 8. U(3) is only an approximate symmetry, and $\Delta Y = \Delta I = 0$ transitions are allowed to occur either via the strong interaction itself or some as yet unidentified medium-strong force. We shall discuss this problem in some detail in Chapter 5. Meanwhile, we note that for equal j^P, the d = 1 state mixes with the I = 0, Y = 0 state in d = 8; from general considerations of quantum mechanics we know that this mixing will be mainly strong if for some other reasons the "original" unmixed levels lie close to each other.

(a) $j = 0^-$. Here $\eta(959, 0^-)$ is the d = 1 and does not mix much with $\eta(549, 0^-)$ of d = 8.

(b) $j = 1^-$. This includes the well-known case[4,8] of a strong mixing in the ϕ-ω states, perhaps related to a further observed selection rule ($\phi \not\rightarrow \rho + \pi$) and explained in triplet models, in which ϕ is $ss^\dagger$ and ω is $(uu^\dagger + dd^\dagger)$. The observed mixing corresponds to a value $\theta = 38°$ of the mixing angle.

(c) $j = 2^+$, with[9] mixed f° (1254) and f°′ (1500), the A_2 (1300) and K(1415). Here $\theta \sim 30°$.

(d) $j = 1^+$, with[10] mixed D(1286) and E(1425), the isovector A_1 (1080) and K(1320). This yields $\theta \sim 30°$.

There are further states like the $B(1220) \rightarrow \omega + \pi$ which could be a 1^+, d = 8 with $\eta_u = -1$, as against the above mentioned 1^+ octet whose $\eta_u = +1$.

INTENSITY RULES

One obvious application of a symmetry postulate, after the assignment of particles to suitable representations, is the derivation of relationships between the amplitudes for processes that have been linked together by the new symmetry assignments. Such results can be found from the Clebsch-Gordan coefficients describing the various allowed amplitudes. One can either read these coefficients directly in some table or compute them easily enough. For example by using Goldberg's table in Appendix II, we can reproduce tables like Table 4-1, which is taken from a calculation of Levinson et al.[11] Note that because of the equivalence of the two (1, 1) channels, there is, in addition to the symmetric and anti-symmetric octects (a convenient choice) an "off-diagonal" element X which couples the two together.

These coefficients will be the same if we replace the mesons or baryons by vector mesons, baryons or antibaryons with the same eightspin (or unitary spin) charges,* though one should also check whether charge-conjugation (or unitary parity) will not close some channels.

An alternative approach, based on Weyl reflections and the I-U-V SU(2) subgroups leads to many shortcuts. It was first used for the Sakata model[11] and then applied to the octet.[12] We shall tackle one example so as to illustrate the method (see Fig. 4-1).

SU(3) contains three SU(2) subgroups, one of which is isospin I. In the weight diagram of Fig. 4-1, $U_{(2)}$ transformations perpendicular to axis "1" correspond to isospin transformations and the Y gauge transformation. However, similar $U_{(2)}$ transformations perpendicular to axis "2" or "3" are also symmetry operations of SU(3) (though, of course, broken by the mass spectrum). Take the axis "2" set. The weight diagrams have been redrawn with axis "2" verticals. Members of the same "U" spin multiplet have the same electric charge. The Weyl reflections in this case would exchange $p - \Sigma^+$, $n - \Xi^0$, $\pi^+ - K^+$, etc. (they correspond to the discrete operation of charge-symmetry in I-spin). This reduces the number of free amplitudes, e.g., we may equate

$$\pi^+ + \Sigma^- \rightarrow K^- + p$$

*To distinguish between the SU(3) charges corresponding to the octet and Sakata "models," I had suggested "eightspin" for the octet base. However the discovery of the Ω^- brought a quick and clearcut proof of the octet choice, and "unitary" spin is now generally identified with this "scale."

Table 4-1
Scattering amplitudes $A^{(\lambda,\mu)}$ for meson-baryon processes.

(λ, μ):	(2, 2)	$(1, 1)_+$	$(1, 1)_-$	(3, 0)	(0, 3)	(0, 0)	X
1. $(K^- n \mid K^- n)$	$\frac{1}{5}$	$\frac{3}{10}$	$\frac{1}{6}$	$\frac{1}{6}$	$\frac{1}{6}$	0	$-\frac{1}{\sqrt{5}}$
2. $(\pi^- p \mid \pi^- p)$	$\frac{1}{5}$	$\frac{3}{10}$	$\frac{1}{6}$	$\frac{1}{6}$	$\frac{1}{6}$	0	$\frac{1}{\sqrt{5}}$
3. $(K^- n \mid K^0 \Xi^-)$	$\frac{1}{5}$	$\frac{3}{10}$	$-\frac{1}{6}$	$-\frac{1}{6}$	$-\frac{1}{6}$	0	0
4. $(\pi^- p \mid K^+ \Sigma^-)$	$\frac{1}{5}$	$\frac{3}{10}$	$-\frac{1}{6}$	$-\frac{1}{6}$	$-\frac{1}{6}$	0	0
5. $(\pi^+ p \mid \pi^+ p)$	$\frac{1}{2}$	0	0	$\frac{1}{2}$	0	0	0
6. $(\pi^+ p \mid K^+ \Sigma^+)$	$\frac{1}{2}$	0	0	$-\frac{1}{2}$	0	0	0
7. $(K^+ n \mid K^0 p)$	$\frac{1}{2}$	0	0	0	$-\frac{1}{2}$	0	0
8. $(K^+ n \mid K^+ n)$	$\frac{1}{2}$	0	0	0	$\frac{1}{2}$	0	0

9. $(K^-p \mid K^-p)$	$\frac{7}{40}$	$\frac{1}{5}$	$\frac{1}{3}$	$\frac{1}{12}$	$\frac{1}{12}$	$\frac{1}{8}$	0
10. $(K^-p \mid \overline{K}^0 n)$	$\frac{1}{40}$	$\frac{1}{10}$	$-\frac{1}{6}$	$\frac{1}{12}$	$\frac{1}{12}$	$-\frac{1}{8}$	$-\frac{1}{\sqrt{5}}$
11. $(K^-p \mid \pi^- \Sigma^+)$	$\frac{1}{40}$	$\frac{1}{10}$	$-\frac{1}{6}$	$\frac{1}{12}$	$\frac{1}{12}$	$-\frac{1}{8}$	$\frac{1}{\sqrt{5}}$
12. $(K^-p \mid \pi^+ \Sigma^-)$	$\frac{1}{40}$	$\frac{1}{10}$	$\frac{1}{6}$	$-\frac{1}{12}$	$-\frac{1}{12}$	$-\frac{1}{8}$	0
13. $(K^-p \mid K^0 \Xi^0)$	$\frac{1}{40}$	$\frac{1}{10}$	$\frac{1}{6}$	$-\frac{1}{12}$	$-\frac{1}{12}$	$-\frac{1}{8}$	0
14. $(K^-p \mid \pi^0 \Sigma^0)$	$\frac{1}{40}$	$\frac{1}{10}$	0	0	0	$-\frac{1}{8}$	$-\frac{1}{2\sqrt{5}}$
15. $(K^-p \mid \pi^0 \Lambda)$	$\frac{\sqrt{3}}{10}$	$-\frac{\sqrt{3}}{10}$	0	$\frac{1}{4\sqrt{3}}$	$-\frac{1}{4\sqrt{3}}$	0	$\frac{1}{2\sqrt{15}}$
16. $(\pi^-p \mid K^0 \Lambda)$	$-\frac{1}{10}\sqrt{\frac{3}{2}}$	$\frac{1}{10}\sqrt{\frac{3}{2}}$	$\frac{1}{2\sqrt{6}}$	0	$-\frac{1}{2\sqrt{6}}$	0	$\sqrt{\frac{2}{15}}$
17. $(\pi^-p \mid \pi^0 n)$	$\frac{3}{10}\sqrt{\frac{1}{2}}$	$-\frac{3}{10}\sqrt{\frac{1}{2}}$	$-\frac{1}{6\sqrt{2}}$	$\frac{1}{3\sqrt{2}}$	$-\frac{1}{6\sqrt{2}}$	0	$-\sqrt{\frac{1}{10}}$

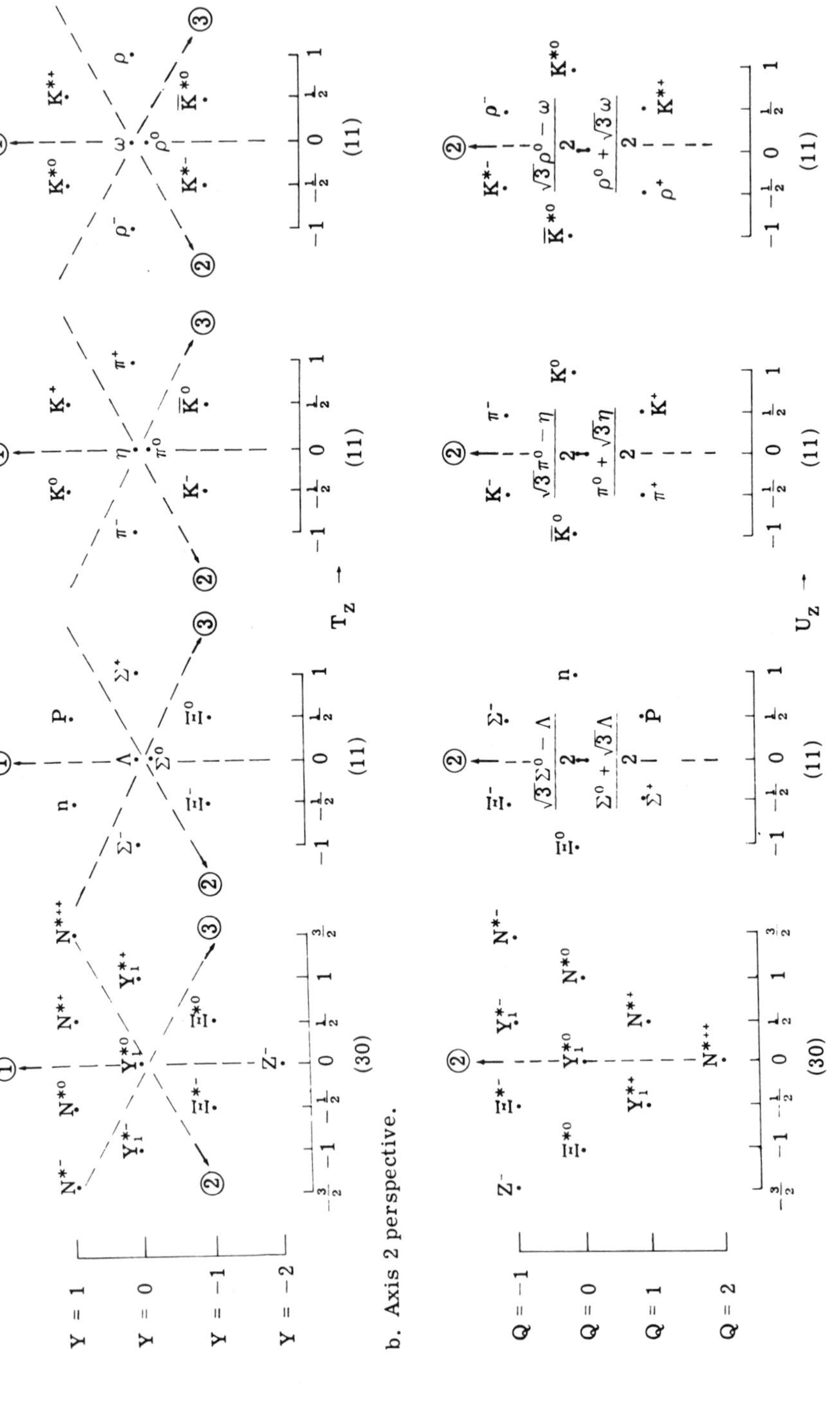

Y = 1
Y = 0
Y = −1
Y = −2
(30)
(11)
(11)
(11)
T_z →
b. Axis 2 perspective.
Q = −1
Q = 0
Q = 1
Q = 2
(30)
(11)
(11)
(11)
U_z →

Fig. 4-1

by adjoining the axes "3" and "1" reflections, with

$$K^- + p \rightarrow K^0 + \Xi^0$$

We find

$$\langle K^-p \,|\, \pi^+\Sigma^- \rangle = \langle K^0\Xi^0 \,|\, K^-p \rangle \tag{4.1}$$

or, similarly,

$$\langle n\pi^+ \,|\, \Sigma^+K^0 \rangle = \langle K^+\Xi^0 \,|\, \overline{K}{}^0 p \rangle \tag{4.2}$$

from axis "2" reflection, and some forty other such expressions.

The next step consists in making use of U-spin in its continuous transformations, instead of the discrete reflections.

Looking at the diagrams in Fig. 4-1 we see that (π^-p) is a system with $U = 1$, $U_Z = 1$. The processes

$$\begin{aligned} \pi^-p &\rightarrow \Delta^-(1238) + \rho^+(750) \\ \pi^-p &\rightarrow Y_1^{*-}(1385) + K^{*+}(880) \end{aligned} \tag{4.3}$$

then depend upon a single $U = 1$ amplitude T. The branching ratio is given by the Clebsch-Gordan coefficients $U_1 U_2 M_1 M_2 \,|\, UM)$ for the allowed coupling of the $U = \frac{3}{2}$ multiplet of Δ^- and Y_1^{*-} with the $U = \frac{1}{2}$ multiplet of ρ^+ and K^{*+},

$$\frac{(\pi^-p \,|\, \Delta^-\rho^+)}{(\pi^-p \,|\, Y_1^{*-}K^{*+})} = \frac{(\frac{3}{2}\,\frac{1}{2}\,\frac{3}{2} - \frac{1}{2} \,|\, 11)T}{(\frac{3}{2}\,\frac{1}{2}\,\frac{1}{2}\,\frac{1}{2} \,|\, 11)T} = -\sqrt{3} \tag{4.4}$$

The following relations are thus deduced,

$$\begin{aligned} (\pi^-p \,|\, Y_1^{*-}K^{*+}) &= (K^-p \,|\, \Xi^{*-}K^{*+}) = (K^-p \,|\, Y_1^{*-}\rho^+) \\ &= -(1/\sqrt{3})(\pi^-p \,|\, \Delta^-\rho^+) \end{aligned} \tag{4.5}$$

or also

$$(\pi^- p \,|\, Y_1^{*-} K^+) = (K^- p \,|\, \Xi^{*-} K^+) = -(K^- p \,|\, Y_1^{*-} \pi^+) \tag{4.6}$$
$$= -(1/\sqrt{3})(\pi^- p \,|\, \Delta^- \pi^+) \qquad \text{etc.}$$

It is interesting to note that the experimental angular distributions for the reactions $(\pi^- p \,|\, Y_1^{*-} K^+)$ and $(K^- p \,|\, Y_1^{*-} \pi^+)$ both show peaking of the Y_1^{*-} in the backward direction. One would therefore expect to see the same behavior in the case of Ξ^{*-} and Δ^-. This is implied by the symmetry here, and corresponds to a wealth of further predictions relating to polarizations—where the symmetry induces a Pauli principle effect, or some time-invariance reduction of the number of available amplitudes.[13] Harari[14] has lately emphasized an alternative technique for the derivation of results like the above equalities—looking at the crossed reaction's U(3) properties. In this case one finds $(\pi^- \pi^- \,|\, \bar{p} \Delta^-)$, $(K^- \pi^- \,|\, \bar{p} Y^{*-})$, $(\pi^- K^- \,|\, \bar{p} Y^{*-})$ and $(K^- K^- \,|\, \bar{p} \Xi^{*-})$. These all describe $Q = -2$ states; in the product of 8×8 on each side, they appear only in representation 27; they thus have to be proportional, and when going back to the uncrossed reaction one gets (4.6).

Sudarshan and collaborators[15] have generalized Shmushkevich's method to parent symmetries in general, and to eightspin in particular. Take for example the decay of Δ(1238) MeV):

$$\begin{array}{ll} \Delta^{++} \to p + \pi^+ (\Gamma_1) & \Delta^0 \to p + \pi^- (\Gamma_4) \\ \Delta^+ \to p + \pi^0 (\Gamma_2) & \Delta^0 \to n + \pi^0 (\Gamma_5) \\ \Delta^+ \to n + \pi^+ (\Gamma_3) & \Delta^- \to n + \pi^- (\Gamma_6) \end{array} \tag{4.7}$$

For isospin conservation, the method consists in stating

$$\Gamma_1 = \Gamma_2 + \Gamma_3 = \Gamma_4 + \Gamma_5 = \Gamma_6 \tag{4.8}$$

(i.e., equal total widths, from the charge independence of Δ).

However, we could read these decays with the nucleon only on the right-hand side. Equalizing for (p, n),

$$\Gamma_1 + \Gamma_2 + \Gamma_4 = \Gamma_3 + \Gamma_5 + \Gamma_6 \qquad (4.9)$$

and similarly for $(\pi^+ \pi^0 \pi^-)$,

$$\Gamma_1 + \Gamma_3 = \Gamma_2 + \Gamma_5 = \Gamma_4 + \Gamma_6 \qquad (4.10)$$

Together we get

$$2\Gamma_1 = 3\Gamma_2 = 6\Gamma_3 = 6\Gamma_4 = 3\Gamma_5 = 2\Gamma_6 \qquad (4.11)$$

which is equivalent to taking the Clebsch-Gordan coefficients. Similarly, for perfect eightspin conservation we get (for squared matrix elements summed over the entire isomultiplets)

$$\begin{aligned} 3(\Delta N\pi) &= 12(Y_1^* N\overline{K}) = 8(Y_1^* \Lambda\pi) = 12(Y_1^* \Sigma\pi) \\ &= 12(\Xi^* \Lambda\overline{K}) = 12(\Xi^* \Sigma\overline{K}) = 6(\Omega\Xi\overline{K}) \\ &= 3(\Delta\Sigma K) = 12(Y_1^* \Xi K) = 8(Y_1^* \Sigma\eta) \\ &= 12(\Xi^* \Xi\eta) = 12(\Xi^* \Xi\pi) \qquad (4.12) \end{aligned}$$

In principle, the predictions of an approximate symmetry regarding reaction amplitudes can only be expected to hold in those cases where the effects of the mass difference can be neglected i.e., at energy and *momentum transfer* so high that the particles which appear (including the ones which are exchanged in the t-channel) are sufficiently relativistic to render unimportant even such a difference in rest mass as in the π-K case.

NUCLEI AND SU(3)

The deuteron, being a $Y = 2$ isoscalar compound of two baryons, belongs to a **10*** representation[16] of SU(3). The SU(3)-breaking mass spacing is such as to make all other components of this **10*** exist only as baryon-baryon resonances—just as the Ω^- is the only stable state in **10**. As will be seen in the next chapter, the mass formula for triangular weight diagrams such as the **10** and **10*** amounts to an equal spacing of the levels. There is some indication[16] that the Σ-N system has a resonance at 2130 MeV; this enables one to predict similar resonances in hyperon-hyperon scattering. Similar studies have been made for nuclei with $B > 2$.

Lipkin[17] has pointed out two difficulties in trying to ascertain the SU(3) classification in hypernuclei:

a. Since the Σ-Λ mass difference is an order of magnitude larger than the binding energy per baryon in a nucleus, the observable hypernuclear states contain only Λ's and are therefore mixtures of states from different eight-spin multiplets (since the latter have eigenstates with both Λ and Σ generally).

b. The ground state of a hypernucleus with $B > 4$ will not belong to the same SU(3) multiplet as any nucleus or nucleon system. This is because the Λ in the ground state will stay in the s orbit, in addition to the 4 nucleons which are normally there. This configuration does not carry over to nuclei, of course.

It has been suggested[17] that true "analog" hypernuclear states, i.e., states which belong to the same representation as some nucleus, can be produced through

$$K^- + (Z, A) \rightarrow \pi^- + {}_{\Lambda}(Z, A) \qquad (4.13)$$

(A is of course the atomic weight, i.e., $A = B$) with very low momentum-transfer to the nucleus, to produce a state in which all nucleons stay in their initial orbits while one nucleon becomes a hyperon. The new state will decay into a hypernucleus with lower-energy Λ, but this will be an

SU(3) breaking interaction and should thus be somewhat slowed-down, enabling us to observe a bump in the spectrum of the outgoing π^-. Another interesting reaction should be

$$K^- + (Z, A) \rightarrow \pi^+ + \pi^- + {}_{\Lambda}(Z - 1, A) \qquad (4.14)$$

THE BROKEN SYMMETRY

While the search for an algebraic description of hadron quantum mechanics was going on between 1954 and 1962, many physicists doubted whether the method would indeed be useful, considering that one clearly had to deal with a broken symmetry. Similar criticisms based upon a cautious examination of the kinematical situation were raised as late as Sept. 1963.[18]

Basically, only I, Y, and B are symmetries of the strong interactions. However we shall see in the next chapter that one may use Gell-Mann's method[19,20] of characterization of an algebra through couplings to weaker interactions, and discuss an algebra of the hadrons even though it is not a symmetry. It is clear that gravitation is a small-coupling force, at least in our part of the universe. One can thus use perturbation theory, work to first order and in principle measure $\theta^{\mu\nu}$, the stress-energy-momentum density tensor, through its matrix elements, coupled as they are to the gravitational field. Thus $\theta^{\mu\nu}$ is a well defined local operator; it can have certain transformation properties under the group we discuss, or in fact certain commutation relations with the generators of our algebra,

$$G^i(t) = \int d^3x\, \mathbf{g}^{oi}(\mathbf{x}, t) \qquad (4.15)$$

(there is a t-dependence in the case of nonconserved currents).

From the mass spectrum, i.e., from the fact that I and Y are conserved, we conjecture that we can project out the non-invariant part of $\mathcal{H}$ by commuting,

$$[G_i, \mathcal{H}] = if_{i8k}\mathcal{H}_k \tag{4.16}$$

The implication of the applicability of SU(3) is that $\mathcal{H}$, i.e., the $-\theta^{44}$ which is the energy density is made mainly of two parts, the larger behaving like an SU(3) scalar $\mathcal{H}_0$ and the smaller like an 8th component $\mathcal{H}_8$ in the octet representation (1, 0, −1).

The trouble with using SU(3) as a symmetry is that relations like Eq. (4.6), for instance, are badly contradicted by experiment. In some cases, when the comparison[22] is made at equal Q-values, thus cancelling out the effects of the mass spectrum, one gets a nice fit. This happens for example in

$$\begin{aligned} |(K^+ p \,|\, \Delta^{++} K^0)|^2 = {} & |(\pi^+ p \,|\, \Delta^{++}\pi^0)|^2 \\ & + 3\,|(\pi^+ p \,|\, \Delta^{++}\eta)|^2 \\ & - 3\,|(\pi^+ p \,|\, Y_1^{*+} K^+)|^2 \end{aligned} \tag{4.17}$$

where the probabilities should be corrected by the appropriate kinematical factors. However, comparing at equal distance from the threshold doesn't help Eq. (4.6). We suffer from the fact that the S-matrix is not really SU(3) symmetric; inserting intermediate states, we could think of the symmetry as being broken repetitively at each stage. This would mean that some kind of spurion behaving like an 8th component of an octet should appear at each vertex, aside from the main symmetric contribution. The complete S-matrix would be describable as a symmetric amplitude plus a series of terms in $\mathcal{H}_8$, $\mathcal{H}_8 \times \mathcal{H}_8$ etc. If the $\mathcal{H}_8$ has a coupling which is smaller than one, i.e., if it is not the true strong interaction, limited only by unitarity in its strength, then we may use perturbation theory and consider the scattering amplitude as corrected by $\mathcal{H}_8$ only. Furthermore the $\mathcal{H}_8 \times \mathcal{H}_8$ term contains a part behaving like 8 and another like 27, because these are the two representations with I = 0, Y = 0 components, in the 8×8 product, and any part of the entire strong interaction should be I-spin and Y-invariant. There again, one could check whether some kinematical factors enhance some specific contribution, making for example the second order 27 as strongly felt as the first order 8, etc. We shall return to this approach later on.

Harari[14] has noted that the failure of the prediction (4.6) when compared at equal Q-values is not surprising: at these Q-values, two of the reactions display a resonant behavior, whereas the two others have not reached the necessary threshold for the equivalent resonances to appear; these resonances correspond to the same unitary multiplet as the previous one, but $\mathcal{H}_8$ moves them much further up. Comparing at equal distances from resonance-thresholds may give a good fit (however, some of the experimental information is missing at present).

There are instances when one can make the $\mathcal{H}_8$ perturbation assumption in the group-theoretical treatment and still get results without too much freedom. Take for example the U(3) symmetric prediction[23]

$$(\pi^- p\,|\,\pi^0 n) \leq \sqrt{3}\,(\pi^- p\,|\,K^0\Lambda) + \sqrt{3}\,(\pi^- p\,|\,\eta n) + (\pi^- p\,|\,K^0\Sigma^0)$$

$$(K^- p\,|\,\bar{K}^0 n) \leq (K^- p\,|\,K^0\Xi^0) + \frac{3}{2}(K^- p\,|\,\eta\Lambda) + \frac{\sqrt{3}}{2}(K^- p\,|\,\eta\Sigma^0) + \frac{\sqrt{3}}{2}(K^- p\,|\,\pi^0\Lambda) + \frac{1}{2}(K^- p\,|\,\pi^0\Sigma^0) \tag{4.18}$$

where $(M^- p|M^0 B^0)$ implies the square root of the kinematically corrected cross section, $[E^2(P_{in}/P_{out})\sigma]^{1/2}$ (E, P_{in}, P_{out} are total energy and initial and final momenta in the c.m. frame). The above inequalities can be reproduced[14] by a U-spin analysis. If one now adds a contribution with a $U = 1$ spurion coupled to the initial states, one gets

$$(K^-p\,|\,\overline{K}^0 n) \le (K^-p\,|\,K^0\Xi^0) + \frac{3}{2}(K^-p\,|\,\eta\Lambda)$$
$$+ \frac{\sqrt{3}}{2}(K^-p\,|\,\pi^0\Lambda) + \frac{\sqrt{3}}{2}(K^-p\,|\,\eta\Sigma^0)$$
$$+ \frac{1}{2}(K^-p\,|\,\pi^0\Sigma^0) + \frac{\sqrt{6}}{2}(\pi^-p\,|\,\eta n)$$
$$+ \frac{\sqrt{2}}{2}(\pi^-p\,|\,\pi^0 n) + \frac{\sqrt{6}}{2}(\pi^-p\,|\,K^0\Lambda^0)$$
$$+ \frac{\sqrt{2}}{2}(\pi^-p\,|\,K^0\Sigma^0) \qquad (4.18')$$

which is extremely well satisfied experimentally. Other relations which include $\mathcal{H}_8$ are,[14]

$$\frac{\sqrt{3}}{3}(\pi^-p\,|\,\pi^+\Delta^-) \le (\pi^-p\,|\,K^+Y^{*-}) + (K^-p\,|\,\pi^+Y^{*-})$$
$$+ (K^-p\,|\,K^+\Xi^{*-}) \qquad (4.19)$$

$$(K^-p\,|\,\overline{K}^0\Delta^-) \le (K^-p\,|\,K^0\Xi^{*0}) + \sqrt{3}(K^-p\,|\,\eta Y^{*0})$$
$$+ (K^-p\,|\,\pi^0 Y^{*0}) + \frac{\sqrt{6}}{2}(\pi^-p\,|\,\eta\Delta^0)$$
$$+ \frac{\sqrt{2}}{2}(\pi^-p\,|\,\pi^0\Delta^0) + \sqrt{2}(\pi^-p\,|\,K^0Y^{*0})$$
$$(4.20)$$

$$(\bar{p}p\,|\,\overline{\Delta}^-\Delta^-) \le 3(\bar{p}p\,|\,\overline{Y^{*-}}Y^{*-}) + 3(\bar{p}p\,|\,\overline{\Xi^{*-}}\Xi^{*-})$$
$$+ (\bar{p}p\,|\,\overline{\Omega}^-\Omega^-) \qquad (4.21)$$

$$(\pi^- p \mid \pi^- \pi^+ n) \leq \frac{\sqrt{6}}{2} (\pi^- p \mid \pi^- K^+ \Lambda) + \frac{\sqrt{2}}{2} (\pi^- p \mid \pi^- K^+ \Sigma^0)$$

$$+ (\pi^- p \mid K^- K^+ n) + (K^- p \mid \pi^- K^+ \Xi^0)$$

$$+ \frac{\sqrt{6}}{2} (K^- p \mid \pi^- \pi^+ \Lambda) + \frac{\sqrt{2}}{2} (K^- p \mid \pi^- \pi^+ \Sigma^0)$$

$$+ \frac{\sqrt{6}}{2} (K^- p \mid K^- K^+ \Lambda) + \frac{\sqrt{2}}{2} (K^- p \mid K^- K^+ \Sigma^0)$$

$$+ (K^- p \mid K^- \pi^+ n) \qquad (4.22)$$

The broken SU(3) results are in agreement with experiment wherever the comparison is possible. Similarly, for decimet resonance decay amplitudes, Gupta and Singh[24] have deduced from a broken SU(3) analysis that

$$2(\Delta \mid N\pi) + 3\sqrt{2}\,(Y^* \mid \Lambda\pi) - 3(Y^* \mid \Sigma\pi)$$

$$+ 2\sqrt{2}\,(\Xi^* \mid \Xi\pi) = 0 \qquad (4.23)$$

which seems to fit the experimental data.

UNIVERSALITY—FROM A GAUGE PRINCIPLE

Up to this point, our results depended only upon the existence of an SU(3) symmetry scheme and the appropriate assignments. We may however go one step further and assume some more detailed model; we combine the symmetry with some structural ideas derived from either field theory or dispersion relations.

The first and most useful such concept is universality. This implies equality—or a simple connection—between the couplings of any hadrons to some particular set of bosons. These bosons are then coupled "universally," just as the photon couples with the same strength to electrons and protons. The exact statement about universal coupling is that the matrix elements are all equal (or proportional, with the proportionality coefficient being given by the group) at zero momentum transfer. A proton does have a different magnetic moment than an electron, but its charge (the non spin-flip form factor, which is the only non-vanishing one at $q^2 = 0$) is equal to the electron's except for the (−1) coefficient.

In conventional Lagrangian field theory, universality is introduced[25] via postulation of a local p-parameter gauge invariance. Assuming a set ψ^a of fermion fields transforming under the local gauge according to the infinitesimal transformation

$$\psi^a \rightarrow \exp(i\epsilon^u(x)\Lambda_u)\psi^a \sim \psi^a + i\epsilon^u(x)\Lambda_u{}^{(a}{}_{b)}\psi^b$$

$$(a, b = 1, \ldots n) \qquad (u = 1, \ldots p)$$

we ensure invariance of the free Lagrangian for ψ^a by adding an interaction term which cancels the $\partial^\mu \epsilon^u(x)$ term arising in the variation and due to the local nature of the gauge. This means that we replace the Dirac equation derivative $\gamma^\mu \partial_\mu$ by a "covariant" derivative $\gamma^\mu(\partial_\mu - (2h)^{-1} \Lambda_u V^u_\mu)$, with V^u_μ a set of vector-fields transforming as

$$V^v_\mu \rightarrow V^v_\mu + i\epsilon^u L_u{}^{(v}{}_{w)} V^w_\mu - (2h)^{-1} \partial_\mu \epsilon^v \qquad (4.24)$$

$$(u, v, w = 1, \ldots p)$$

with gauge-invariant field strengths.

$$F^u_{\mu\nu} = \partial_\mu V^u_\nu - \partial_\nu V^u_\mu + 2h\, L^{u(v}{}_{w)} V_{\mu v} V^w_\nu \qquad (4.25)$$

and a Lagrangian

$$-\bar{\psi}_a \gamma_\mu \left(\partial^\mu - (2h)^{-1} \Lambda^{(a}{}_{ub)} V^{\mu u}\right) \psi^b - M\bar{\psi}^u \psi_u$$
$$- \tfrac{1}{4} F^u_{\mu\nu} F^{\mu\nu}_u \qquad (4.26)$$

The Λ_u are an abstract representation of the gauge generators; the V_μ, like the current densities (2.23)

$$j_\mu^u = i\bar{\psi}_a \gamma_\mu \Lambda^{u(a}{}_{b)} \psi^b \qquad (4.27)$$

span a basis for the adjoint representation $L^{(v}{}_{uw)}$ of the algebra. When unitary spin[3,4] was discovered, it was introduced as a gauge, following a series of arguments[25] for the existence of vector meson fields. The role of ψ_a was played by the baryon octet; the $\Lambda^{(a}{}_{ub)}$ were then identical with the structure constants f_{uab}, i.e., the Λ_u and L_u were really antisymmetric F-type couplings. Indeed, every experimental verification fits roughly with the theoretical result of F-couplings for vector mesons. Within SU(3) itself, there is no such direct argument for baryon-pseudoscalar meson couplings; experimentally, these are largely D-type. We shall see in Chapter 7 that this may be connected with a symmetry and gauge larger than SU(3), the chiral SU(3) × SU(3).

With couplings defined by the symmetry plus the gauge, or determined by experiment—one may try to proceed dynamically by using Born-approximation methods, or dispersion theory. The physics literature of the years 1962-64 is saturated with such applications.

We have brought the above derivation of universality from a Lagrangian field theory because this brings out the group-theory features. However, little is known about the applicability of such a field theory to hadrons. In the coming chapters, we shall rederive universality using a different approach in which the dynamical content of the assumptions involved is clarified.

THE BOOTSTRAP AS AN ORIGIN FOR SU(3) SYMMETRY

We now try to gather some insight from the study of possible "origins" of unitary symmetry.

Cutkosky[26] has shown in an elegant proof how a symmetry such as SU(3) could emerge from a bootstrap mechanism with no fundamental fields. To simplify matters, one deals only with one kind of particle; the simplest choice is one in which N vector-mesons (with equal masses) generate themselves.

The forces are taken in the Born approximation, so that any two vector mesons A and B interact by exchanging vector mesons R in both "u" and "t" channels, the result being a vector meson Q produced as an AB resonance in the s-channel. This is shown in Fig. 4-2. On the right we draw a field theory vertex-diagram supplying identical results when one assumes that the Q-A-B vertex renormalized coupling constant is entirely due to renormalization effects (i.e., zero bare couplings) approximated by the lowest order contribution. This amounts to regarding the QAB vertex as the resulting eigenfunction of a potential

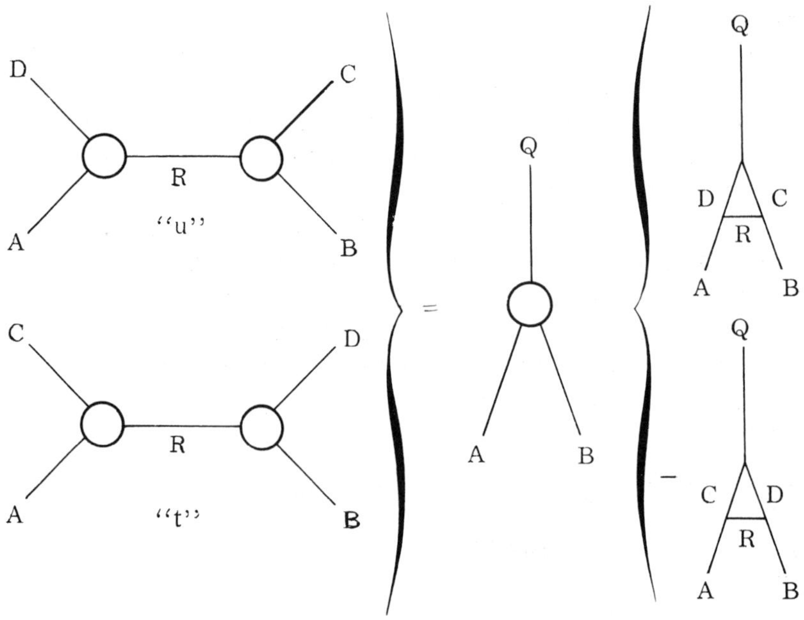

Fig. 4-2

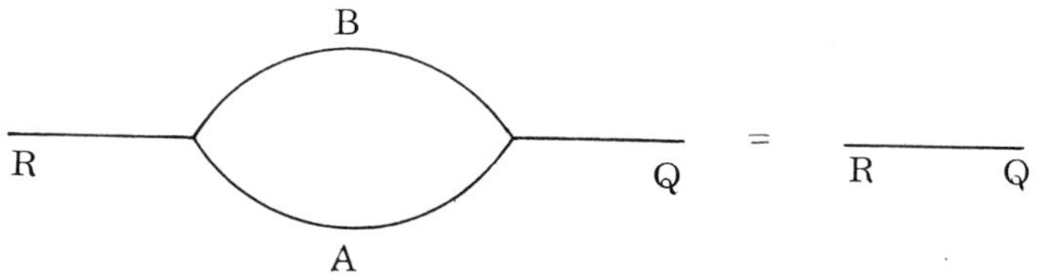

Fig. 4-3

$$V_{AB,\,CD} = F_{ADR}\,F_{BCR} - F_{ACR}\,F_{BDR}$$

(summation is implied over all repeated indices) applied to the simple vertex F_{CDQ}. A positive λ eigenvalue implies binding, and there have to be N such degenerate eigenvalues,

$$\lambda F_{ABQ} = V_{AB,\,CD}\,F_{CDQ} \tag{4.28}$$

One can normalize the couplings by requiring wave-function algebraic invariance under lowest order bubble diagrams (see Fig. 4-3)

$$F_{ABR}\,F_{BAQ} = \delta_{RQ} \tag{4.29}$$

Lastly, the symmetry properties of vector mesons require the F_{ABR} to be antisymmetric at least in two indices; however, we take for simplicity and crossing symmetry the case of a coupling totally antisymmetric in all pairs

$$\begin{aligned} F_{ABR} &= -F_{BAR} = -F_{ARB} \\ &= -F_{RBA} = F_{RAB} = F_{BRA} \end{aligned} \tag{4.30}$$

Self-consistency requires that out of the $N(N-1)/2$ sets of antisymmetric AB pairs, there will be an N-degenerate λ such that

$$\lambda > \lambda_i$$

where λ_i are the d_i degenerate eigenvalues of Eq. (4.28) for all solutions other than our N vector mesons. We now get a connection between λ and λ_i by multiplying Eq. (4.28) by F_{BAQ} from the left and summing over A, B:

$$\begin{aligned} N\lambda &= F_{BAQ} V_{AB,CD} F_{CDQ} \\ &= F_{BAQ}(F_{ADR} F_{BCR} - F_{ACR} F_{BDR}) F_{CDQ} \\ &= 2F_{BAQ} F_{ADR} F_{BCR} F_{CDQ} \end{aligned} \qquad (4.31)$$

where we have made use of the fact that all indices have become "dummies," and transform the second term under the replacements

$$A \to C \qquad C \to D \qquad D \to A \qquad R \to Q$$

We now use (4.31) to evaluate (P_i represents a pair of indices AB etc.)

$$\begin{aligned} \mathrm{Tr}\, V^2 &= \sum_{P_1 = P_3} \sum_{P_2} (V_{P_1 P_2} V_{P_2 P_3}) \\ &= \sum_{P_1 P_1'} \sum_{P_2 P_2'} (F_{P_1 R} F_{P_2 R} - F_{P_1' R} F_{P_2' R}) \\ &\quad \times (F_{P_2 Q} F_{P_1 Q} - F_{P_2' Q} F_{P_1' Q}) \\ &= \sum_{P_1 P_1'} \sum_{P_2, P_2'} \{(F_{P_1 R} F_{P_2 R} F_{P_2 Q} F_{P_1 Q} \\ &\quad + F_{P_1' R} F_{P_2' R} F_{P_2' Q} F_{P_1' Q}) \\ &\quad - (F_{P_1' R} F_{P_2' R} F_{P_2 Q} F_{P_1 Q} \\ &\quad + F_{P_1 R} F_{P_2 R} F_{P_2' Q} F_{P_1' Q})\} \end{aligned}$$

The first bracket reduces through Eq. (4.29) to 2N, the second one is of the type (4.31) so that we get

$$\mathrm{Tr}\ V^2 = 2N - N\lambda \tag{4.32}$$

while we can also write by definition,

$$\mathrm{Tr}\ V^2 = N\lambda^2 + d_i \lambda_i^2 \tag{4.33}$$

which gives us the correlation

$$\lambda(\lambda + 1) = 2 - N^{-1} d_i \lambda_i^2 \tag{4.34}$$

so that

$$\lambda \leq 1$$

and $\lambda = 1$ only if all λ_i vanish.

One now performs an orthogonal transformation on the indices A, B etc.

$$\phi'_A = 0_{AB}\, \phi_B \tag{4.35}$$

under which we have covariance of Eqs. (4.28) and (4.29).

The infinitesimal variation $F^{(\alpha)}_{ABC}$ in

$$F'_{ABC} = F_{ABC} + i\epsilon^{\alpha} F^{(\alpha)}_{ABC}$$

is given by

$$\Delta F^{(\alpha)}_{ABC} = G^{(\alpha)}_{XA} F_{XBC} + G^{(\alpha)}_{XB} F_{AXC} + G^{(\alpha)}_{XC} F_{ABX} \tag{4.36}$$

where

$$0_{AB} = \delta_{AB} + i\epsilon^{\alpha} G^{(\alpha)}_{AB}$$

At this stage, Cutkosky assumes conservation of electric charge E. This implies that some (α) will coincide with the generator of the electric charge gauge. One then has

$$G_{XA}{}^{E} F_{XBC} + G_{XB}{}^{E} F_{AXC} + G_{XC}{}^{E} F_{ABX} = 0 \tag{4.37}$$

We now multiply this result by F_{BAD}, obtaining (with $G^{E}_{CD} = -G^{E}_{DC}$)

$$G^{E}_{CD} = V_{CD,AB}\, G^{E}_{AB} \tag{4.38}$$

which shows that G^{E}_{CD} is an eigenfunction with $\lambda' = 1$. This λ' can be either a λ_i or λ itself. If it is a λ_i we find from (4.34) that $\lambda < 1$, which means $\lambda < \lambda'$, contradicting our self-consistency approach (i.e., the N vector mesons are *not* the solution bound states); if λ' is λ itself, we have

$$\lambda = 1 \qquad \lambda_i = 0$$

This then allows us to write (4.28) as

$$V_{AB,CD} = F_{ABQ} F_{DCQ}$$

which can be rewritten as

$$F_{ABR} F_{CDR} + F_{BCR} F_{ADR} + F_{CAR} F_{BDR} = 0 \tag{4.39}$$

This is the equation for the structure constants of a compact Lie group. If we can assume r *a priori* good quantum numbers (instead of just E), its rank will be at least r. If one assumes that the N vector mesons cannot be reduced into $N = N_1 + N_2 + \cdots N_m$, with these bosons interacting only within the respective subsets, the algebra is simple.

Note that if $N \to \infty$, this proof fails since the trace becomes meaningless; we are dealing with a noncompact group. It is also interesting that the coupling we got for the vector mesons is indeed the same universal F-type coupling.

THE QUARK MODEL

In Chapter 2, we noticed[27] that the baryon $\frac{1}{2}^+$ octet (2, 1, 0) and $\frac{3}{2}^+$ decimet (3, 0, 0) can be regarded as products of three "quarks" (1, 0, 0),

$$(1, 0, 0) \times (1, 0, 0) \times (1, 0, 0)$$

$$= (3, 0, 0) + (2, 1, 0) + (2, 1, 0) + (0, 0, 0)$$

It was suggested[27-29] that such triplet fields could provide a workable model for hadrons. More recently, it has become obvious that the observed hadrons should not be considered as basic, elementary fields. Stability or metastability is no criterion for elementarity: we have seen the metastable Ω^- in the same multiplet with nine resonances with fast decays. If one wishes to formulate an SU(3)-invariant Lagrangian theory, one can either do it with "quarks" or, if one were to keep to the baryon octet as a fundamental field, we would be forced to include the vector-meson octet as elementary fields as well. Otherwise one would get an SU(8) system. In the chapter dealing with the vector and axial vector currents, we shall see that the same result applies to the chiral algebra: only quark fields yield the observed algebra SU(3) × SU(3) directly. Other models would be even more complicated to adapt there.

Quarks have fractional charges; they also create some difficulties with the spin-statistics correlation. The $\frac{3}{2}^+$ decimet is totally symmetric in both spin and unitary spin indices; so is the entire **56** baryon multiplet (16 states of the $j = \frac{1}{2}^+$ octet and 40 states of the $j = \frac{3}{2}^+$ decimet, counting spin states) which has certainly provided the most interesting results of SU(6), as we shall see in Chapter 8. This difficulty has been attacked in several ways, all of which involve an added dimensionality:

a. Quarks could be parafermions[30] of order 3, that is, they would constitute each an indistinguishable superposition of three fermion fields, with only triple products allowing for ordinary statistics.

b. Quarks could be replaced by two or three sets of triplets. Such attempts have been numerous,[31-37] mainly prompted by the urge to avoid fractional charges. One then starts out from two or three "different" U(3) systems; the charge is represented by a properly displaced generator in each, arranged so that the displacements cancel out in $\tau = 0$ representations of the product U(3) group. (See for example Gell-Mann's original mathematical lepton and meson triplets.[4]) All such schemes imply a larger group structure such as $U(1) \times U(3)$, U(4), $U(3) \times U(3)$ or Sp(3). The models are concocted so as to provide for maximal attraction when the bound state is a $\tau = 0$ multiplet of "total" unitary spin. The $\tau \neq 0$ states are therefore heavier (rough arguments for $m \approx 10$ BeV have been given for the triplets themselves—mainly the fact that this would explain why first order mass formulae work, since 1 BeV is then a minor perturbation. On the other hand, if the triplet states are so heavy—and this applies to quarks also—one wonders to what extent it will be possible to give some dynamical meaning to their role as fundamental particles. In what sense is a proton a binding of two or three triplet states rather than bootstrap of the baryon-meson octets? Can the ρ be said to be mainly a quark-antiquark bound state, rather to the π-π resonance?

To reproduce the observed particles, in two-triplet models the two "fundamental" triplets have to be [B, (1, 0, 0)] and [B − 1, (0, 0, 1)] respectively. There are in fact two free parameters, as we can now displace the Y by equal amounts in the two systems in oppositve direction; it is convenient to use as a parameter the lowest charge z in the triplet [B, (z + 1, z, z)], so that

$$Y = \frac{1}{3}(h_1 + h_2 - 2h_3) + 2(z + \frac{1}{3}) \tag{4.40}$$

or alternatively one adds a new Quantum Number $c = z + \frac{1}{3}$ to the Gell-Mann-Nishijima relation. The second triplet has to be $[B - 1, (-z - 1, -z, -z)]$.

The multiple triplet theories have their electric charge corresponding to a direct product $Q' \times Q''$ yielding $z' + z''$. The number of independent amplitudes is increased, and the SU(3) predictions. The electromagnetic structure may yet provide proof of the existence of several fundamental triplets. Alternatively, one can look for stable, metastable or unstable $\tau = 1$ states at higher energies. The difficulty is that the situation is ambivalent if they are not found, as we do not have a good argument for the choice of their couplings; how can we determine their production cross sections? Using rough plausibility arguments, one can already put a lower limit of some 15 BeV (from cosmic rays) on stable and metastable states, and perhaps 3 BeV for unstable ones.[38]

We would like to stress that a situation where only $\tau = 0$ representations of U(3) appear in nature would be perfectly consistent with a dynamical symmetry, perhaps of the bootstrap nature. In the 3-dimensional harmonic oscillator problem, there is a dynamical U(3) symmetry but only representations of the type (n, 0, 0) appear; in strong coupling theory, only (j, I) with j = I, etc. At the same time, however, we should note that quark-fields (of the simplest type, but with the statistics difficulty) do provide a host of useful results in our study of hadron physics. They certainly form the neatest realization of the algebraic commutation relations deduced from observation.

In Chapter 9 we shall describe a sequence of results which were first derived from a "naive" quark model, in which the methods of nuclear physics were used to describe a nucleon as a composite state. However, all such results were then reproduced with a formalism where no such quarks enter, so that there is still no convincing evidence of the existence of quarks.

REFERENCES

1. A. H. Rosenfeld, A. Barbaro-Galtieri, W. H. Barkas, P. L. Bastien, J. Kirz, and M. Roos, *Rev. Mod. Phys.* **37**, 633 (1965).
2. A. H. Rosenfeld, A. Barbaro-Galtieri, J. Kirz, W. J. Podolsky, M. Roos, W. J. Willis, and C. C. Wohl, UCRL-8030 (revised), August 1966. To be published in *Rev. Mod. Phys.*
3. Y. Ne'eman, *Nucl. Phys.* **26**, 222 (1961).
4. M. Gell-Mann, Report CTSL-20 (1961), published in "The Eightfold Way," W. A. Benjamin, Inc., New York (1964).
5. M. Gell-Mann, *Proc. Intern. Conf. High Energy Phys.* (CERN, 1962), p. 805; Y. Ne'eman, private communication to G. Goldhaber at same conference; S. L. Glashow and J. J. Sakurai, *Nuovo Cimento* **26**, 622 (1962).
6. See in this context Y. Dothan, *Phys. Rev.* **137**, B637 (1965).
7. S. L. Glashow and A. H. Rosenfeld, *Phys. Rev. Letters* **10**, 192 (1963).
8. J. J. Sakurai, *Phys. Rev. Letters* **9**, 472 (1962).
9. S. L. Glashow and R. Socolow, *Phys. Rev. Letters* **15**, 329 (1965)
10. G. Goldhaber, *Proc. Intern. Conf. High Energy Phys. (Berkeley, 1966)*, to be published.
11. C. A. Levinson, H. J. Lipkin, and S. Meshkov, *Phys. Letters* **1**, 44 (1962)
12. S. Meshkov, C. A. Levinson, and H. J. Lipkin, *Phys. Rev. Letters* **10**, 361 (1963).
13. H. Ruegg and S. B. Treiman, *Phys. Rev.* **132**, 384 (1963).
14. H. Harari, *High Energy Physics and Elementary Particles (IAEA, Vienna 1965)*, p. 353.
15. C. Dullemond, A. J. Macfarlane, and E. C. G. Sudarshan, *Phys. Rev. Letters* **10**, 423 (1963) and other papers by the same group.
16. R. J. Oakes, *Phys. Rev.* **131**, 2239 (1963).
17. H. J. Lipkin, *Phys. Rev. Letters* **14**, 18 (1965).
18. C. N. Yang and R. J. Oakes, *Phys. Rev. Letters* **11**, 173 (1963).
19. M. Gell-Mann, *Phys. Rev.* **125**, 1067 (1962).

20. M. Gell-Mann, *Physics* **1**, 63 (1964).
21. Y. Ne'eman, *Nuclear Phys.* **26**, 230 (1961).
22. S. Meshkov, G. A. Snow, and G. B. Yodh, *Phys. Rev. Letters* **12**, 87 (1964).
23. M. Konuma and K. Tomozawa, *Phys. Rev. Letters* **12**, 493 (1964).
24. V. Gupta and V. Singh, *Phys. Rev.* **135**, B1443 (1964).
25. C. N. Yang and H. Mills, *Phys. Rev.* **96**, 192 (1954), and R. Shaw, dissertation, unpublished (1954). The method was generalized by R. Utiyama, *Phys. Rev.* **101**, 1597 (1956). J. J. Sakurai, *Ann. of Phys.* **11**, 1 (1960) emphasized its observational implications. V. V. Ogievetski and I. V. Polubarinov, *Nuovo Cimento* **23**, 173 (1962) have pointed to the nonuniqueness of the method. However, provided vector particles do exist, the couplings are bound to be universal, as pointed out by the same authors in JETP (translations) **18**, 166 (1964).
26. R. E. Cutkosky, *Phys. Rev.* **131**, 1888 (1963).
27. H. Goldberg and Y. Ne'eman, *Nuovo Cimento* **27**, 1 (1963).
28. M. Gell-Mann, *Phys. Letters* **8**, 214 (1964).
29. G. Zweig, "Symmetries in Elementary Particle Physics," A. Zichichi, ed., Academic Press, New York, 1965, p. 192.
30. O. W. Greenberg, *Phys. Rev. Letters* **13**, 598 (1964).
31. J. Schwinger, *Phys. Rev.* **135**, B816 (1964).
32. F. Gürsey, T. D. Lee, and M. Nauenberg, *Phys. Rev.* **135**, B467 (1964).
33. Z. Maki, *Prog. Theoret. Phys. (Kyoto)* **31**, 331 (1964).
34. Y. Hara, *Phys. Rev.* **134**, B701 (1964).
35. H. Bacry, J. Nuyts, and L. Van Hove, *Phys. Letters* **9**, 279 (1964), and **12**, 285 (1964).
36. M. Han and Y. Nambu, Phys. Rev. **139**, B1006 (1965).
37. S. Okubo, Ann. of Phys. **38**, 377 (1966) has studied methods of distinguishing between these models through their contributions to various commutators (see Chapter 8).
38. D. E. Dorfan, J. Eades, L. M. Lederman, W. Lee, and C. C. Ting, *Phys. Rev. Letters* **14**, 999 (1965); L. B. Leipuner, W. T. Chu, R. C. Larsen, and R. K. Adair, *Phys. Rev. Letters* **12**, 423 (1964); H. Kasha, L. B. Leipuner, and R. K. Adair, *Phys. Rev.* **150**, 1140 (1966)

5

THE PHYSICAL ALGEBRA OF UNITARY SPIN

SYMMETRIES AND ALGEBRAS OF THE LEPTONS

The system of leptons can be described by a 4-spinor ψ

$$\psi_\ell = \begin{vmatrix} e^- \\ \nu_e \\ \mu^- \\ \nu_\mu \end{vmatrix} \tag{5.1}$$

with the free Lagrangian (leptons have no strong interaction and a Lagrangian is thus meaningful)

$$\mathcal{L} = -\overline{\psi}_\ell (\not{\partial} + M) \psi_\ell + \text{h.c.} \tag{5.2}$$

We introduce a set of eight linearly independent 4×4 matrices σ_e^i, σ_μ^i $(i = 0, 1, 2, 3)$ where σ^0 stands for a 2×2 identity and σ^{1-3} are hermitian Pauli 2×2 matrices; the σ_e^i operate in the upper left hand corner and the σ_μ^i in the lower right-hand corner. All eight matrices are normalized to

$$\mathrm{Tr}(\sigma^i_\ell)^2 = \tfrac{1}{2} \qquad [\sigma^i_\ell, \sigma^j_n] = i\,\epsilon^{ij}{}_k\,\delta_{\ell n}\,\sigma^k \tag{5.3}$$

(the commutator vanishes for i or j = 0). We note that the electric charge eigenvalue is

$$Q = -\sum_\ell (\sigma^0_\ell + \sigma^3_\ell) \tag{5.4}$$

and the masses

$$M = m^\ell (\sigma^0_\ell + \sigma^3_\ell) \tag{5.5}$$

where the summation runs over $\ell = e, \mu$. Besides Q, we know from observation that

$$L_e = 2\,\sigma^0_e \qquad L_\mu = 2\,\sigma^0_\mu$$

are abstract matrices corresponding to conserved quantum numbers. Moreover, the atonous (weak) current densities are

$$\begin{aligned} j^{\alpha(\ell)}_{A\pm} &= \bar{\psi}_\ell\,\gamma^\alpha\,(1 + \gamma_5)(\sigma^\pm_e + \sigma^\pm_\mu)\,\psi_\ell \\ &= \bar{\psi}_\ell\gamma^\alpha\,\tfrac{1}{2}(1 \pm \gamma_5)\,2(\sigma^\pm_e + \sigma^\pm_\mu)\,\psi_\ell \\ &= \bar{\psi}_\ell\,\gamma^\alpha(\sigma^\pm_e + \sigma^\pm_\mu)\,\psi_\ell + \psi_\ell\,\gamma^\alpha\,\gamma_5\,(\sigma^\pm_e + \sigma^\pm_\mu)\,\psi_\ell \end{aligned} \tag{5.6}$$

with $\sigma^\pm_\ell = (\sigma^1_\ell + i\,\sigma^2_\ell)$.

From the comparison between processes such as

$$n \to p + e^- + \bar{\nu}_e$$

$$\nu_\mu + n \to p + \mu^-$$

etc.

it appears that the two terms $(\bar{e}\nu_e)$ and $(\bar{\mu}\nu_\mu)$ of the weak leptonic $j^{(\ell)}_{A+}$ current are coupled with equal strengths. This is at least a symmetry result, i.e., equal unrenormalized couplings fixed by the equal coefficients heading those terms in the weak Hamiltonian. The symmetry is lepton-type symmetry, a rotation by 180° performed with $(\sigma^0_e - \sigma^0_\mu)$. However, the coefficients are given by the matrices $\frac{1}{2} A^i = \sigma^i_e + \sigma^i_\mu$ of Eq. (5.6); they thus happen also to correspond to the identification of the leptonic weak charge with an operator $(A_1 \pm i A_2)$ inserted between $\bar{\psi}_\ell \gamma^\alpha (1 + \gamma_5)/2$ and $\frac{1}{2}(1 + \gamma_5)\psi_\ell$, where A_1 and A_2 have the commutation relations

$$[A_i, A_j] = 2i\, \epsilon_{ij}{}^k A_k \tag{5.7}$$

This is also certainly true separately for the vector part of A-spin, where we observe almost-exact equality of μ and e couplings and as we shall further see we can in fact recover *exact* equality of the renormalized couplings even for hadrons. Writing $A^i = A^i_V + A^i_X$ with

$$A^i_V = \int d^3x\, \bar{\psi} \gamma^0 (\sigma^i_e + \sigma^i_\mu) \psi \tag{5.8$'$}$$

$$A^i_X = \int d^3x\, \bar{\psi} \gamma^0 \gamma^5 (\sigma^i_e + \sigma^i_\mu) \psi \tag{5.8$''$}$$

we can thus use

$$A^i_{v,\ell} = \sigma^i_e + \sigma^i_\mu \, ; \, A^i_{x,\ell} = \gamma_5 (\sigma^i_e + \sigma^i_\mu)$$

$$[A^v_i, A^v_j] = i \, \epsilon_{ij}{}^k A^v_k \qquad (5.9)$$

and the leptonic weak vector charge is represented by $(A^v_1 \pm i A^v_2)$ inserted between $\bar{\psi}_\ell \gamma^\alpha$ and ψ_ℓ. We concentrate in the following on the applications of A^v; note however that for (5.7) and (5.9) to hold at the same time, we have

$$[A^x_i, A^x_j] = i \, \epsilon_{ij}{}^k A^v_k \qquad (5.7')$$

"Exact" equality of couplings for *hadrons* and leptons goes beyond symmetry, it implies universality. By "exact" we mean to all orders in the strong interaction, but we do not include the nonstrong effects, except to first order. If indeed the weak interactions conserve this A^v-spin, we could rest assured that whatever their own renormalization effects, they would combine so as to conserve this coupling, i.e., all virtual states would still have the same total A^v-spin and produce *the same form factor at zero-momentum transfer*. It is not clear that this result is necessary here, as we cannot be sure that the nondetection of such renormalization effects is not due to the smallness of higher order terms in the weak interaction. To check this point we would require a method of removing divergences, which does not exist to date. Moreover, it seems clear that the weak Hamiltonian does not conserve A-spin anyhow: invariance would have required a neutral term $j^{+(\ell)}_{A_3} j^{(\ell)}_{A_3}$, which does not seem to be there. Also, $m_e \neq m_\mu \neq m_\nu$, and the mass term breaks the symmetry.

Before we leave the lepton system, it is worth noting that

$$A_3^V = \sigma_e^3 + \sigma_\mu^3$$

$$Q = -\left(\sum_\ell \tfrac{1}{2} L_\ell + A_3\right) \tag{5.10}$$

so that A-spin and electric charge close upon a system generating SU(2) × U(1); this system contains the total lepton number as well. To distinguish between L_e and L_μ and describe lepton-type symmetry we have to add another generator $(L_e - L_\mu)$ and the full lepton endo-algebra generates U(1) × U(1) × SU(2).

THE HADRONS A^V-SPIN

We can now go over to the hadrons and derive an important result from the universality of weak couplings. It is observed that the decays

$$n \to p + e^- + \bar{\nu}_e$$

$$\mu^- \to e^- + \bar{\nu}_e + \nu_\mu$$

for instance, display equal vector couplings and slightly different ones (1.18:1) for the axial-vector parts. Thus the existence of a virtual meson cloud surrounding the neutrons does not renormalize the vector current at least. This physical result implies, as we have seen, the conservation of A^V-spin in the hadron cloud by the strong interaction. Indeed we are observing the renormalized coefficient in the $(\bar{n}$-p) term $j_{A^+}^{(h)}$ of j_{A^+}; since it is about equal to the lepton's, we have to assume that under the A-spin generators, the nucleon appears as a 2-spinor, and that $2(A_1 \pm i A_2)$ has the same matrix elements between nucleons as between leptons. This was the original idea of the conserved vector current theory, but we now have to include $\Delta S = 1$ decays like

$$\Lambda \to p + e^- + \bar{\nu}_e$$

Had there been but one neutrino, we could have constructed spinors

$$\begin{pmatrix} \alpha\, \mu^- + \beta\, e^- \\ \nu \end{pmatrix} \qquad \begin{pmatrix} \gamma\, n + \delta\, \Lambda \\ p \end{pmatrix}$$

lepton universality implying $\alpha = \beta = \sqrt{2}/2$. Since $\alpha \sim \gamma$, $\gamma = \sqrt{2}/2$, $\delta = \sqrt{2}/2$.

However in the present picture we compare

$$\begin{pmatrix} e^- \\ \nu_e \end{pmatrix} \quad \begin{pmatrix} u^- \\ \nu_\mu \end{pmatrix} \quad \begin{pmatrix} \gamma\, n + \delta\, \Lambda \\ p \end{pmatrix}$$

and the fact that $\gamma \sim 1$ implies $\delta = (1 - \gamma^2)^{1/2}$, a small number. This is characterized by an angle θ, and we now know[2] that the hadrons appear as

$$\cos\theta\; j_A^{(h)}\,(\Delta S = 0) + \sin\theta\; j_A^{(h)}\,(\Delta S = 1) \tag{5.11}$$

which is the Cabibbo component of the j^μ octet. Thus the strong interactions have to display an approximate symmetry under an SU(2) set of transformations whose electrically charged components are proportional to the atonous charge they carry, i.e., to A-spin; in other words, the strong S-matrix is roughly invariant under the action of the generators defined by the space integrals of atonous densities; the smallness of the renormalization effects in the axial vector term similarly implies the existence of a larger "chiral" very rough symmetry of the strong S-matrix, with a partially-conserved axial-vector charge. We shall return to this problem at a later stage. We also notice that the very small but non-zero renormalization of the vector current implies that the generators of the hadron endosymmetry corresponding to A-spin do not exactly commute with the

Hamiltonian. The $\Delta S = 0$ part seems really unrenormalized; its corresponding generators thus have to represent a good hadron symmetry (this is indeed I-spin).

UNITARY SPIN GENERATORS

We now take up the view according to which the starting point lies in the system of hadron currents participating in the nonstrong interactions. We follow Gell-Mann[3] in regarding this as our formal physical starting point, to which we have recently added[5] an alternative or complementary set of currents coupled to the Regge trajectories of strong transitions.

We assume that the hadron electromagnetic current density is given by [we have factorized out $(\sqrt{3}/3)e$, so that the actual current is $(\sqrt{3}/3)ej^{\mu}_{\text{electric}}$]

$$j^{\mu}_{el} \begin{cases} j^0_{el} \equiv g(\sigma^0 \lambda_{el}) \text{ or } g(\lambda_{el}) \\ j^k_{el} \equiv g(\gamma^5 \sigma^k \lambda_{el}) \end{cases} \tag{5.12}$$

where

$$\lambda_{\text{electric}} = \sqrt{3}\ \lambda_3/2 + \lambda_8/2 \tag{5.12'}$$

and σ^0, σ^k denote the identity and the Pauli matrices in a 2-spinor space. In a "quark-field" picture, this would indeed be the quark-spin space, since

$$j^k_{el} = \bar{\psi}\gamma^k \lambda_{el}\psi = \psi^{\dagger}\gamma_5 \sigma^k \lambda_{el}\psi \tag{5.12''}$$

Note that we have used a more general definition, independent of a particular field model, but ensuring certain commutation relations among these density-components—apart from Schwinger terms,[6] which we shall discuss in Chapter 8.

Similarly we assume, following our analysis of the implications of atonous (weak) universality, that the atonous (weak) vector current is given as,

$$j^{\mu}_{at} \begin{cases} j^0_{at} \equiv g(\sigma^0 \lambda_{at}\,; x, t) \text{ or } g(\lambda_{at}, x) \\ j^k_{at} \equiv g(\gamma_5\, \sigma^k\, \lambda_{at}\,; x, t) \end{cases} \tag{5.13}$$

(we use $g^{11} = g^{22} = g^{33} = -g^{00} = -1$; $\{\gamma^i, \gamma^k\}_+ = 2\, g^{ik}$; $(\gamma^k)^\dagger = g^{kk}\, \gamma^k$; $\beta = \gamma^0$; $\gamma_5 = i\, \gamma^0\gamma^1\gamma^2\gamma^3 = \gamma_5^\dagger$) where[2]

$$\lambda_{at} = \cos\theta\, \sqrt{2}\, (\lambda_1 + i\lambda_2)/2 + \sin\theta\, \sqrt{2}\, (\lambda_4 + i\, \lambda_5)/2 \tag{5.13'}$$

We may assume that the symmetry-breaking interaction is generated by a nonstrong coupling to the strangeness-current; alternatively, we use our identification of hypercharge and isospin as conserved quantum numbers of the hadrons in strong-interactions, and break up the above j^{μ}_{at} into $j^{\mu}_{at}\,(\Delta S = 0)$ and $j^{\mu}_{at}\,(\Delta S = 1)$; similarly, we separate the isovector and isoscalar parts of the electromagnetic current density. We now have a system of densities behaving like an SU(3) octet,

$$[\, G(\lambda^i),\ g(\lambda^j)\,] = i\, f^{ijk}\, g(\lambda^k) \tag{5.14}$$

$$[G(\lambda^i),\ g(\gamma^5\, \sigma\lambda^j)] = i\, f^{ijk}\, g(\gamma^5\, \sigma\lambda^k) \tag{5.14'}$$

where $G(\lambda^i)$ are the SU(3) generators. We now further postulate the connection,

$$G(\lambda^i) = \int d^3x\, g(\lambda^i; \mathbf{x}, t) \tag{5.15}$$

thus assuming that the space integrals of the $g(\lambda^i; \mathbf{x}, t)$ span an SU(3) algebra, and that this algebra coincides with the phenomenological approximate symmetry of the strong interactions.

In the limit of unitary symmetry, the $G(\lambda^i)$ are constants of the motion; in the actual situation, they are functions of the time. We can then consider their commutators with other $G(\lambda^i)$ or with the $g(\lambda^i, x)$ at equal times. We know that

$$[G(\lambda^i; t), G(\lambda^j; t')]_{t=t'} = i f^{ijk} G(\lambda^k; t) \qquad (5.16)$$

This is the physical algebra of unitary spin. Most of the results we shall describe derive from its definition, i.e., from the fact that it is an *exactly-defined system in the hadron world.* The structure constants are fixed and exact; we replace from now on the picture of an approximate symmetry (ASA) by that of an exact TOA.

SAKURAI UNIVERSALITY FROM POLE ARGUMENTS

In Chapter 4, we discussed the emergence of universal couplings in Lagrangian field theory. Experimentally, vector meson couplings do display a rough universality. However the field theory derivation has the following disadvantages:

(a) Vector mesons play a special role; other mesons lose their standing as mediators. There is no gauge invariant way of emitting or absorbing single pseudoscalar mesons, for instance.

(b) To ensure true gauge invariance, the vector mesons have to be massless. One way out, however, is to assume that this is true of their bare mass, and that the actual observed mass stems from the nonlinear interaction they undergo in the $F^u_{\mu\nu} F^{\mu\nu}_u$ term $(u = 1 \cdots p)$.

(c) We have, of course, all the other imponderables of local field theory: nonrenormalizability of vector meson theories for $p > 1$, no justification for a perturbation treatment, ambiguities of off-mass shell matrix elements, etc.

(d) To achieve similar universality-like results for mesons other than the vector-mesons, special multiplets have to be introduced. For instance, the introduction of a σ-meson was used to produce a field-theory derivation of the Goldberger-Treiman relations[7] between the pion-lifetime, the renormalization of the axial vector weak current coupling, and the strong pion-nucleon vertex. Such a system in the case of SU(3) would be more complicated. Note that we do not as yet know of any definitely observed scalar meson.

Originally, the Goldberger-Treiman relation was derived through a dispersion analysis of the beta-decay matrix element. This was considered fortuitous at the time. In present thinking, a phenomenological derivation based upon pole dominance assumptions seems more substantiated than the gauge field postulate. (However, the modern phenomenological derivation differs from the original dispersion derivation in that it does not require the meson to decay via a $N + \bar{N}$ channel.) Similar derivations can be given[3] for the vector mesons, etc. Incidentally, we also have here an example of the type of sum-rule used in dealing with the algebra of the currents, as we shall later see. Take a one-photon nucleon electromagnetic[3] matrix element; this is a matrix element of (5.12), a component of $\mathbf{j}_\mu$, the unitary spin current [e has been extracted, $F_1(0) = 1$].

$$\langle N | j_\mu | N \rangle = \tfrac{1}{2} \bar{u}_f \gamma_\mu \Lambda F_1(t) u_i + \text{magnetic term } (F_2(t)) \quad (5.17)$$

$$t = k^2 = k^\mu k_\mu, \; k^\mu \text{ is the 4-momentum transfer.}$$

We now break up the vertex-bubble in two (see Fig. 5-1). The electromagnetic interaction is in the right hand bubble

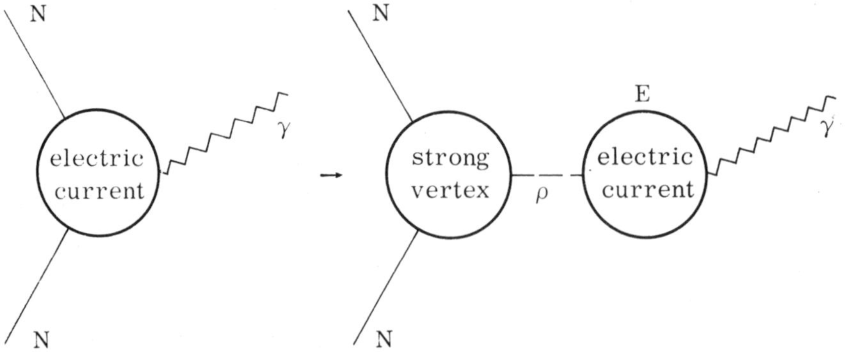

Fig. 5-1

E; on the left, we have strong-interactions only. The intermediate states have to conserve the quantum numbers of the unitary spin current, i.e., they should have unit angular momentum, octet eightspin and odd parity. The lowest—and as yet the only known—such single particle state is the vector meson octet $\mathbf{V}_\mu$ (or ρ for the I-spin subalgebra). We use boldface for the eightspin vector.

We describe the bubble E in terms of a constant g_V ($\mathbf{V}_\mu$ is a wave function)

$$\langle 0 | \mathbf{j}_\mu | \mathbf{V}_\mu \rangle = m_V^2 (2g_V)^{-1} \mathbf{V}_\mu \tag{5.18}$$

We now write the dispersion relation (unsubtracted, for simplicity) for F_1, the unitary octet form factor

$$F_1(t) = (g_{\overline{N}NV}/g_V)\, m_V{}^2 (m_V{}^2 - t)^{-1} + \int dM^2\, \sigma_1(M^2)\, M^2 (M^2 - t - i\epsilon)^{-1} \tag{5.19}$$

where the integral takes care of the many-particle states such as 2π, 3π etc. We get for $t = 0$,

$$1 = (g_{\overline{N}NV}/g_V) + \int dM^2\, \sigma_1(M^2) \tag{5.20}$$

and universality now appears as the approximation in which we assume that the low $|t|$ region is dominated by the vector meson pole.

$$g_V = g_{\overline{N}NV} = g_{\pi\pi V} = \cdots \tag{5.21}$$

For the pseudoscalar octet, we shall see that we may derive a generalized Goldberger-Treiman result in a similar fashion. Another application of similar ideas consists[4] in the Gell-Mann-Sharp-Wagner approach to the problem of meson decays, such as $\omega \to \pi^\circ + \gamma$. This is assumed to be dominated by $\omega \to \pi^0 + \rho$; one again takes the single particle ρ state as dominant in the electric current matrix element as in (5.18).

THE ALGEBRA OF UNITARY SPIN TIME-DERIVATIVES

Our TOA, whether it is unitary spin or some of its extensions, was defined in terms of the atonous and electromagnetic currents. We now have to pay the price of having avoided the symmetry issue: quantum-mechanical states are eigenstates of the Hamiltonian, and if our TOA does not exactly commute with the strong Hamiltonian, we cannot guarantee that the actual physical particles form complete representation space of the TOA. This may lead to two types of results.

Representation Mixing

At the level of the $j = \frac{1}{2}^+$ octet, the two algebras (the strong Hamiltonian approximate symmetry algebra and the current TOA) coincide. However, the H_8 part of the strong Hamiltonian implies that $\Delta I = \Delta Y = 0$ transitions are not strongly forbidden; they can mix representations, as in the ϕ-ω case. As far as SU(3) is concerned, this is identical to the symmetry-breaking picture. However, when using SU(3) extensions, we may have to deal with velocity-dependent mixings. We shall study this problem mainly when working with the action of the SU(3) $\times$ SU(3) algebra of vector and axial vector currents upon states with infinite momenta $\mathbf{p} \to \infty$ in Chapter 8.

Operator Leakage

This is the complementary effect. Not only do particles belong at times to more than one representation—it is the representations themselves which are not really complete without some contributions from many-particle states. For instance, when $G(\lambda^4 + i\lambda^5)$ acts on a $|\Lambda\rangle$, it may "leak" out of the one-particle **8** of baryons. Besides leading to a $|p\rangle$, it may also yield $|n + \pi\rangle$, $|n + \eta\rangle$, $|n + p + \bar{p}\rangle$ etc. From the good fit at the $j = \frac{1}{2}^+$, **8** level, we know that such contributions in SU(3) are not really important. However, when using some SU(3)-extension involving motion, we are sure to have important matrix elements leading to many-particle states. Indeed, it has been shown that such states have to occur.[8,9] This means that these generators do have the one-particle matrix elements defined by the currents' algebraic properties, but they also have in addition large matrix elements between a one-particle state and extraneous many-particle states. In such situations, we shall have to find means of projecting out the one-particle matrix elements only, either by picking commutators and expressions where the other parts cancel out, or by working with states where such appendages are not allowed to occur (putting the states at $\mathbf{p} \to \infty$ does it).

We have in fact come across such situations in the preceding derivation of universality results via a dispersion relation. In that case we were using densities rather than generators, so that the one-particle states had no reason to saturate the matrix elements. With the density acting on the hadron vacuum in E we separated a one-particle result (a pole in the dispersion relation at the vector-meson—or pion mass in Chapter 7) in the product **1** (the vacuum) $\times$ **8** (the density) = **8**, from an integral containing all many particle contributions. We had a sum rule

$$1 = (g_{\overline{N}NV}/g_V) + \int dM^2\, \sigma(M^2) \qquad (5.20)$$

To deal with these algebraic corrections and connect them with the physical renormalizations, we work with the algebra's time derivatives. The algebra itself does not commute with the Hamiltonian, or rather does not commute with some part of it H_Δ. We have

$$[G^i, H] = [G^i, H_\Delta] = i\frac{d}{dt} G^i = R^i \qquad (5.21)$$

$$R^i = i \int r^i(\mathbf{x}, t)\, d^3\mathbf{x} \qquad (5.21')$$

$$r^i = \partial_\mu\, j^{\mu i} \qquad (5.21'')$$

These divergences and their integrals R^i provide a good

description of symmetry-breaking effects. Taking the matrix elements

$$(E_b - E_a)\langle a|G^i|b\rangle = \langle a|R^i|b\rangle \tag{5.22}$$

we see that the mass-spectrum within the representation is proportional to the matrix elements of the R^i,

$$E_b - E_a = \frac{\langle a|R^i|b\rangle}{\langle a|G^i|b\rangle} \tag{5.22$'$}$$

We can also use the R^i to evaluate the "leakage" of G^i, by taking b to be a many-particle state n,

$$\langle a|G^i|n\rangle = \frac{\langle a|R^i|n\rangle}{E_n - E_a} \tag{5.22$''$}$$

We see that many-particle states which are distant energy-wise will contribute less. This clarifies the connection between operator-leakage and convergence problems, which are important in the use of dispersion relations.

We can also use the R^i to estimate the self-renormalization of the leaking operators,[10,11] i.e., the effect of the leakage upon the size of matrix elements within the representations themselves. We take the defining commutators between states A^a, A^b inside the representation; completeness will ensure that intermediate states include both the corresponding components in the same representation, and the many-particle states of the leakage. For the latter we use the R^i replacement.

$$\begin{aligned}\sum_{m,m'} \{&\langle A^a|G^i|A^m\rangle\langle A^m|G^j|A^b\rangle \\ &- \langle A^a|G^j|A^{m'}\rangle\langle A^{m'}|G^i|A^b\rangle\} \\ &- \sum_{n,n'} \frac{\langle A^a|R^i|n\rangle\langle n|R^j|A^b\rangle}{(E_n - E_a)(E_n - E_b)} \\ &- \frac{\langle A^a|R^j|n'\rangle\langle n'|R^i|A^b\rangle}{(E_{n'} - E_a)(E_{n'} - E_b)} \\ &= i f^{ijk}\langle A^a|G^k|A^b\rangle\end{aligned} \tag{5.23}$$

and we can now rewrite the left hand side transitions to intermediate states *within* the A representation as (K is a kinematical factor, t^{ℓ}_{cd} the C.G. coefficient)

$$\langle A^c | G^{\ell} | A^d \rangle = K^{\ell}_{c,d}(\mathbf{p}_c, \mathbf{p}_d)\, t^{\ell}_{cd}\, \delta^3(\mathbf{p}_c - \mathbf{p}_d) \quad (5.24)$$

The function $K^{\ell}_{c,d}$ represents the effect of the internal-algebra leakage, i.e., the renormalization due to the leakage to many-particle states (it is $K = 1$ for a symmetry). It contains a factor depending upon velocities and masses, occurring mainly in the SU(3) extensions, but present even within SU(3) itself as we shall see.

The R^i system can be treated in several ways. On the one hand, we may get a direct estimate of their matrix elements by using some dispersion relation and assuming they are dominated by scalar mesons (which however have as yet not been discovered). Alternatively one may try to make some further algebraic postulate, such as the assumption that the $[R^i, R^j]$ commutator yields G^k and we close on a $U(3) \times U(3)$ algebra.[3] This possibility has as yet not been thoroughly explored.

RENORMALIZATION OF A TRANSITION INTEGRATED GENERATOR

The assumption of an exact commutator relates to physical Heisenberg states. These states are eigenstates of the Hamiltonian and are related to each other ideally by the symmetry generators. As long as there is no symmetry breaking the generators are unrenormalized. In Eq. (5.23) we are now dealing with renormalized generators. Our system is thus normalized via the commutator. In practice, this normalization will be useful for the computation of physical transitions in the following way: we take the right-hand side between a particle A^a and itself, using some diagonal generator [i.e., a conserved quantity as far as strong and electromagnetic interactions go, within the U(3) system]. Dividing everywhere by $G_V^{(0)}$, the unrenormalized strength of the diagonal term (e.g., the weak current unrenormalized conserved vector coupling) we can then get an equation for the renormalization factor $(K_{i,a,m})^2$, where m labels an intermediate one-particle state, with momentum $\mathbf{p}_m = \mathbf{p}_a$

$$\{K_{i,a,m}(\mathbf{p}_a, \mathbf{p}_m)\, t^i_{am}\}^2 - \sum \{\text{leakage terms}\} = 1 \tag{5.23'}$$

This is one way of evaluating quantities like $G_V/G_V^{(0)}$ both for the $\Delta I = 0$, $\Delta S = 0$ ($\cos\theta$) term (renormalized by electromagnetic leakage) and the $|\Delta S| = 1$ ($\sin\theta$) term (renormalized through leakage caused by SU(3)-breaking and electromagnetism). The result can be considered as a slight renormalization of the θ angle and incorporated in it so that $G_V = G_V^{(0)}$ and $\sin^2\theta_{V,\text{eff}} + \cos^2\theta_{V,\text{eff}} \neq 1$. However, θ itself is a parameter which cannot be computed from the algebra.[12] Of course, an essential requirement for the application of these ideas is to find computational devices that will yield an actual estimate of the leakage contribution, a question we shall discuss in later chapters.

Rewriting (5.23′) as an equation for K^2, we have:

$$(t^i_{am})^2\, \beta\, K^2 = 1 + \beta \sum_{n,n'} \left\{ \left(\frac{R^i_{an}}{\Delta E_{na}}\right)^2 - \left(\frac{R^j_{an'}}{\Delta E_{n'a}}\right)^2 \right\} \tag{5.25}$$

where we have redefined the right-hand side of equation (5.23) by introducing

$$\beta^{-1} = i\, f^{ijk}\, t^k_{aa} .$$

We have found the Fubini-Furlan[10] sum rule, remindful of the universality results (5.20) or of the Källen-Lehmann[13] sum rules for renormalization constants

$$Z_3^{-1} = 1 + \int_{M_0^2}^{\infty} \sigma(m^2)\, dm^2$$

We note that

(a) The leakage terms appear in second-order in H_Δ of equation (5.21). This is a generalized Ademollo-Gatto theorem[14]; the original result was derived for the SU(3) breaking contribution to the renormalization of the $|\Delta S| = 1$ vector current transitions in leptonic decays. We see that it should hold for electromagnetic corrections to the $|\Delta S| = 0$ currents etc.

(b) The contribution of many-particle states at higher energies is strongly damped by factors $(\Delta E_{na})^2$, leading to a "convergent commutator." When extending the algebra, we shall have to check whether such factors still appear, otherwise we may be faced with divergent expressions.

(c) Using the identity (for $\mathbf{p}_n = \mathbf{p}_a$)

$$(E_n - E_a)^2 (E_n + E_a)^2 = (m_n^2 - m_a^2)^2 \tag{5.26$'$}$$

and

$$t = (E_n - E_a)^2$$

we can rewrite the leakage contributions as

$$\beta \sum_{n,n'} \left\{ \frac{|\, r^i_{an}(t)\,|^2}{m_n^2 - m_a^2} \quad \frac{(E_n + E_a)^2}{|\, 4E_n E_a\,|} \right\}$$

$$- \text{ similar exp. for } r^j_{an'} \tag{5.27}$$

where we have used the matrix element value for the scalar densities $r^i(\mathbf{x}, t)$ of (5.21) which we have inserted in (5.25),

$$\langle A^a | r^i | A^n \rangle = \frac{r^i_{an}(t)}{(4E_a E_n)^{1/2}} \tag{5.26$''$}$$

We note that aside from the damping factor $m_n^2 - m_a^2$ which we discussed in (b), there is a velocity dependence given by

$$\frac{(m_n + m_a)^2}{4m_n m_a} \xleftarrow[0 \leftarrow \mathbf{p}]{} \frac{(E_n + E_a)^2}{|4E_n E_a|} \xrightarrow[\mathbf{p} \to \infty]{} 1 \qquad (5.28)$$

i.e., we get the "best" sum rule, with least possible divergence when the commutator is taken between states with infinite momentum. At $\mathbf{p} \to 0$ we even lose one power of m_n in the overall damping.

The term $r^i_{an}(t)$ is a form factor about which little is known. However, if the $r(t)$ are of the usual form (with a meson dominance), we know we shall get a finite value at $t = 0$, which corresponds to $\mathbf{p} \to \infty$. At $\mathbf{p} = 0$, $r^i(t = (m_n - m_a)^2)$ is difficult to evaluate at the present time; any hope of good results at $\mathbf{p} = 0$ would depend upon some effect reducing r^i very rapidly at large time-like values.

(d) We can also consider[10] an alternative formulation. Instead of normalizing the commutator itself for renormalized generators, we can use a normalization in which the renormalized and unrenormalized generators have the same one-particle matrix elements between physical states. The usual commutator we postulate for the renormalized generators G^i is equivalent, in terms of bare generators $F^i_{(0)}$ to $[Z^{-1} = K$ of Eq. (5.24)]

$$[G^i, G^j] = [Z^{-1} G^i_{(0)}, Z^{-1} G^j_{(0)}] = Z^{-2} [G^i_{(0)}, G^j_{(0)}]$$

whereas the right-hand side is

$$i f^{ijk} G^k = i f^{ijk} Z^{-1} G^k_{(0)}$$

so that we have an "unrenormalized" commutator

$$[G^i_{(0)}, G^j_{(0)}] = i f^{ijk} Z\, G^k_{(0)} \qquad (5.29)$$

we get in (5.23) for the right-hand side if $a \equiv b$ and G^k is diagonal

$$= \frac{(Z^i_{a,m})^2}{Z^k_{aa}} \sum_{m,m'} \{ |\langle A^a | G^i_R | A^m \rangle|^2 - |\langle A^a | G^j_R | A^{m'} \rangle|^2 \}$$

The multiplier in brackets is $\Sigma_{m,m'} (t^i_{am})^2 - (t^j_{am'})^2$; dividing by this number we get a sum rule

$$\frac{(Z^i_{a,m})^2}{Z^k_{aa}} = 1 - \frac{\sum_{n,n'} \{ (R^i_{an} \Delta E^{-1}_{na})^2 - (R^i_{an'} \Delta E^{-1}_{n'a})^2 \}}{\sum_{mm'} \{ (t^i_{am})^2 - (t^j_{am'})^2 \}} \tag{5.29''}$$

which is useful in view of the insight it provides with respect to the connection with field theory renormalizations.

MASS FORMULAE

We can now go on and formalize our use of the TOA for mass formulae.[11,15] We pick[16] a time-dependent generator, e.g., the $\sqrt{2}\ \omega_{U^+}$ operator $G\{(\lambda_6 + i\lambda_7)/2\}$ (see Fig. 5-2) and commute it with its time-derivative (this is extremely similar to our derivation of the Thomas-Reiche-Kuhn sum rule in a preceding chapter). Our choice of U^+ was motivated by the fact that the Hamiltonian has $I = Y = 0$, i.e., a linear combination of $U = 1$ and $U = 0$. The $I = U = 0$ does not break SU(3), so that ΔM behaves like $U = 1$, $U_Z = 0$, i.e., like U_Z. The U^+ is thus a mass-raising operator with the mass differences as divergences.

$$[[G\{(\lambda_6 + i\,\lambda_7)/2\}, H], G\{(\lambda_6 + i\,\lambda_7)/2\}]$$

$$= [R^{U^+}, G^{U^+}] = 0 \qquad (5.30)$$

Take the matrix elements between N^0 and Ξ^0. We have as the only one-particle intermediate state the $U = 1$, $U_Z = 0$ state $(\frac{1}{2}\Sigma^0 - (\sqrt{3}/2)\Lambda^0)$ which is orthogonal to the $U = 0$ electric charge combination $(\sqrt{3}/2)\lambda_3 + \frac{1}{2}\lambda_8)$. For the R^{U^+} we can use (5.22) so that the vanishing commutator in (5.30) provides a sum rule (all one particle states are taken at rest); note that the G_{U^+} transition is given by the above coefficients $\frac{1}{2}$ and $(-\sqrt{3}/2)$ of Σ^0 and Λ.

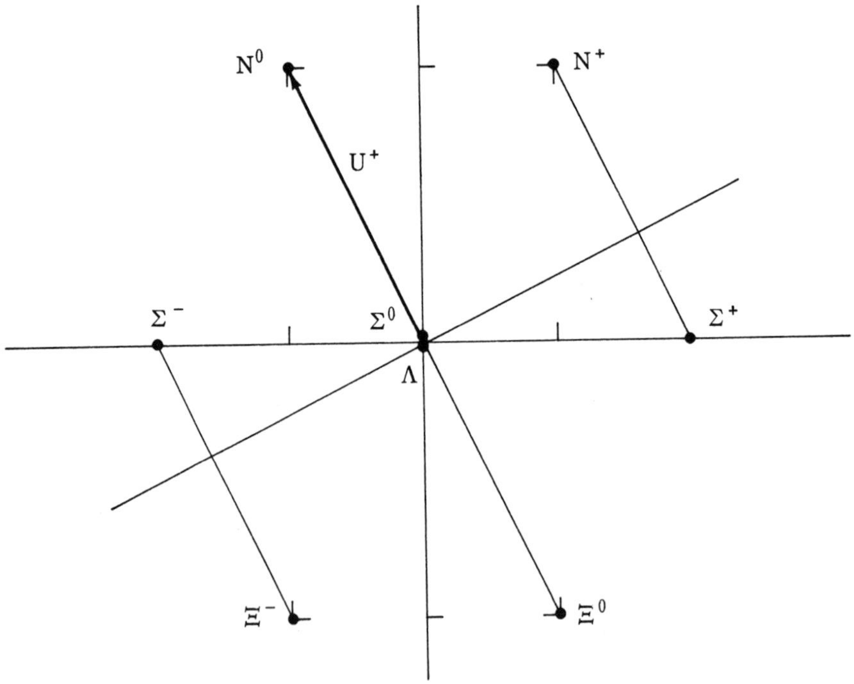

Fig. 5-2

$$(m_\Sigma - m_N)\langle N^0 | G_{U^+} | \Sigma^0\rangle\langle \Sigma^0 | G_{U^+} | \Xi^0\rangle$$

$$+ (m_\Lambda - m_N)\langle N^0 | G_{U^+} | \Lambda\rangle\langle \Lambda | G_{U^+} | \Xi^0\rangle$$

$$- (m_\Xi - m_\Sigma)\langle N^0 | G_{U^+} | \Sigma^0\rangle\langle \Sigma^0 | G_{U^+} | \Xi^0\rangle$$

$$- (m_\Xi - m_\Lambda)\langle N^0 | G_{U^+} | \Lambda\rangle\langle \Lambda | G_{U^+} | \Xi^0\rangle$$

$$+ 0(n) = 0$$

where $0(n)$ represents contributions from transitions to many particle states n. This yields

$$0 = \bar{g}\left\{\tfrac{1}{4}(m_\Sigma - m_N) + \tfrac{3}{4}(m_\Lambda - m_N) - \tfrac{1}{4}(m_\Xi - m_\Sigma) - \tfrac{3}{4}(m_\Xi - m_\Lambda)\right\} + 0(n)$$

where $\bar{g}$ is the product of the two U^+ coefficients. We find, assuming $0(n) \sim 0$

$$m_\Sigma + 3m_\Lambda = 2m_N + 2m_\Xi \tag{5.30'}$$

i.e., the Gell-Mann first order mass formula.[17] A dispersion study of $0(n)$ could provide an evaluation of the corrections to it. Note that the sum rule may be **k** dependent; taking (5.30) between states at rest gave us a rule for masses, but as we really get here $(E_\Sigma - E_N)$ etc. we would get other results between states with $\mathbf{k} \neq 0$ (Lorentz invariance ensures equal **k** for bra and ket states). Indeed[9] we find that $\mathbf{k} \to \infty$ would yield a Δm^2 sum rule,

$$\Delta E = E_1 - E_2 = (m_1^2 + \mathbf{k}^2)^{1/2} - (m_2^2 + \mathbf{k}^2)^{1/2}$$

$$2k\,\Delta E = (4\mathbf{k}^2 m_1^2 + 4\mathbf{k}^4)^{1/2} - (4\mathbf{k}^2 m_2^2 + 4\mathbf{k}^4)^{1/2}$$

$$\sim (2\mathbf{k}^2 + m_1^2) - (2\mathbf{k}^2 + m_2^2) \sim \Delta m^2$$

$$\Delta E \sim \frac{\Delta m^2}{2\mathbf{k}} \qquad (5.31)$$

An alternative prescription for the choice between Δm and Δm^2 can be derived directly from the structure of the R^{U^+} density $r^{U^+} = \partial^\mu j_\mu^{U^+}$ matrix elements. Between fermions this is Δm, from $\partial^\mu(\bar{u}\gamma_\mu u)$, whereas we find Δm^2 for a boson, where we have $\partial^\mu(\partial^\mu \phi^* \phi - \partial^\mu \phi \phi^*)$. This is related to the structure of the Dirac and Klein-Gordon equations, but the argument is more general than the use of a specific Lagrangian.

One can use the formalism to derive sum rules for the second order corrections to the mass formula,[18] etc.

OKUBO'S FORMULA

The mass operator (or its square for mesons) thus has certain tensorial properties under a given algebra. For unitary spin, the assumption (4.16) that it behaves like a component of (1, 0, −1) enabled Okubo to derive the general formula[19]

$$M = a + b\,BY + c\,[I(I + 1) - Y^2/4] \qquad (5.32)$$

For the derivation of this formula, we refer the reader to Okubo's paper or to the simplified proof by Goldberg and Lehrer-Ilamed.[20]

For octets, (5.32) reduces to (5.30′); for mesons it should correspond to (5.30′) for M^2. Present figures for the left-hand side of (5.30′) are 4539.7 MeV, with 4512.8 for the right-hand side for baryons. For the 0^- mesons, the formula predicted a mass of 563 MeV for the η, whose actual mass is 548.6 MeV.

In the $j = \frac{3}{2}^+$ decuplet the same approach yields equal-spacings (present experimental figures are 149, 145, 145).

Such predictions are expected to hold, provided the states themselves are unmixed. The latter is an unexpected fact: why does the symmetry breaking $\mathcal{H}_8$ not mix representations, when these result from strong binding between states of previously defined representations? For the decimet resonances, for instance, when considering the **10** as being made from **8** (baryons) × **8** (mesons), one would expect in some models the **10** to come out with an admixture of **27**. Also, if the masses in **8** go like **1** + **8**, why does the product-mass transform like **1** + **8** and not **1** + **27**, for instance?

Let us just study the second effect, retention of the octet character of the mass operator. That this is fixed we can conclude directly from our approach, in which we determined the octet behavior as a general feature of the operator; but this is a description, not an explanation of the dynamical and kinematical machinery responsible for the effect. Cutkosky and Tarjanne[21] verified that in a model bootstrap, a perturbation behaving like an octet in the input (i.e., a study of the binding of nondegenerate sets of states, with an **8**-like mass spectrum) reproduces the same symmetry breaking in the output masses. On the other hand, a **27**-like perturbation does not reproduce itself in the output; instead, the emerging bound states have predominantly an **8**-like spectrum. Thus the kinematics of the bootstrap tend to make it "unstable" against an octet perturbation, and "stable" against **27** breaking. This has been termed "octet enhancement." Dashen and Frautschi[22] have applied the idea to the entire set of U(3) breaking disturbances, i.e., to electromagnetism and the weak interactions too; we shall return to their results later, but we note here that the implication is that whatever the actual level of binding, **8** × **8** in most cases enhances an **8**-like term, leaving the **27** contribution at a weaker level, provided the whole system of disturbances can be considered as a perturbation. The equivalent derivation if field theory requires the existence of a 0^+ octet dominating the various "spurion" Hamiltonians.

We now come to the other effect—the approximate purity of representation. Again, in a bootstrap approach, these representations are the outcome of a non-linear self-coupling system of hadron matter[22]; the system is characterized by some group structures and the U(3) representation are embedded in fact in one infinite-dimensional (probably only in an idealized sense) representation of a huge group, containing all U(3) $\times$ spin-parity multiplets. Thus admixture or non-admixture is a matter of *identification of the larger representations.*

This again is a static description and not a kinematical check. The actual kinematical check has been provided case by case by the bootstrap analysts, who found that the deepest-bound solutions indeed fitted the observed representations. In all these bootstrap checks, the crucial role is played by the SU(3) crossing matrices. However, there certainly are cases of real admixture, like the famous ϕ-ω mixing; at first, this was conjectured from the quantum-mechanics of the two isoscalar states in **8** + **1**. We shall also return to these in our discussion of U(6) and $[U(6) \times U(6)]_\beta$ in Chapter 8, because we now replace the phenomenological fixing of the mixing angle by a U(6) identification.

CONNECTION BETWEEN UNITARY SYMMETRY OF THE STRONG INTERACTIONS AND THE UNITARY SPIN DEFINED BY THE CURRENTS

In Chapter 9 we shall deal with a novel speculative approach dealing with this issue.[5] However, in either case, we have introduced the symmetries *a priori.* True bootstrapists hope as we have seen to get the symmetry entirely as a result of their kinematics. If these "extremist" views were right, we would be faced with two problems:

1. We would have to prove the emergence of the broken SU(3) in the strong interactions, as a kinematical result.

2. We would have to explain why certain particular directions in the SU(3) algebra's space, at definite angles to the symmetry-breaking axis, are projected into the weaker interactions, where they appear as electric charge and the weak currents. These, of course, now happen to be multiplied by some small number and to serve as the source term for nonstrongly interacting fields.

To this one may propose the following alternative:

1. The first problem is to explain these weaker interactions, ending up with an electromagnetic current and a weak current, etc.

2. Problem II then does not exist, since it has been solved in principle by the bootstrapists, as they have proved that a Lie group structure emerges from the system of three-particle vertices (see our discussion in Chapter 4). One does not get a specific group; if we now require some structure constant of the emerging algebra to be proportional to electric charge, two to the almost-conserved weak vector couplings, and another one with strangeness, the machine yields SU(3). This also happens in the hadron current-algebra, where the observed weak and electric current matrix elements yield U(3) through repeated equal time commutation (up to closure), provided one adjoins the strangeness-current, for instance.

THE FIFTH INTERACTION

In this view, hadron matter displays the dynamical symmetry of SU(3) as a result of the bootstrap mechanism, but only upon injection of some information by the weaker interactions. This has to be sufficient to fix the symmetry, or at least its generator algebra. The weaker interaction currents start out at certain angles to each other and widely different coupling scales; the bootstrap sees to it that the strong interactions display the same algebra, with all couplings now brought to one scale (in fact, 1 : 1) and particles appearing as representations of the group.

To achieve this result, we need one more *a priori* current, since the weak and the electric currents would close on U(1) × SU(2). This is one reason to look for another set of well-defined current matrix elements; we have picked the eighth component, since we do observe an effect linked to it —the mass spectrum. From

$$Q = (\sqrt{3}\, G_3 + G_8)/2$$

with

$$S_5 = \frac{(aG_0 + bG_8)}{(a^2 + b^2)}$$

and

$$W^{\pm} = \frac{\cos\theta}{\sqrt{2}}(G_1 \pm i\, G_2) + \frac{\sin\theta}{\sqrt{2}}(G_4 \pm i\, G_5)$$

we generate the whole U(3). Note that it has to be a vector current. If, for example, we take the space integral of the gravitational matrix elements, i.e., the Hamiltonian, its commutator with $W^{\pm}$ will give a different result, since it involves a derivative and yields a current divergence instead of a current.

When one is studying the effects of symmetry breaking in the bootstrap, one can get a self-consistent "spontaneous" symmetry breaking, except that one can't make the breaking choose the G_8 direction. Indeed, considering that electromagnetism exists as a perturbation, one would almost expect particles to arrange themselves in U-spin instead of I-spin multiplets. If, however, there is a stronger *a priori* perturbation in the G_8 direction, we understand the observed multiplet structure. Moreover, it seems that axiomatic field theory may forbid "spontaneous" breakdowns, if they are not accompanied by a massless (here K-like) particle.[29] This is the Goldstone theorem; we refer the reader to the extensive literature on this subject.

Evidently, there is no room for such a massless particle in strong interactions. This is why we have suggested[24] that a "fifth force" is really responsible for the mass spectrum, i.e., a force which has a given parameter—a coupling of

$g^2/4\pi$ ~~ 0.1 to 0.3. The simplest model is one with a vector meson coupled to the strangeness current, or equivalently a current-current interaction involving only linear combinations of the strangeness and baryon-number currents.

Beder, Dashen, and Frautschi[25] have made a thorough analysis of the experimental data bearing on the mass of such a vector meson. Small masses seem excluded, and a two-pion mass is probably a minimum. Both the ϕ and the ω meson are eleigible candidates; ω-ϕ mixing would still result in any case. The experimental criteria identifying our ω meson are eligible candidates; ω-ϕ mixing would still Regge trajectory from a C.D.D. pole. The fifth force's meson is not on a Regge trajectory and would be identified through Levinson's theorem, for instance.[26] Unfortunately, these are extremely difficult criteria at the present stage, though perhaps a possibility of the future. Such a meson will look like a ϕ or ω; let us hope that helpful nature will provide us with a clearcut case of a new meson whose late appearance will have been due to the relative weakness of its coupling. It should be seen in the K $\bar{K}$ channel, for instance, provided it is heavy enough.

Sometime in the future we may be able to observe fifth force reactions directly, in channels where an SU(3)-invariant interaction is forbidden. A $\Delta(5^+/2)$ resonance in the $\Delta(3^+/2) + \pi$ system, for instance, could belong with a $\psi(5/2, 5/2)$ in a **35** of U(3). Its decay into $N + \pi$ is allowed only via fifth forces.[27]

Recently, some calculations have been performed, using a current-current Hamiltonian for the fifth force, with encouraging results.[28] The mass differences were computed in terms of one parameter only, using as input the experimental form factors corresponding to such currents.

ϕ-ω MIXING

When vector mesons were being discovered, it was expected[17,29] that one would be faced with two isoscalar, nonstrange states; for the gauge-believers, these were required as Yang-Mills fields coupled to B and Y respectively. In terms of SU(3), they corresponded to the λ_8 and λ_0 directions, the one in **8** and the other in **1**. The SU(3) breaking interaction may connect two such states; if they happen to lie at nearby energies, a large mixing and repulsion of levels would follow, and the actual observed mesons would no more couple purely to B and Y respectively, for instance.

Actual calculations were performed for the observed $\phi-\omega$ pair.[30] Assuming that the "original" V_8^μ vector meson in the **8** was where the Gell-Mann mass formula would require it to have been (i.e., at 925 MeV), and using the values of the actual ϕ, ω masses, one diagonalizes the Hamiltonian

$$H = \begin{vmatrix} M(V_8) & H_{mix} \\ H_{mix} & M(V_0) \end{vmatrix} \tag{5.33}$$

and gets for the observed states

$$M(\phi) = 1020 = M(V_8) + H_{mix} = 925 + H_{mix}$$

$$M(\omega) = 790 = M(V_0) - H_{mix}$$

which gives $H_{mix} \sim 100$ MeV and $M(V_0) \sim 900$ MeV, i.e., $M(V_0) \sim M(V_8)$. This gives a mixing angle with $\cos\theta \sim 0.78$

$$|\phi\rangle = V_8 \cos\theta + V_0 \sin\theta$$
$$|\omega\rangle = V_0 \cos\theta - V_8 \sin\theta \tag{5.34}$$

so that the $|\phi\rangle$ is slightly more in **8**, the ω in **1**.

From these results one may derive a large number of predictions. Considering that V_0 is uncoupled to the electric current (this would not be true in some models with integer-charge triplets), we have the following couplings to the photon for the physical particles (f_8 is the $\mathbf{V_8} - \gamma$ coupling)

$$g_{\phi\text{-}\gamma} = -e \cos\theta \frac{m_\phi^2}{2f_8} \qquad g_{\omega\text{-}\gamma} = +e \sin\theta \frac{m_\omega^2}{2f_8} \tag{5.35}$$

which leads to

$$\Gamma(\omega \to e^+ + e^-) \approx \frac{\alpha^2}{12} \sin^2\theta \, (f_8^2/4\pi)^{-1} \, m_\omega$$
$$\Gamma(\phi \to e^+ + e^-) \approx \frac{\alpha^2}{12} \cos^2\theta \, (f_8^2/4\pi)^{-1} \, m_\phi \tag{5.36}$$

These numbers can be evaluated by deriving f_8 via SU(3) from the $\Gamma(\rho \to 2\pi)$ width: for $\Gamma(\rho) \sim 100$ MeV, $f_\rho^2/4\pi \sim 2$ and $f_8^2/4\pi \sim 1.5$. On the other hand one may check directly the mixing idea by measuring

$$\frac{\Gamma(\omega \to e^+ + e^-)}{\Gamma(\phi \to e^+ + e^-)} \approx \text{tg}^2\theta \, \frac{m_\omega}{m_\phi} \approx 0.48 \tag{5.37}$$

Note that in this approach, the angle is derived phenomenologically. An alternative interpretation provides us with an "ideal" mixing angle: in triplet theories (in terms of quarks for instance)

$$V_8 \sim \frac{\sqrt{6}}{6} (uu^\dagger + dd^\dagger - 2ss^\dagger) \tag{5.38$'$}$$

$$V_0 \sim \frac{\sqrt{3}}{3} (uu^\dagger + dd^\dagger + ss^\dagger) \tag{5.38$''$}$$

on the other hand, the $V_{1\text{-}2\text{-}3}$ triplet (i.e., the ρ meson) is

$$\rho^\dagger \sim ud^\dagger, \; \rho^0 \sim \frac{\sqrt{2}}{2} (uu^\dagger - dd^\dagger), \; \rho^- \sim du^\dagger \tag{5.38$'''$}$$

If one assumes that the SU(3) breaking is basically represented by s being heavier than the (u, d) doublet, one may use the approximation

$$m_{\omega} \approx m_{\rho} \qquad (5.39)$$
$$(790) \qquad (750)$$

and assume that the actual physical ϕ-ω are

$$\phi = ss^{\dagger}$$
$$\omega = \frac{\sqrt{2}}{2}(uu^{\dagger} + dd^{\dagger}) \qquad (5.40)$$

which implies $\cos\theta \sim 0.81$. In this approach, there is a further mixing representing the nonlinear contributions and responsible also for $m_{\omega} - m_{\rho} \neq 0$. One can also use (5.40) to derive mass formulae for mixed nonets[31] (see Chapter 8).

Mixings similar to the ω-ϕ situation occur in other multiplets. It appears that the $\eta - \chi$ pseudoscalar mesons have very little mixing; this can be understood in terms of SU(6) and $[U(6) \times U(6)]_{\beta}$ as we shall see. The 2^{+} mesons do mix, though it is not clear whether the angle is exactly the same as for ϕ-ω. Mixing may be responsible for the difficulties in identifying the $\frac{3}{2}^{-}$ octet, whose Λ-state may be mixed with a **1** at least (there can also be general mixing with **10** or **27** if such $\frac{3}{2}^{-}$ multiplets exist).

Note that the existence of algebras larger than SU(3) classifying hadrons, even if only as SGA, entails numerous cases of mixing, since each super representation of the SGA contains several SU(3) multiplets, some with equal j^{P}. We may thus find that the Gell-Mann Okubo mass formula will be more useful in evaluating the amount of mixing than in actual prediction of masses.

FUBINI FURLAN AND ROSSETTI METHOD FOR INTEGRATED COMMUTATORS

Before going on to the direct applications of U(3) and its extensions we should stress that Fubini's analysis[10] of the dispersion structure of algebraic operators has led to the development of a number of practical algorithms. These are methods whose main purpose is to relate a commutator —between integrated generators, between densities or between a generator and a density—to scattering cross sections.

As an example we give here one of the most widely used methods, due to Fubini and collaborators.[32] Starting from

$$[G^a(x^0 = 0), d^b(\mathbf{x}, 0)] = e_c^{ab}\, d^c(\mathbf{x}, 0)$$

i.e., a commutator at equal time $x^0 = 0$, between a generator and some density, we get by Gauss' theorem for 4 dimensions,

$$\begin{aligned} G^a(x^0) &= \int g^{0a}(\mathbf{x}, x^0)\, d^3x \\ &= \int \partial_\mu\, g^{\mu a}(y)\, \theta(x^0 - y^0)\, d^4y \\ &\quad + \int g^{0a}(\mathbf{x}, -\infty)\, d^3x \end{aligned} \tag{5.41}$$

(if $\partial_\mu\, g^\mu = 0$, we get the conservation law for G). The last term on the right-hand side effectively vanishes for a non-conserved current because $G^a(x^0)$, the total charge, has an oscillating behavior (for exceptions and a more careful statement see Ref. 33)

$$\begin{aligned} \langle A|G^a(x^0)|B\rangle &= \exp[i(E_B - E_A)x^0] \\ &\quad \times \langle A|G^a(0)|B\rangle \end{aligned} \tag{5.41'}$$

so that

$$\begin{aligned} &\langle A|[G^a(0), d^b(\mathbf{x}, 0)]|B\rangle \\ &= \int d^4y\, \theta(-y^0)\, \langle A|[\partial_\mu\, g^{\mu a}(y), d^b(\mathbf{x}, 0)]|B\rangle \\ &= e_c^{ab}\, \langle A|d^c(\mathbf{x}, 0)|B\rangle \end{aligned}$$

leading to (writing $z = y-x$, and translating by $\exp[i(\mathbf{p}_A - \mathbf{p}_B)\cdot\mathbf{x}]$)

$$M = \int \langle A|[\partial_\mu g^{\mu a}(z), d^b(0)]|B\rangle\, \theta(-z^0)\, dz$$

$$= e^{ab}_c \langle A|d^c(0)|B\rangle \qquad (5.42)$$

One now makes the microcausality assumption

$$[\partial_\mu g^{\mu a}(x), t^b(y)] = 0 \qquad (x-y)^2 < 0 \qquad (5.43)$$

which is needed to give (5.42) an invariant meaning. To introduce dispersion relations, Fubini et al. use

$$F(k) = \int d^4z\, \theta(-z^0) \langle A|[\partial_\mu g^{\mu a}(z), t^c(0)]|B\rangle\, e^{ikz} \qquad (5.44)$$

so that

$$M = \lim_{k \to 0} F(k) \qquad (5.45)$$

F(k) being the Fourier transform of an advanced causal commutator, vanishing outside the light cone, one-dimensional dispersion relations in k can be applied. For example, if A and B are spinless and t^c is a scalar density, M is a scalar function of m^2_A, m^2_B and $q = (p_A - p_B)^2$; for F(k) we introduce two four vectors k^μ_A and k^μ_B s.t.,

$$p_A + k_A = p_B + k_B$$

$$p_A \cdot k_A = p_B \cdot k_A \text{ or } q \cdot k_A = 0 \qquad (5.46)$$

$$k_A = k \qquad k^2_A = k^2 = 0 \qquad k^2_B = (q + k_A)^2 = q^2$$

and the "energy"

$$\nu = k_A \frac{p_A + p_B}{2m_A} = \frac{k_A \cdot p_A}{m_A} \tag{5.47}$$

From Eq. (5.44) onwards, we have here a series of devices which have been introduced so as to simulate a scattering problem. The $\partial_\mu g^{\mu a}$ and t^c can now be regarded as "mesons" with external masses $k_A^2 = 0$ and $k_B^2 = q^2$, in a process A + "$\partial_\mu g^\mu$" $\longleftrightarrow$ B + "t^c" ; the amplitude is a function of these "masses" k_A^2 and k_B^2 and of ν and q^2. From the study of the analytical properties of such a scattering amplitude, one is led to write,

$$F(\nu, q^2) = \frac{1}{\pi} \int_0^\infty \frac{F^I(\nu', q^2)}{\nu' - \nu} d\nu' - \frac{1}{\pi} \int_{-\infty}^0 \frac{F^{II}(\nu', q^2)}{\nu' - \nu} d\nu' \tag{5.48}$$

with the spectral functions,

$$\begin{aligned} F^I &= \frac{i}{2} \sum_n (2\pi)^4 \, \delta\,(p_A + k_A - p_n) \\ &\quad \times \langle A | \partial_\mu g^{\mu a}(0) | n \rangle \langle n | d^b(0) | B \rangle \\ F^{II} &= \frac{i}{2} \sum_n (2\pi)^4 \, \delta\,(p_B - k_A - p_n) \langle A | d^b(0) | n \rangle \\ &\quad \times \langle n | \partial_\mu g^{\mu a}(0) | B \rangle \end{aligned} \tag{5.49}$$

and we have again on the one hand contributions from one-particle states A′ in the same representations as A and B, with poles

$$\partial_\mu \, g^{\mu a}_{An}(0) \, d^{b}_{nB}(0) \, / \, \nu - \left(\frac{m^2_A - m^2_{A'}}{2m_A} \right)$$

and a "leakage" contribution from many-particle states. Clearly, at the end of this calculation, we take the limit $k \to 0$ to get back to M.

If the original problem deals with a commutator between two integrated generators, we can use similar results. Taking the simple case where the right-hand side is a diagonal charge (G_α and $G_{-\alpha}$ are the raising and lowering generators with root-vectors $\alpha, -\alpha$)

$$[G_\alpha \, , G_{-\alpha}] = \alpha_i \, G^i \tag{5.50}$$

we find (with G^i diagonal, A and B are the same particle)

$$\begin{aligned} \langle A(p_1)|[G_\alpha \, , G_{-\alpha}]| A(p_2) \rangle & \\ = - \int d^4x \, d^4y \, \langle A_1 | [\partial_\mu \, g^\mu_\alpha (x), \partial_\nu \, g^\mu_{-\alpha} (y)]| A_2 \rangle & \\ \times \, \theta(-x^0) \, \theta(-y^0) & \\ = (2\pi)^3 \delta^3 (\mathbf{p}_A - \mathbf{p}_B) M & \qquad (5.51) \end{aligned}$$

with

$$M = \int z^0 \, \theta(-z^0) \, d^4z \, \langle A_1 | [\partial_\mu \, g^\mu_\alpha (z), \partial_\nu \, g^\nu_{-\alpha} (0)]| A_2 \rangle \tag{5.52}$$

To disperse, we again create a fictitious scattering matrix (elastic here), with

$$F(k) = \int \theta(-z^0) \, d^4z \, \langle A_1 | [\partial_\mu \, g^\mu_\alpha (z), \partial_\nu \, g^\nu_{-\alpha} (0)]| A_2 \rangle \, e^{ikz} \tag{5.53}$$

a forward scattering problem, as we have equal masses

$p_1^2 = p_2^2$, $k_1^2 = k_2^2 = 0$ and thus $q^2 = 0$. This time, using (5.47)

$$M = -i \lim_{k \to 0} \frac{\partial}{\partial k^0} F(k) = -i \frac{E_A}{m_A} \lim_{\nu \to 0} \frac{\partial}{\partial \nu} F(\nu) \tag{5.54}$$

Using now the right-hand side of (5.50)

$$\langle A_1 | G^i | A_2 \rangle = e^i_{AA} (2\pi)^3 \delta(\mathbf{p}_1 - \mathbf{p}_2) 2 E_A$$

we get a sum rule

$$\frac{-i}{\alpha_i e^i_{AA}} \frac{1}{2m_A} \lim_{\nu \to 0} \frac{\partial F}{\partial \nu} = 1 \tag{5.55}$$

From here on, we may disperse as in (5.48), (5.49), etc. Note that (5.55) is a relativistic equivalent to the sum rules we studied for renormalization problems.

REFERENCES

1. M. Gell-Mann, *Proc. Intern. Conf. High Energy Phys., Rochester (1960)*, p. 508.
2. N. Cabibbo, *Phys. Rev. Letters* **10**, 531 (1963).
3. M. Gell-Mann, *Phys. Rev.* **125**, 1067 (1962); *Physics* **1**, 63 (1964).
4. M. Gell-Mann, D. H. Sharp, and W. Wagner, *Phys. Rev. Letters* **8**, 261 (1962).
5. N. Cabibbo, L. Horwitz, and Y. Ne'eman, *Phys. Letters* **22**, 336 (1966).
6. J. Schwinger, *Phys. Rev. Letters* **3**, 296 (1959); *Phys. Rev.* **130**, 406 (1961).
7. M. Goldberger and S. B. Treiman, *Phys. Rev.* **110**, 1478 (1958).
8. S. Coleman, *Phys. Letters* **19**, 144 (1965).
9. R. Dashen and M. Gell-Mann, *Proc. Third Coral Gables Conf. Symmetry High Energy*, p. 000.
10. S. Fubini and G. Furlan, *Physics* **1**, 229 (1965).
11. G. Furlan, F. G. Lannoy, C. Rossetti, and G. Segre, *Nuovo Cimento* **38**, 1747 (1965).

12. L. K. Pandit and J. Schechter, *Phys. Letters* **19**, 56 (1965).
13. G. Källen and H. Lehmann, *Kgl. Dansk. Vid. Sels. Mat. Fys. Medd.* **27** No. 12 (1954).
14. M. Ademollo and R. Gatto, *Phys. Rev. Letters* **13**, 264 (1964).
15. S. Fubini, G. Furlan and C. Rossetti, *High Energy Physics and Elementary Particles,* (IAEA, Vienna 1965), p. 739.
16. H. J. Lipkin, "Lie Groups for Pedestrians," North Holland (1965), p. 117.
17. M. Gell-Mann, report CTSL-20 (1961) unpublished.
18. M. Boiti and C. Rebbi, *Nuovo Cimento* **43**, 214 (1966).
19. S. Okubo, *Prog. Theoret. Phys. (Kyoto)* **27**, 949 (1962).
20. H. Goldberg and Y. Lehrer-Ilamed, *Jour. Math. Phys.* **4**, 501 (1963).
21. R. E. Cutkosky and P. Tarjanne, *Phys. Rev.* **132**, 1354 (1963).
22. Y. Ne'eman, Physics **1**, 203 (1965).
23. J. Goldstone, *Nuovo Cimento* **19**, 154 (1961).
24. Y. Ne'eman, *Phys. Rev.* **134**, B1355 (1964).
25. D. Beder, R. Dashen, and S. Frantschi, *Phys. Rev.* **136**, B1777 (1964).
26. See for example S. C. Frantschi, "Regge Poles and S-Matrix Theory," W. A. Benjamin, Inc., New York (1963), p. 34.
27. H. Harari and H. J. Lipkin, *Phys. Rev. Letters* **13**, 345 (1964).
28. Y. T. Chiu and J. Schechter, report EFINS 66-61, University of Chicago (1966).
29. J. J. Sakurai, *Phys. Rev. Letters* **9**, 472 (1962); *Ann. of Physics* **11**, 48 (1963).
30. S. L. Glashow, *Phys. Rev. Letters* **11**, 48 (1963); R. F. Dashen and D. H. Sharp, *Phys. Rev.* **133**, B1585 (1964); S. Okubo, *Phys. Letters* **5**, 165 (1963).
31. J. Schwinger, *Phys. Rev.* **135**, B816 (1964).
32. S. Fubini, G. Furlan and C. Rossetti, *Nuovo Cimento* **40**, A1172 (1965).
33. S. Okubo, *Nuovo Cimento* **41**, 586 (1966).

6

APPLYING SU(3) TO HADRON ELECTROMAGNETIC AND WEAK INTERACTIONS

ELECTRIC CHARGE AND MAGNETIC MOMENTS

We have seen that electric charge is proportional to a certain generator of SU(3).

$$Q = \frac{e}{2}(\lambda_3 + (\tfrac{1}{3})^{1/2}\lambda_8)$$

$$= e(G(\lambda_3) + (\tfrac{1}{3})^{1/2}G(\lambda_8))$$

$$= eG(Q) \qquad (6.1)$$

i.e., electric charge is proportional to one of the "eight-spin" charges. It therefore has the transformation properties of an octet component. For an electromagnetic transition, we have as many eightspin form factors n^a (a denotes the appropriate Poincaré group Γ^a reduction operator, i.e., γ^μ, k^μ, $\sigma^{\mu\nu}k_\nu$ etc.)

$$\langle A | j^\mu_Q | B \rangle A_\mu = \phi(A^*)\, n_{ABQ}\, \Gamma^a\, F_{an}(q^2)\, \phi(B)^j \qquad (6.2)$$

as there are octets in the product $D(A^*) \times D(B)$; for example, for the baryon octet we have f_{ABQ} and d_{ABQ} "γ^μ"

form factors, F_{1f} and F_{1d}; and again F_{2f} and F_{2d} for the $\sigma^{\mu\nu}k_\nu$ form factors. Experimentally F_{1d}, $G_{Ed} = F_{1d} - (q^2/2M)F_{2d}$ both seem to vanish, a fact which we shall try to understand in terms of larger algebras. The baryon **10** has only one eightspin form factor for every Γ^n as

$$\mathbf{10}^* \times \mathbf{10} = \mathbf{1} + \mathbf{8} + \mathbf{27} + \mathbf{64}$$

contains only one **8**. Meson octets also have only f_{ABQ} form factors because charge-conjugation invariance of a spin 1 coupling of mesons leaves only antisymmetric combinations.

One may thus obtain unitary *symmetry* requirements with respect to the electromagnetic properties of the hadrons. These could provide a good approximation, since we have seen in (5.25) that the symmetry-breaking appears in second order provided $(g_\Delta^2/4\pi) < 1$. Coleman and Glashow showed[1] that the baryon magnetic moments and the $F_2(q^2)$ should satisfy

$$\mu(\Sigma^+) = \mu(p) \tag{6.3}$$

$$\mu(\Xi^0) = \mu(n) \tag{6.4}$$

$$\mu(\Xi^-) = \mu(\Sigma^-) = -[\mu(p) + \mu(n)] \tag{6.5}$$

$$\mu(\Lambda) = -\mu(\Sigma^0) = \tfrac{1}{2}\mu(n) \tag{6.6}$$

$$\mu(\Sigma^0 \rightarrow \Lambda) = \frac{(3)^{1/2}}{2}\mu(n) \tag{6.7}$$

in addition to the one condition derived from I-spin,

$$\mu(\Sigma^+) + \mu(\Sigma^0) = 2\mu(\Sigma^0) \tag{6.8}$$

In deriving predictions relating to electromagnetism, it is often convenient[2] to use U-spin, since Q and j_Q^μ are U-scalars.

Equation (6.3) and the first part of Eq. (6.5) can be visualized as resulting from rotations within the U-spinors (p, Σ^+) and (Ξ^-, Σ^-). Similarly, Eq. (6.4) represents a rotation within the U-vector. The other relations are more difficult to derive directly, and it seems simplest to read them out of a table of f_{ijk} and d_{ijk} coefficients. For the decimet, particles fall into exact U-spin multiplets and the results of type (6.3) are direct.

We have to remember that (5.25), the Ademollo-Gatto theorem,[3] holds only for the generators, i.e., for couplings at $t = 0$. When considering the matrix elements of a density coupled to the photon or lepton current, we are using perturbation theory to define what we mean; however, perturbation theory also says that there are diagrams where the one-photon exchange is accompanied by the "emission" of an $\mathcal{H}_8$ spurion, for instance. These terms may introduce symmetry-breaking in first order for $t \neq 0$. Okubo[4] has derived an equation which survives after consideration of $\mathcal{H}_8$ of (4.16) to first order, in addition to Eq. (6.8):

$$\mu(\Sigma^0, \Lambda) = \frac{1}{2\sqrt{3}}[\mu(\Sigma^0) + 3\mu(\Lambda) - 2\mu(\Xi^0) - 2\mu(n)] \tag{6.9}$$

the right-hand side is chosen so as to cancel out the $\mathcal{H}_8$ effects by (5.30′).

For the **10**, we have vanishing μ for all neutral particles and also no F_1 to zeroth order in $\mathcal{H}_8$. Moreover,[5]

$$\begin{aligned}\mu(\Omega^-) &= \mu(\Xi^-_{10}) = \mu(\Sigma^-_{10}) = \mu(\Delta^-)\\ &= -\ \mu(\Sigma^+_{10}) = -\mu(\Delta^+) = -\tfrac{1}{2}\,\mu(\Delta^{++})\end{aligned} \tag{6.10}$$

For the electromagnetic mass splittings, we arrange things so as to balance $U = 0$, U-multiplet contributions δ^e acquired by particles other than the $I_z = Y = 0$ pair:

$$\begin{array}{cccccc} p & n & \Sigma^+ & \Sigma^- & \Xi^0 & \Xi^- \\ m_N + \delta^+ & m_N + \delta^0 & m_\Sigma + \delta^+ & m_\Sigma + \delta^- & m_\Xi + \delta^0 & m_\Xi + \delta^- \end{array}$$

$$m_{\Xi^-} - m_{\Xi^0} = m_{\Xi^-} - m_{\Sigma^+} + m_p - m_n \qquad (6.11)$$

This is the Coleman-Glashow formula[1]; present experimental figures are 7.- and 6.5 MeV respectively for left-hand side and right-hand side. For the decimet we have[5,6]

$$\begin{aligned} m(\Delta^{++}) + 3m(\Delta^0) &= 3m(\Delta^+) + m(\Delta^-) \\ m(\Delta^+) - m(\Delta^0) &= m(\Sigma^+_{10}) - m(\Sigma^0_{10}) \qquad (6.12) \\ m(\Delta^0) - m(\Delta^-) &= m(\Sigma^0_{10}) - m(\Sigma^-_{10}) \\ &= m(\Xi^0_{10}) - m(\Xi^-_{10}) \end{aligned}$$

where X_d denotes an I-spin X-type multiplet in **d** of SU(3).

One may derive intensity rules for all types of electromagnetic reactions[1,5-7]: Compton scattering, photoproduction, decays, etc. We shall note some samples,

$$\langle \Sigma^-_{10}(1385) \,|\, \Sigma^-_8, \gamma \rangle = 0 \qquad (6.13)$$

by U-spin conservation[2]: the left-hand side has $U = \frac{3}{2}$, the right-hand side $U = \frac{1}{2}$. On the other hand

$$\langle \Sigma^+_{10}(1385) \,|\, \Sigma^+_8, \gamma \rangle \neq 0 \qquad (6.13')$$

as it conserves U-spin.

Similarly,

$$\langle \Delta^+ | p, \gamma \rangle \neq 0 \qquad (6.14)$$

$$\langle \Xi^-_{10}(1535) \,|\, \Xi^-_8, \gamma \rangle = 0 \qquad (6.14')$$

For Compton scattering, we have[6] from U-spin conservation,

$$\langle \gamma p | \gamma p \rangle = \langle \gamma \Sigma^{+} | \gamma \Sigma^{+} \rangle$$

$$\langle \gamma n | \gamma n \rangle = \langle \gamma \Xi^{0} | \gamma \Xi^{0} \rangle$$

$$\langle \gamma \Sigma^{-} | \gamma \Sigma^{-} \rangle = \langle \gamma \Xi^{-} | \gamma \Xi^{-} \rangle$$

$$2\langle \gamma \Lambda | \gamma \Sigma^{0} \rangle = \sqrt{3}\, \langle \gamma \Sigma^{0} | \gamma \Sigma^{0} \rangle - \sqrt{3}\, \langle \gamma \Lambda | \gamma \Lambda \rangle \tag{6.15}$$

$$\sqrt{3}\, \langle \gamma \Lambda | \gamma \Sigma^{0} \rangle = \langle \gamma \Sigma^{0} | \gamma \Sigma^{0} \rangle - \langle \gamma n | \gamma n \rangle$$

$$\langle \gamma \Lambda | \gamma \Sigma^{0} \rangle = \sqrt{3}\, \langle \gamma \Lambda | \gamma \Lambda \rangle - \sqrt{3}\, \langle \gamma n | \gamma n \rangle$$

For decays one has[6] [ϕ_8^0 is the SU(3) octet-component of the mixed ϕ^0, ω^0]

$$\langle \rho^{+} | \pi^{+}, \gamma \rangle = \langle \rho^{0} | \pi^{0}, \gamma \rangle = \langle K^{*+} | K^{+}, \gamma \rangle$$

$$= -\langle \phi_8^0 | \eta^0, \gamma \rangle = \frac{1}{\sqrt{3}} \langle \phi_8^0 | \pi^0, \gamma \rangle$$

$$= \frac{1}{\sqrt{3}} \langle \rho^0 | \eta^0, \gamma \rangle = -\tfrac{1}{2} \langle K^{0*} | K^0, \gamma \rangle \tag{6.16}$$

and

$$\langle \eta^0 | 2\gamma \rangle = -\frac{1}{\sqrt{3}} \langle \pi^0 | 2\gamma \rangle \tag{6.17}$$

Inclusion of $\mathcal{H}_8$ to first order yields just

$$\frac{1}{\sqrt{3}} [\langle \phi_8^0 | \pi^0, \gamma \rangle + \langle \rho^0 | \eta^0, \gamma \rangle]$$

$$= \langle \phi_8^0 | \eta^0, \gamma \rangle - \tfrac{4}{3} \langle K^{0*} | K^0, \gamma \rangle + \tfrac{1}{3} \langle \rho^0 | \pi^0, \gamma \rangle \tag{6.18}$$

For photoproduction of the decimet states we get

$$\langle \Delta^0 \pi^+ | p\gamma \rangle = -\sqrt{2}\, \langle \Sigma_{10}^0 K^+ | p\gamma \rangle \tag{6.19}$$

ATONOUS (WEAK) LEPTONIC DECAYS

These are given in the same way by the identification of the transformation properties of the atonous current.[8] Its vector part (5.13) is in fact one of the SU(3) densities,

$$j^4_A(x) = \cos\theta\, g\left(\frac{\lambda_1 + i\lambda_2}{\sqrt{2}},\ x\right) + \sin\theta\, g\left(\frac{\lambda_4 + i\lambda_5}{\sqrt{2}},\ x\right) \tag{6.20}$$

with matrix elements of the F and D type. However, for zero-momentum-transfer (which is good enough as an approximation for these decays), we have to consider the atonous "charge" only, i.e., the F part. The form factors $F_{an}(q^2)$ are the same as in electromagnetism, because of our identification of both densities with components of the SU(3) system.

For the axial vector current, all we can assume at this state is **8** behavior. The axial current will have both F and D allowed contributions at $t = 0$.

All baryon leptonic decays thus depend upon the parameters θ and $(F/D)_A$, with $(F/D)_V$ fixed by electromagnetic nucleon structure experiments (i.e., $D_V \sim 0$). One may also infer from the strong interactions the value of $(F/D)_A$, as it should reappear there—by the Goldberger Treiman relation (see Chapter 7)—in the coupling of the pseudoscalar mesons. We can therefore fit all the leptonic decays with just one parameter θ. There are 5 octet-hyperon decays (in terms of I-spin multiplets) and three K_{ℓ_2} and K_{ℓ_3} decays. By comparing one such decay with the parallel nonstrange case, we may fix θ. We give in Tables 6-1 and 6-2 the results derived by Brene et al[9]; these authors derived both θ and $(D/F)_A$ from the above 8 decays, finding $\alpha_A = 0.67 \pm 0.03$ in

$$\alpha d_{BAL} + (1 - \alpha) f_{BAL} \tag{6.21}$$

as against estimates[10-12] of 0.67, 0.66 and 0.61 for α in the

Table 6-1
Leptonic decay branching ratios (Brene et al[9])

Decay	Experiment	Reference	Theory
$K^+ \to \pi^0 e^+ \nu_e$	$(4.73 \pm 0.25)\%$	a	
$K^+ \to \mu^+ \nu_\mu$	$(62.8 \pm 0.6)\%$	a	
$\pi^+ \to \pi^0 e^+ \nu_e$	$(1.19 \pm 0.15) \times 10^{-8}$	b	
$\Lambda \to pe^- \bar{\nu}_e$	$(0.80 \pm 0.09) \times 10^{-3}$	c	0.77×10^{-3}
$\Lambda \to p\mu^- \bar{\nu}_\mu$	$(2.35 \pm 1.3) \times 10^{-4}$	d	1.9×10^{-4}
$\Sigma^- ne^- \bar{\nu}_e$	$(1.3 \pm 0.2) \times 10^{-3}$	e	1.35×10^{-3}
$\Sigma^- \to n\mu^- \bar{\nu}_\mu$	$(0.72 \pm 0.15) \times 10^{-3}$	f	0.64×10^{-3}
$\Sigma^- \to \Lambda e^- \bar{\nu}_e$	$(0.81 \pm 0.3) \times 10^{-4}$	f	0.68×10^{-4}
$\Sigma^+ \to \Lambda e^+ \bar{\nu}_e$	$(0.7 \pm 0.4) \times 10^{-4}$	g	0.20×10^{-4}
$\Xi^- \to \Lambda e^- \bar{\nu}_e$	$\cong 0.6\%$	h	0.51×10^{-3}
$\Xi^- \to \Lambda \mu^- \bar{\nu}_\mu$			1.5×10^{-4}
$\Xi^- \to \Sigma^0 e^- \bar{\nu}_e$			0.82×10^{-4}
$\Xi^0 \to \Sigma^+ e^- \bar{\nu}_e$			2.4×10^{-4}

a. Galtieri, Roos and Rosenfeld, UCRL-8030 rev. (June 1964, to be published in the Rev. Mod. Phys.)
b. Wu, Rev. Mod. Phys. 36 (1964) 618.
c. Average of Ely et al., Phys. Rev. 131 (1963) 868, and Baglin et al., Proc. of the Sienna Int. Conf. on Elementary Particles, 1 (1963) 8.
d. Normal distribution fit to data of Kernan et al., Phys. Rev. 133 (1964) B1271.
e. Average of ref. g, Murphy et al., Phys. Rev. (to be published) and Nauenberg et al., Phys. Rev. Letters 12 (1964) 679.
f. CERN-Maryland Cooperation (June 1964, private communication).
g. Courant et al., (CERN-Maryland Cooperation), Proc. of the Sienna Int. Conf. on Elementary Particles 1 (1963) 15.
h. Carmony et al., Phys. Rev. Letters 10 (1963) 381. Conolly et al., Proc. of the Sienna Int. Conf. on Elementary Particles 1 (1963) 34, find one certain and one uncertain event in 164, in agreement with this.

Table 6-2
Effective coupling constant.

Decay	V_{charge}	$V_{magn.}$	A
$\Lambda \to pe^-\bar{\nu}_e$ $\Lambda \to p\mu^-\bar{\nu}_\mu$	$-(0.291 \pm 0.017)$	$-(0.141 \pm 0.008)$	$-(0.185 \pm 0.013)$
$\Sigma^- \to ne^-\bar{\nu}_e$ $\Sigma^- \to n\mu^-\bar{\nu}_\mu$	$-(0.238 \pm 0.014)$	$+(0.130 \pm 0.008)$	$+(0.093 \pm 0.017)$
$\Sigma^- \to \Lambda e^-\bar{\nu}_e$ $\Sigma^+ \to \Lambda e^+\nu_e$	0.000	$+(0.614 \pm 0.002)$	$+(0.611 \pm 0.027)$
$\Xi^- \to \Lambda e^-\bar{\nu}_e$ $\Xi^- \to \Lambda\mu^-\bar{\nu}_\mu$	$+(0.291 \pm 0.017)$	$-(0.009 \pm 0.001)$	$+(0.036 \pm 0.014)$
$\Xi^- \to \Sigma^0 e^-\bar{\nu}_e$	$+(0.168 \pm 0.010)$	$+(0.168 \pm 0.010)$	$+(0.193 \pm 0.011)$
$\Xi^0 \to \Sigma^+ e^-\bar{\nu}_e$	$+(0.238 \pm 0.014)$	$+(0.238 \pm 0.014)$	$+(0.273 \pm 0.016)$

The predicted combined effect of Cabibbo angle, SU_3 coefficients and d/f mixing parameters on the vector term (charge term V_{charge} and anomalous magnetic moment term $V_{magn.}$ respectively) and on the axial vector term A is shown in the three last columns of table 2. After multiplication by the Fermi coupling constant $G/\sqrt{2}$ these numbers act as effective coupling constants for the corresponding terms in the simple V–A theory. In our notation the three coefficients are in neutron decay $V_{charge} = +0.97$, $V_{magn.} = +0.97$ and $A = +1.12$.

coupling of pseudoscalar mesons to baryons. For θ they got a value 0.240 ± 0.014 from the baryon decays, 0.264 ± 0.004 and 0.218 ± 0.015 for axial and vector K-decays.

NONLEPTONIC WEAK DECAYS

For hadronic decays we cannot derive any direct results from the current-current structure of the weak Hamiltonian density $\mathcal{H}_A$, with perturbation theory loosing its grip the moment both currents are subject to strong interactions. However, we may use this hypothetical structure (it is a plausible generalization from the CVC theory[13] which works so well with leptonic decays) to abstract out the transformation properties of $\mathcal{H}_A$.

$\mathcal{H}_A$ should belong to the symmetric part of **8** × **8**, i.e., it can contain an **8**-like and a **27**-like piece.

$$\mathcal{H}_A = \mathcal{H}_{A,8} + \mathcal{H}_{A,27} \tag{6.22}$$

Phenomenologically, it appears that[14] $\mathcal{H}_A$ has only $|\Delta \mathbf{I}| = \frac{1}{2}$. This corresponds to

$$\langle Y | \mathcal{H}_A | N, \pi \rangle \sim \langle Y | \mathcal{H}_{A,8} | N, \pi \rangle \tag{6.23}$$

where Y is a hyperon, and to a similar octet-transition result in K-meson decays. There are two ways of explaining this fact:

a. $\mathcal{H}_A$ may contain further $(j^\dagger)^\mu j_\mu$ terms which cancel out $\mathcal{H}_{A,27}$. Such terms would consist of neutral weak currents $\{j^3_\mu, j^{6\mu}\}_+$ which would be difficult to observe directly, as they are not coupled to leptons.

b. $\mathcal{H}_{A,8}$ may be enhanced kinematically. This would be one more case of octet-enhancement.

In either case, if $\mathcal{H}_{A,8}$ is the dominant term, one may derive[15,16] for the s-wave parity-violating amplitudes

$$-\langle \Lambda | p, \pi^- \rangle + 2 \langle \Xi^- | \Lambda, \pi^- \rangle = \sqrt{3} \langle \Sigma^+ | p \pi^0 \rangle \tag{6.22}$$

which is compatible with experiment. To derive this result, we use the unitary-parity[17,15] eigenvalues η_U of $\mathcal{H}^{\text{scalar}}_{A,8}$ and $\mathcal{H}^{\text{ps}}_{A,8}$ [see p. 36].

Remembering that $\eta_U = \eta_C(\phi_{1,3,4,6,8}) = -\eta_C(\phi_{2,5,7})$ of an octet ϕ_i, we note that the vector and axial vector currents have

$$\eta_U(j^\mu) = -1$$

$$\eta_U(a^\mu) = +1$$

In $\mathcal{H}_{A,8}$ we use a symmetrized product, i.e., d_{ijk} couplings with $\eta_U = +1$. This yields

$$\eta_U(\mathcal{H}^{\text{scalar}}_{A,8}) = \eta_U(j^{\mu\dagger}\, j_\mu + a^{\mu\dagger}\, a_\mu) = +1 \qquad (6.23)$$

$$\eta_U(\mathcal{H}^{\text{ps}}_{A,8}) = \eta_U(j^{\mu\dagger}\, a_\mu + a^\mu\, j^\dagger_\mu + \text{h.c.}) = -1 \qquad (6.24)$$

The SU(3) behavior of $\mathcal{H}_{A,8}$ is that of a sixth component, as we have to get CP = +1 for both parts. This is sufficient to relate the $\mathcal{H}^{\text{ps}}_{A,8}$ contributions and get (6.22).

There is one more result which is derivable from the above analysis,

$$\langle K^0_1 | \mathcal{H}_{A,8} | \pi\pi \rangle = 0 \qquad \text{for } t = 0 \qquad (6.25)$$

This process involves $\mathcal{H}^{\text{ps}}_{A,8}$ only, by angular momentum conservation. The $K^0_1\pi\pi$ matrix element is symmetric (we deal with an s-state of 3 mesons); therefore it has

$$\eta_U(K^0_1\,\pi\pi)_{\text{sym}} = [\eta_C(\pi^0)]^3 \times \eta_U(\text{coupling}) = +1 \qquad (6.26)$$

like the K_1^0 (which is a ϕ_7 with $\eta_C = -1$, $\eta_U = +1$) and cannot be mediated by $\mathcal{H}^{ps}_{A,8}$ with $\eta_U = -1$.

The physical implications of (6.25) are not clear. On the one hand, one may write a derivative matrix element, coupling together the three mesons in a totally antisymmetric pattern.

$$\epsilon^{ijk}\, \partial_i \phi^q\, \partial_j \phi^b\, \partial_k \phi^c$$

which is allowed, though centrifugally depressed. On the other hand, the observed ratio

$$\frac{K_1^0 \rightarrow 2\pi}{K^+ \rightarrow 2\pi} \sim 500$$

can now be explained[16] without involving $\mathcal{H}_{A,27}$. In this case

$$\langle K^+ | 2\pi \rangle \propto \langle K^+ | \mathcal{H}_{A,8}\, \mathcal{H}_{el} | 2\pi \rangle \tag{6.27}$$

i.e., it is due entirely to an electromagnetic correction, and the K_1^0/K^+ ratio should be $\sim 10^4$ in the rates. One can then deduce that the reduction to 500 is due to SU(3)-forbiddenness, and that

$$\langle K_1^0 | 2\pi \rangle \propto \langle K_1^0 | \mathcal{H}_{A,8}\, \mathcal{H}_8 | 2\pi \rangle \tag{6.28}$$

This would imply $g_8^2 \sim e^2\sqrt{500} \sim 0.16$ which is rather plausible ($g_8 \sim 0.4$).

EXISTENCE OF $\mathcal{H}_{A,27}$

We now return to the two possibilities of explaining (6.23). To simplify our analysis, we perform an SU(3) transformation[16] which rotates the A-spin into an I-spin. This implies replacing $\lambda^4 + i\lambda^5$ or ω_{V^-} (with the quantum numbers of a

K^+) by $\lambda^1 + i\lambda^2$ or ω_{I^+} (transforming like π^+) and ω_{V^+} by ω_{I^-}; the generator is then λ^7, which connects $\phi^1 \to \phi^4$ and $\phi^2 \to \phi^5$ through f^{ijk}. Clearly, $\mathcal{H}_A$ now conserves Y′, as $[Y', I'] = 0$

$$[\mathcal{H}_A, Y'] = 0 \tag{6.29}$$

$$\mathcal{H}_A\,(\text{hadrons}) = (z_1'^{\mu}(x))^2 + (z_2'^{\mu}(x))^2 \tag{6.30}$$

where

$$z'^{\mu} = j'^{\mu} + a'^{\mu}$$

This can now be rewritten[18] as

$$\mathcal{H}_A = \mathcal{H}_{A,1} + \mathcal{H}_{A,8} + \mathcal{H}_{A,27} \tag{6.31}$$

with

$$4\mathcal{H}_{A,1} = \sum_{i=1}^{8} (z_i'^{\mu}(x))^2 \equiv Z_1 \tag{6.31′}$$

$$\tfrac{5}{2}\mathcal{H}^{(8)\prime}_{A,8} = \sum_{i=1}^{3} (z_i'^{\mu}(x))^2 - \tfrac{1}{2}\sum_{i=4}^{7} (z_i'^{\mu}(x))^2 - (z_8'^{\mu}(x))^2$$

$$\equiv Z_8^8 \tag{6.31″}$$

$$20\mathcal{H}_{A,27} = 7\sum_{i=1}^{3} (z_i'^{\mu}(x))^2 - 20(z_3'^{\mu}(x))^2$$

$$- \sum_{i=4}^{7} (z_i'^{\mu}(x))^2 + 3(z_8'^{\mu}(x))^2$$

$$\equiv Z_{27} \tag{6.31‴}$$

We have written in the (8)′ upper index in $\mathcal{H}^{(8)\prime}_{A,8}$ of Eq. (6.31″)

because this is an eighth component (in the rotated octet); however, Y′ conservation as such allows the existence of an additional third component piece,

$$\mathcal{H}^{(3)\prime}_{A,8} \propto \frac{\sqrt{3}}{2} \sum_{i=4,5} (z_i'^{\mu}(x))^2 - \sum_{i=6,7} (z_i'^{\mu}(x))^2$$

$$+ 2\, z_3'^{\mu}(x)\, z_8'^{\mu}(x)$$

$$\equiv Z_8^3 \tag{6.32}$$

To achieve cancellation of the $\mathcal{H}_{A,27}$ contribution as derived from the CVC theory with the observed $z_1'^{\mu}(x)$ and $z_2'^{\mu}(x)$ we would thus have to add all other terms in (6.31″) i.e., have an interaction involving additional charged currents. Alternatively we can take a linear combination of $\mathcal{H}^{(8)\prime}_{A,8}$ and $\mathcal{H}^{(3)\prime}_{A,8}$ which involves only neutral currents in the additional terms. The total weak nonleptonic Hamiltonian density would then be,

$$\hat{\mathcal{H}}_A^{\text{nonlept}} = \tfrac{2}{3} Z_1 + \tfrac{1}{3} Z_8^8 - \frac{1}{\sqrt{3}} Z_8^3$$

$$= \sum_{i=1,2,3,6,7,8} (z_i'^{\mu}(x))^2 - \{z_3'^{\mu}(x), z_8'^{\mu}(x)_+\}$$

$$\tag{6.33}$$

This result can also be reinterpreted as the effective second-order coupling[19] produced by a Hamiltonian density

$$\hat{\mathcal{H}}_A = \sqrt{G}\, z_i^{\mu}(x)\, W_{\mu}^{i}(x) \tag{6.34}$$

with coupling strength $\sqrt{G}$ and mediation by a triplet W_{μ}^{i} and an antitriplet $\overline{W}_{\mu}^{i}$ of intermediate bosons. This $\hat{\mathcal{H}}_A$ may be assumed to behave like **3** in **3** × **8**, and the effective $\hat{\mathcal{H}}_A^{\text{eff}}$ would then behave like

$$\mathbf{3} \times \overline{\mathbf{3}} = \mathbf{8} + \mathbf{1}$$

which would reduce to the terms of Eq. (6.33).

The existence of Z_8^3 may be detected via the parity-nonconserving component of nuclear forces. This is a $\Delta Y = 0$ nonleptonic atonous interaction result; Z_8^3 would display a $|\Delta I| = 1$ component of order unity (as $\cos^2 \theta \sim 1$). No such term would appear if only Z_8^8 exists, or if the Hamiltonian density is the complete expression of Eq. (6.31), even with kinematical enhancements of its **8** part. The $\mathcal{H}_A^{\text{nonlept}}$ contains only $|\Delta I| = 0,2$ for $\Delta Y = 0$; enhancement would intensify the $|\Delta I| = 0$ component. The ratio between the $|\Delta I| = 1$ component in $\hat{\hat{\mathcal{H}}}_A$ and $\mathcal{H}_A$ is $\cos\theta/\sin\theta \sim 15$. One may therefore hope that some experiment on light nuclei, distinguishing the $|\Delta I| = 0,1,2$ contributions and detecting the strength of parity violations may point to the right composition of the weak Hamiltonian density. Detailed estimates[18] predict a ratio

$$\frac{|\Delta I| = 0}{|\Delta I| = 1}$$

of 1 for $\hat{\hat{\mathcal{H}}}_A$ and 15 for $\mathcal{H}_A$ with octet enhancement. The detection of $|\Delta I| = 2$ (or an upper limit) could provide an estimate of the **8**-enhancement by a comparison with $|\Delta I| = 0$.

The bootstrap-perturbation N/D model[20] has been used to derive a self-consistent mechanism of octet-enhancement for the nonleptonic decays. It provides a positive answer for s-wave (parity-violating) hyperon decays, but enhances[21] both **8** and **27** in the P-wave (parity-conserving) ones.

REFERENCES

1. S. Coleman and S. L. Glashow, *Phys. Rev. Letters* **6**, 423 (1961).
2. H. J. Lipkin, "Lie Groups for Pedestrians," North Holland Pub., Amsterdam 1965, p. 000.
3. M. Ademollo and R. Gatto, *Phys. Rev. Letters* **13**, 264 (1964).
4. S. Okubo, *Physics Letters* **4**, 14 (1963).
5. S. P. Rosen, *Phys. Rev. Letters* **11**, 100 (1963).
6. R. J. Oakes, *Phys. Rev.* **132**, 2349 (1963).
7. N. Cabibbo and R. Gatto, *Nuovo Cimento* **21**, 872 (1961).
8. N. Cabibbo, *Phys. Rev. Letters* **10**, 531 (1963).
9. N. Brene, B. Hellesen, and M. Roos, *Phys. Letters* **11**, 346 (1964).
10. R. Cutkosky, *Ann. Phys.* **23**, 415 (1963).
11. S. L. Glashow and A. Rosenfeld, *Phys. Rev. Letters* **10**, 192 (1963).
12. A. Martin and K. Wali, *Nuovo Cimento* **31**, 1324 (1964).
13. R. P. Feynman and M. Gell-Mann, *Phys. Rev.* **109**, 193 (1958); E. C. G. Sudarshan and R. E. Marshak, *Phys. Rev.* **109**, 1860 (1958); S. S. Gershtein and J. B. Zeldovich, *JETP* **29**, 698 (1955).
14. M. Gell-Mann and A. Pais, *Phys. Rev.* **97**, 1387 (1955).
15. M. Gell-Mann, *Phys. Rev. Letters* **12**, 155 (1964).
16. N. Cabibbo, *Phys. Rev. Letters* **12**, 62 (1964)
17. Y. Dothan, *Nuovo Cimento* **30**, 399 (1963).
18. R. F. Dashen, S. C. Frautschi, M. Gell-Mann, and Y. Hara, *Proc. Intern. Conf. High Energy Phys. Dubna (1964)*, p. See M. Gell-Mann and Y. Ne'eman, The Eight-
19. fold Way, W. A. Benjamin, N.Y. (1964), p. 254.
20. R. F. Dashen, S. C. Frautschi, and D. H. Sharp, *Phys. Rev. Letters* 13, 777 (1964).
21. R. F. Dashen, Y. Dothan, S. C. Frautschi, and D. H. Sharp, *Phys. Rev.* **151**, 1267 (1966)

7

THE ALGEBRA OF SCALAR AND PSEUDOSCALAR INTEGRATED CHARGES

THE CHIRAL ALGEBRA $U(3) \times U(3)_\chi$

In Chapter 5 we saw how the U(3) algebra was defined in terms of space-integrals of local charge densities $v^{0a}(\mathbf{x}, t) = g(\sigma^0 \lambda^a; \mathbf{x}, t)$ carried by a current $v^{\mu a}(\mathbf{x}, t)$. These $g(\lambda^a)$ enter physics via their role as atonous (weak) and electromagnetic currents. Now the vector current $v^{\mu a}(\mathbf{x}, t)$ is not the only atonous current: we also have the axial vector $a^{\mu a}(\mathbf{x}, t)$. The approximate universality of weak couplings had long been taken to imply that a larger group, the "chiral" symmetry[1] is involved, with the strong interactions approximately invariant under it. Indeed, in a Lagrangian model, one could have generators whose densities would be given by axial-vector charge-currents, provided there were no fermion mass term[2]. (Below, we shall examine a model[3] in which the meson masses vanish in the symmetry limit).

The analysis we performed at the lepton level in Chapter 5 revealed the existence of an A-spin algebra whose densities describe atonous vector couplings. The fact that the axial-vector coupling is almost the same as the vector coupling for leptons (in μ-decay, for instance) can be taken to imply that the axial-vector charges should be included in our definition of the atonous algebra of A-spin; in fact we are dealing with the $\frac{1}{2}(1 + \gamma_5)$ "left-handed" lepton current rather than with either the vector or axial-vector densities. Moreover, $|G_A| \sim 1.18|G_V|$ in β-decay, which indicates that even in hadrons the expected renormalization of the axial-vector part is not too strong and both couplings could be considered to have "originated" with equal unrenormalized strengths. Of course, these equal strengths would appear at the level of the defining representation. If the currents are written as

$$\bar{\psi}_a \gamma^{\mu} \tfrac{1}{2}(1 + \gamma_5)\, 2A_i^{(a,b)} \psi_b = \bar{\psi}_a \gamma^{\mu} (A_i^V + A_i^X)^{(a,b)} \psi_b \tag{7.1}$$

where ψ_a represents the baryon octet, we would have $G_A^{(0)} = G_V^{(0)}$ for the unrenormalized couplings. However, if ψ_a is a triplet, the actual unrenormalized relation would depend upon the choice of a representation for the nucleons. We do not make the choice at this point. Rather, we stick to the much closer $G_A(\mu) \sim G_V(\mu)$ and taking our cue from the lepton part, we write for the total A-spin, assuming the hadron and lepton parts commute with each other

$$[A_i, A_j] = 2i\epsilon_{ijk} A_k \tag{7.2}$$

and since

$$[A_i^V, A_j^V] = i\epsilon_{ijk} A_k^V \tag{7.3}$$

and

$$[A_i^V, A_j^X] = i\epsilon_{ijk} A_k^X \tag{7.4}$$

because of the fact that A^X is an "A^V-vector" under the A^V SU(2) algebra, we get

$$[A_i^x, A_j^x] = i\epsilon_{ijk} A_k^v \qquad (7.5)$$

which is indeed the answer we got using the lepton system of matrices of Chapter 5.

In going over to the hadrons, we follow the previous chapter's identification[4]

$$A^v_{\text{hadrons}} = \cos\theta\ \mathbf{I} + \sin\theta\ \mathbf{U} \qquad (7.6)$$

To fulfill (7.5) we have to take the same angle θ for the A^x system. Indeed, only octet-like axial currents have been observed to date. This is consistent with the "$\Delta S/\Delta Q = +1$" rule. In terms of U(3) generators $G(\lambda^i)$ we have

$$A^{\pm} = n\{\cos\theta\,(G(\lambda^1) + iG(\lambda^2) + G(\gamma_5\lambda^1) + iG(\gamma_5\lambda^2))$$
$$+ \sin\theta\,(G(\lambda^4) + iG(\lambda^5) + G(\gamma_5\lambda^4) + iG(\gamma_5\lambda^5)) \qquad (7.7)$$

where

$$G(\gamma_5\lambda^a; t) = \int d^3x\, g(\gamma_5\lambda^a; \mathbf{x}, t) \qquad (7.8)$$

and

$$g(\gamma_5\lambda^a; \mathbf{x}, t) = g(\gamma_5\,\sigma^0\lambda^a; \mathbf{x}, t) = a^{0a}(\mathbf{x}, t) \qquad (7.9)$$

is the axial vector charge density, and

$$g(\sigma^i\lambda^a; \mathbf{x}, t) = a^{ia}(\mathbf{x}, t) \qquad (7.10)$$

are the space components of this current, as can readily be checked

$$\overline{\psi}\gamma^i\gamma_5\gamma^a\,\psi = \psi^+\beta\gamma^i\,\gamma_5\,\gamma^a\,\psi = \psi^+\sigma^i\lambda^a\,\psi \qquad (7.10')$$

The scale of $G(\gamma_5 \lambda^a)$ is chosen so that they appear with equal coefficients in (7.7). We have left the scale n undetermined, to be fixed by the commutation relations.

We can perform a unitary transformation belonging to SU(3) which will "rotate" A^V in (7.6) into I-spin, i.e., put $\theta \to 0$. It will have the same effect in A^X and we get

$$A^{\pm'} = n\{G^1 + iG^2 + G^1(\gamma^5) + iG^2(\gamma^5)\} \qquad (7.11)$$

where G^i denotes $G(\lambda^i)$ and $G^i(\gamma_5)$ is $G(\gamma_5 \lambda^i)$. We now require

$$[n(G^i + G^i(\gamma_5)),\ n(G^j + G^j(\gamma_5))]$$

$$= 2in\, \epsilon^{ijk}(G^k + G^k(\gamma_5)) \quad \text{for } i, j, k = 1, 2, 3 \qquad (7.12)$$

Equating pseudoscalar terms (the $G^i(\gamma_5)$) on both sides of (7.12) we obtain n = 1. Setting n = 1 and equating scalar terms, we have

$$[G^i(\gamma_5), G^j(\gamma_5)] = i\epsilon^{ijk} G^k \qquad (7.13)$$

We now make use of the U(3) behavior of the $G^i(\gamma_5)$. They are octets, and (7.13) should lie in the antisymmetric part of **8** × **8**:

$$[G^i(\gamma_5), G^j(\gamma_5)] = if^{ijk} E^k + ig^{ijn} T^n + ig*^{ijn} U^n \qquad (7.14)$$

where E^k is an **8**(k = 1, 2, . . . 8), T^n is a **10** and U^n is **10***
(n = 1, 2, . . . 10). Now **8**, **10** and **10*** each contain one iso-triplet with Y = 0. Taking i, j, k, n = 1, 2, 3, not only do we have $f^{ijk} = \epsilon^{ijk}$ but also (with suitable normalization) $g^{ijn} = g*^{ijn} = \epsilon^{ijn}$ and

$$[G^i(\gamma_5), G^j(\gamma_5)] = i\epsilon^{ijk}(E^k + T^k + U^k) \qquad (7.15)$$

for i, j, k = 1, 2, 3.

Comparing with (7.13), since G^k is an **8**, we find

$$E^k = G^k \qquad T^k = U^k = 0$$

which implies that no new generators other than the G^i octet will arise in (7.14). This proves[5] that our algebra is the algebra[6] of

$$SU(3) \times SU(3)$$

which is the only one with just two octets of generators and the commutator (7.13). The two commuting SU(3) algebras [they can be completed with λ^0 and $\gamma^5\lambda^0$ to form U(3) nonets] are

$$G(\tfrac{1}{2}(1 \pm \gamma^5)\, \sigma^0 \lambda^\alpha) \tag{7.16}$$

with

$$\begin{aligned} [G(\lambda^a), G(\lambda^b)] &= if^{ab}{}_c\, G(\lambda^c), \\ [G(\lambda^a), G(\gamma_5\lambda^b)] &= if^{ab}{}_c\, G(\gamma_5\lambda^c) \\ [G(\gamma_5\lambda^a), G(\gamma_5\lambda^b)] &= if^{ab}{}_c\, G(\lambda^c) \end{aligned} \tag{7.16'}$$

TRIPLET-FIELD REALIZATION

If we try to realize the $g[\frac{1}{2}(1 + \gamma_5)\sigma^0 \lambda^\alpha]$ in terms of some set of fields, we find that the only choice where the SU(3) × SU(3) commutation relations are reproduced uniquely consists of a *triplet spinor field*.[7] This makes the bilinears behave like **8** and **1** only. Working with a spinor octet, i.e., taking the baryon octet as the fundamental set, we have minimally all the freedom of SU(8). It is observed that the axial-vector couplings follow roughly the D-octet pattern in the baryon-antibaryon product. If we commute two such currents, we will not reproduce (7.13), and the algebra will yield **10, 10*** vector currents. These will subsequently create

27 pieces in the axial vector currents. Similarly, it is clear that we cannot use a model of fundamental fields including the pseudoscalar mesons, for instance, as they would clash with (7.13). This results from the fact that one cannot have an axial vector current of pseudoscalars "canonically," and any ad-hoc choice such as $\partial^{\mu} \phi^{\alpha}$ will not yield the vector currents upon commutation. It is of course conceivable that a structure containing both scalar and pseudoscalar mesons could fulfill (7.13), but this would require at least 16 additional "fundamental" fields. A triplet spinor field is certainly the minimal assumption, satisfying our commutation relations with no further conditions.

APPLYING THE ALGEBRA AS AN ASA

Having settled on $U(3) \times U(3)_{\chi}$ as the chiral algebra, we now have to find the transformation properties of baryons and mesons under it and under P, since parity is a good quantum number. The simplest way of making the baryon octet from triplets—quarks—is to use a direct product $3 \times 3 \times 3$, which would make use of the normalization we used for the baryon number generator. In the $U(3) \times U(3)_{\chi}$ system, a quark is either right-handed

$$q_R : (\mathbf{3}, \mathbf{1})$$

or left-handed

$$q_L : (\mathbf{1}, \mathbf{3})$$

in the symmetry limit. For the baryons, we require two octets, one for each chirality component, with parity interchanging them. The **8** behavior should of course arise in the product $\mathbf{a} \times \mathbf{b}$ of $(\mathbf{a}, \mathbf{b})$, since the U(3) algebra is given by the sum of $U(3)_R \oplus U(3)_L$. We may choose from

$$(\mathbf{3}, \mathbf{3}^*) + (\mathbf{3}^*, \mathbf{3}), (\mathbf{8}, \mathbf{1}) + (\mathbf{1}, \mathbf{8}), (\mathbf{6}, \mathbf{3}) + (\mathbf{3}, \mathbf{6})$$

whose content in terms of U(3) is respectively

8 + **1**, **8**, **8** + **10**

All generators connect each bracket to itself only. In the (**8**, **1**) and (**1**, **8**) choice the two $U(3)_L$ and $U(3)_R$ are clearly F^{ijk} matrices, so that the axial vector coupling would be of f-type as well; experimentally, it is rather more d than f. For the other allowed choices, (**3***, **3**) contains both **8** and **1**, and the $G(\gamma_5\lambda^0)$ may connect the two different U(3) representations; the same is true for (**6**, **3**) where 10 and 8 can be connected by **8**. For (**3***, **3**), the axial vector coupling comes out to be of the d-type entirely; for (**6**, **3**) one gets $D/F = \frac{3}{2}$, or an effective current,

$$-\, if_{abc}\, \psi_b \gamma_\mu \psi_c + (d_{abc} - \tfrac{2}{3} if_{abc})\, \psi_b \gamma_\mu \gamma_5 \psi_c \tag{7.17}$$

where ψ_a is the baryon **8**. This pattern also yields

$$(-G_A/G_V) = \tfrac{5}{3} \tag{7.18}$$

for the unrenormalized couplings; as against $G_A = -G_V$ in the (**3*** , **3**) case. The experimental value is 1.2, which is between the two theoretical numbers. A variety of calculations had been performed[6] with the (**3**, **3***) choice, with no clear cut verification. However, the more recent successes of SU(6) point[8] to the (**6**, **3**) choice, which is the appropriate choice for an embedding of $U(3) \times U(3)_\chi$ in U(6) or U(6) × U(6) with the baryons in the **56** representations of U(6). We shall discuss these possibilities in the next chapters.

$U(3) \times U(3)_\chi$ is a broken symmetry. In a quark field model, it does not commute with the quark mass term

$$m\bar{q}q = m(\bar{q}_L q_R + \bar{q}_R q_L) \tag{7.19}$$

which mixes the two subspaces. We abstract the corresponding algebraic properties and assume that the Hamiltonian density contains a piece $\mathcal{H}_m$ which behaves like the U(3) scalar component of $(\mathbf{3}, \mathbf{3}^*) + (\mathbf{3}^*, \mathbf{3})$. Using this assignment and McDowell's transformation, i.e., interpreting a negative mass eigenvalue as a positive mass for $\gamma_5 \psi$, a baryon with odd relative parity with respect to the **8**, we find that the **10** in $(\mathbf{6}, \mathbf{3}) + (\mathbf{3}, \mathbf{6})$ should have $j = \frac{1}{2}^-$, and its mass should be twice the octet mass. There is a recently[9] reported $\Delta(1670; \frac{1}{2}^-)$; the center of mass of a **10** with this Δ could very well lie around 1.9 to 2.0 BeV. As to the J = 1 mesons, they should be assigned to the same representation $(\mathbf{8}, \mathbf{1}) + (\mathbf{1}, \mathbf{8})$ as the currents, so as to fit a meson pole-dominance picture.

The photon transforms like a component of $(\mathbf{8}, \mathbf{1}) + (\mathbf{1}, \mathbf{8})$. There is no limitation on the D/F structure of the electric matrix element, other than that it is pure F at $q^2 = 0$ (from universality). The anomalous magnetic part of the matrix element vanishes at the $U(3) \times U(3)_\chi$ symmetry limit: it should relate components with opposite helicity, i.e., connect $(\mathbf{6}, \mathbf{3})$ with $(\mathbf{3}, \mathbf{6})$. This cannot be achieved by $(\mathbf{8}, \mathbf{1})$ and $(\mathbf{1}, \mathbf{8})$; however, if we leave the symmetry limit and count in the $\mathcal{H}_m$ effect to first order, i.e., we take the matrix element of $[(\mathbf{3}, \mathbf{3}^*) + (\mathbf{3}^*, \mathbf{3})] \times [(\mathbf{6}, \mathbf{3}) + (\mathbf{3}, \mathbf{6})]$ between $(\mathbf{6}, \mathbf{3})$ and $(\mathbf{3}, \mathbf{6})$, this has a number of independent channels available; if we restrict our choice to the $(\mathbf{3}, \mathbf{3}^*) + (\mathbf{3}^*, \mathbf{3})$ part of $\mathcal{H}_m$ $\mathcal{H}_{em}$, we get

$$\frac{\mu(n)}{\mu(p)} = -\frac{2}{3} \tag{7.20}$$

which is rather near to the experimental value -0.68. The choice here seems highly arbitrary, however it is picked out by the larger U(6) structure, as we shall see. Moreover, we note that the magnetic moment emerges from a picture in which $\mathcal{H}_m$ is acting, i.e., we are consistent with the static model.

POLE DOMINANCE OF THE AXIAL CURRENT DIVERGENCE—A UNIVERSALITY RELATION

Like many other important results, the Goldberger-Treiman relation was originally derived from a set of somewhat implausible assumptions. Once it was found to lead to correct predictions, several attempts were made to incorporate it in a symmetry-picture. The symmetry was the chiral one, with axial vector currents; however, there were two views with respect to the role of the pseudoscalar mesons. In the Gell-Mann and Levy[2] picture, these mesons have to be a part of a complete multiplet of $[U(3) \times U(3)]_\chi$ (or in ref[2] $[U(2) \times U(2)]_\chi$); to make this multiplet a representation of the parity operator too, the additional mesons [only one "σ" isosinglet was sufficient before SU(3); one now requires 8] have 0^+ spin-parity assignments. This then produces a meson term $\sigma \partial^\mu \phi_\pi$ in the axial vector current; taking the divergence, one now breaks the symmetry by letting the σ connect with the vacuum in a tadpole-like diagram. This then yields

$$\partial^\mu a_\mu = C \phi_\pi \tag{7.21}$$

In the Nambu picture,[3] the pseudoscalar meson plays an almost opposite role. When writing a matrix element of the nonvanishing divergence of the axial vector nonconserved current, we note that we *could* make it vanish provided there were some accidental cancellation between form factors. For this to occur,

$$0 = \langle N|\partial^\mu a_\mu |N\rangle \propto \bar{u}(p_2) i\gamma_5 [2m_N F_A(k^2) - k^2 F_P(k^2)] u(p_1) \tag{7.22}$$

so that

$$F_P(k^2) = 2m_N F_A(k^2)/k^2$$

and the one then says that $F_P(k^2)$ has a pole at $k^2 = 0$, corresponding to a zero mass meson meson. The idea is then that the pseudoscalar mesons indeed are not a complete multiplet of the chiral group; they exist for the non-conserved part only, and would in the limit of $m_\pi^2 \to 0$ make all matrix elements of $\partial^\mu a_\mu$ vanish. This view has been called a "spontaneous" symmetry breakdown; in theories that have attempted to provide SU(3) itself with such a "spontaneous" symmetry breaking, one needs a K-meson like *scalar* meson whose zero-mass limit contribution would cancel the symmetry-breaking part of $\langle\Lambda|\partial^\mu j_\mu|N\rangle \propto (m_\Lambda - m_N)$, for instance.[11]

In our dispersion-analysis algebraic approach, the Goldberger-Treiman relation is derived in the same way that we got the Sakurai vector-meson universality. Consider the β-decay of any baryon B_a. Because of the weakness of the atonous interaction, we may factor out the lepton current term. We are now analyzing the matrix element

$$\langle B_a|\mathbf{a}_\mu|B_b\rangle = \tfrac{1}{2}\bar{u}_{fa}(\gamma_\mu F_A^{\bullet}(t) + k_\mu F_P(t)) \times \gamma_5 \boldsymbol{\Lambda}(a, b)\, u_{ib} \qquad (7.23)$$

[the actual atonous hadron current corresponds of course to a pair of components $\Lambda^\pm = \cos\theta(\Lambda_1 \pm i\Lambda_2) + \sin\theta(\Lambda_4 \pm i\Lambda_5)$ of unitary spin]. Again G_V has been extracted and $F_A(0) = -G_A/G_V$. We now take the matrix element of the divergence,

$$\langle B_a|\partial^\mu \mathbf{a}_\mu|B_b\rangle = \frac{i}{2}\bar{u}_{fa}\gamma_5\Lambda^{(a,b)}u_{ib} \times [(m_a + m_b)F_A(t) + tF_P(t)] \qquad (7.23')$$

The right hand blob for this matrix element would be

$$\langle 0|\partial^\mu \mathbf{a}_\mu|\boldsymbol{\phi}\rangle = m_\phi^2\, g_\phi^{-1}\, \boldsymbol{\phi} \qquad (7.24)$$

(ϕ denotes here a wave function) where we have inserted the pseudoscalar octet as intermediate states. The constant g_ϕ has been evaluated for the $\Delta S = 0$ case by Goldberger and Treiman from the pion muonic decay. [Note that the right hand blob in Fig. 7.1 is indeed the pion-decay amplitude (7.24).]

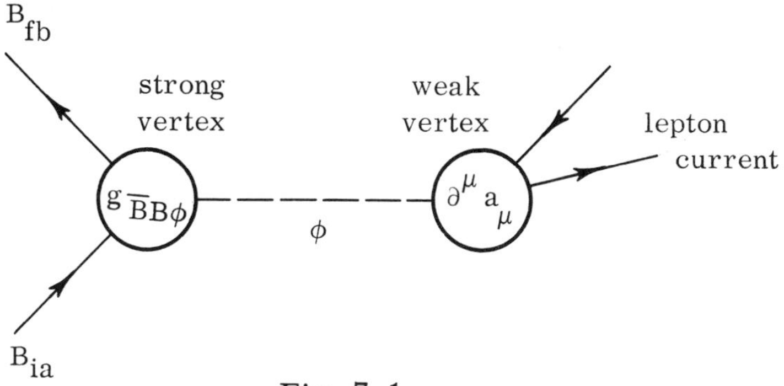

Fig. 7-1.

Again we assume an unsubtracted dispersion relation for $\partial^\mu a_\mu$, with the meson pole plus an integral representing many-particle contributions entering

$$(m_a + m_b)\, F_A(t) + tF_P(t) = (g_{\overline{B}B\phi}/g_\phi)\, m_\phi^2$$

$$\times\, (m_\phi^2 - t)^{-1} + \int dM^2\, \sigma_A(M^2)\, M^2 (M^2 - t - i\epsilon)^{-1} \tag{7.25}$$

at $t = 0$, we get

$$(m_a + m_b)\, (-G_A/G_V)^{ab} = (g_{\overline{B}B\phi}/g_\phi) + \int dM^2\, \sigma_A(M^2) \tag{7.26}$$

and with pole-dominance assumed for low t, we get the relation,

$$g_\phi (m_a + m_b)\, (-G_A/G_V)^{ab} \approx g_{\overline{B}_a B_b \phi} \tag{7.27}$$

This represents a quasi-universality for the couplings $g_{xy\phi}$. However, the above formulae have to be corrected for the variation over the range of t, between $t = -m_\phi^2$ where the dispersion relation is written and $t = 0$. We deal below with this correction.

(7.27) is satisfied experimentally within 10%, in the πNN case [i.e., the $\gamma_5(\lambda^1 \pm i\lambda^2)$, $\Delta S = 0$ current],

$$g_{\overline{N}N\pi} \sim 2g_\pi m_N F_A(0) \tag{7.28}$$

where $g_{\overline{N}N\pi}$ is the rationalized, renormalized π-N coupling constant, $F_A(0)$ is the beta decay axial vector form-factor at $t = 0$, and m_N is the nucleon mass:

$$g^2_{\overline{N}N\pi}/4\pi = 14 \qquad F_A(0) = -\frac{G_A}{G_V} = 1.19$$

We find $g_\pi \sim \frac{11}{2} m_N^{-1}$ from (7.28); experimentally, from π-decay we get $g_\pi \sim 5m_N^{-1}$. There are various other experimental predictions arising from the pole dominance assumption (generally known as PCAC, for "partial conservation of axial vector currents") in itself, either in its matrix element formulation (7.24), or in the perhaps stronger formulation (7.21) in which ϕ_π is a renormalized phenomenological field operator creating a pion; computing C of (7.21) from $\langle N | \partial^\mu a_\mu | N \rangle$ one finds[12]

$$\partial^\mu \mathbf{a}_\mu = \frac{2m_N m_\pi^2 F_A(0)}{g_{\overline{N}N\pi} K_{\overline{N}N\pi}(0)} \phi_\pi + R \tag{7.29}$$

R has small matrix elements for $-m_\pi^2$, and where $K_{\overline{N}N\pi}(t)$ is the π-N form factor, taken as 1 at $t = -m_\pi^2$. From (7.29), one predicts[13] that in the reaction

$\nu + N \rightarrow \ell + N'$

(ℓ is e or μ, N′ is a system of hadrons)

$$k^{\mu}\langle N'|a_{\mu}|N\rangle = (2k^0)^{1/2}\, A(\pi^+ + N \rightarrow N') \times 2^{1/2} m_N G_A g^{-1}_{\overline{N}N\pi} \times [1 - k^2(k^2 + m^2_{\pi})^{-1}] \tag{7.30}$$

where the momentum of the incident π^+ in the strong interaction $A(\pi^+ + N \rightarrow N')$ should be taken parallel to **k** and its energy is k^0. This is computed with m_ℓ neglected; a more complicated expression corresponds[13] to $m_\ell \neq 0$.

Universality results are derived from pole-dominance postulates, as we have seen. On the other hand, they are finally statements about the strong interactions themselves —like the approximate universality of ρ couplings. The same is true of (7.28) or (7.29), which impose conditions on π-couplings, such as Adler's,

$$g^2_{\overline{N}N\pi}/m_N = A(\pi_i N_i \rightarrow \pi_f N_f)^{\{+\}}_{\nu=\nu_B=k^2_{\pi i}=0}/K_{\overline{N}N\pi}(0) \tag{7.31}$$

where $\{+\}$ denotes the symmetric part in isospin, $m^2_{\pi f} = m^2_{\pi}$, $\nu = -(P_{Ni} + P_{Nf})\cdot k/2m_N$, $\nu_B = q_{\pi f}\cdot k_{\pi i}/2m_N$. To compare with experiment, one has to devise proper methods of extrapolating from the mass shell to $k^2_{\pi i} = 0$; a study of models leads us to expect a change of some 2 percent of $g^2_{\overline{N}N\pi}/m_N$, i.e., a small correction only. The results show that (7.31) is satisfied to within less than 10 per cent, perhaps as low as 5 per cent. Several similar conclusions from (7.29) have been derived for π-π, π-Λ, etc.

Note that when considering electromagnetic corrections to first order, one should use[14]

$$(\partial^{\mu} \mp ie A^{\mu})\, a_{\mu}^{(\pm)} = C\, \phi_{\pi(\pm)}$$
$$\partial^{\mu} a_{\mu}^{(0)} = 2^{1/2} C\, \phi_{\pi(0)} \qquad (7.32)$$

where (±) and (0) denote charges, and C is the constant in (7.29).

SOFT PION EMISSION RELATIONS

One of the most interesting physical results from the pion dominance postulate is a relation holding between any two processes one of which differs from the other only in that an additional zero-mass, zero-energy pion is emitted or absorbed. This idea, developed by Nambu[15-17] and collaborators has been extensively used in deriving physical results from current commutators.

From the postulate (7.21) or (7.29) we find for any two hadron states α and β,

$$\langle\beta|\partial^{\mu} a_{\mu}|\alpha\rangle = \frac{2m_N m_{\pi}^2 F_A(0)}{g_{\overline{N}N\pi} K_{\overline{N}N\pi}(0)} (k^2 + m_{\pi}^2)^{-1} (2k_0)^{1/2} \times A(\pi^+ + \alpha \to \beta)_{k^2=(p_{\beta}-p_{\alpha})^2} \qquad (7.33)$$

This in itself contains such a relationship. The right-hand side contains the on-mass shell radiative (or emittive) amplitude explicitly; the left-hand side can be computed from the $\langle\beta|S|\alpha\rangle$ amplitude by the insertion of an a_{μ} vertex in all possible ways into the external lines, followed by taking the divergence of the summed expression. The left hand side has at $k^2 \neq 0$ several invariant matrix elements which do not allow us to make direct identifications on both sides; taking $k^2 = 0$ everywhere gives a one-to-one correspondence between the invariant matrix elements on both sides. The result (7.31) is an example of such a soft-pion emission theorem; it is computed from $\langle N\pi|\partial^{\mu} a_{\mu}|N\rangle$. Similarly, the π-π result is derived from $\langle\pi\pi|\partial^{\mu} a_{\mu}|\pi\rangle$, etc.

The theory has been generalized by Weinberg[18] so as to give a definite prescription for the production of any number n_{π} of soft pions, with all four components of their $k^{\mu} \to 0$, all at the same time. Using field theory and the reduction formula, this matrix element is shown to contain two parts:

1. A quantity corresponding exactly to what one would get from assuming perturbation theory and a pseudovector pion coupling $g_{\overline{N}N\pi}/2m_N$ in the standard way. This is the result of the parallelism between the matrix-element identifications which fixed C of (7.21), and Foldy's transformation in perturbation theory, or the various field-theory models of chiral symmetries.

2. A quantity produced by the reduction formula and containing multiple commutators

$$[a_i^0(x), a_j^{\mu}(y)]_{x^0 = y^0} \qquad \text{etc.}$$

between components of axial densities. It is in the evaluation of these commutators that the algebraic structure produces new results.

In Chapter 5, we described some of the algorithms used to turn an expression for a commutator-between integrated generators, or between a generator and a density—into a fictitious scattering problem, amenable to a dispersion treatment.[19,20] Note that the expressions we got described the scattering of zero-mass fictitious bosons; whenever an integrated generator appeared in the original commutator, its place was taken by $\partial^{\mu} g_{\mu a}$, the divergence of its density, acting as our fictitious meson. We now see that the use of (7.21) replaces this fictitious meson by a soft pion, and we can thus expect a variety of further theorems for soft pion emission to be derived from commutators involving $G(\gamma_5 \lambda^a)$

EVALUATING A COMMUTATOR BETWEEN DENSITITIES; SEMI-INTEGRATED COMMUTATORS

There are cases in which it is more fruitful to use the local commutation relations of the algebraic densities directly; at this stage we are interested in commutators between the charge density on the one hand, and other components on the other hand. Such commutators give rise to a particular type of singular terms discovered by Schwinger[21]; we shall leave our discussion of these terms to another chapter, and assume the commutation relations we would get from (7.16′) and quark fields.[6]

$$\begin{aligned}
&[g^0(\lambda^a_;\, x),\, g^\mu(\lambda^b_;\, y)]_{x^0=y^0} \\
&\qquad = if^{ab}{}_c\, g^\mu(\lambda^c_;\, x)\, \delta^3(\mathbf{x}-\mathbf{y}) \\
&[g^0(\lambda^a_;\, x),\, g^\mu(\gamma_5\lambda^b_;\, y)]_{x^0=y^0} \\
&\qquad = if^{ab}{}_c\, g^\mu(\gamma_5\lambda^c_;\, x)\, \delta^3(\mathbf{x}-\mathbf{y}) \qquad (7.34)\\
&[g^0(\gamma_5\lambda^a_;\, x),\, g^\mu(\lambda^b_;\, y)]_{x^0=y^0} \\
&\qquad = if^{ab}{}_c\, g^\mu(\gamma_5\lambda^c_;\, x)\, \delta^3(\mathbf{x}-\mathbf{y}) \\
&[g^0(\gamma_5\lambda^a_;\, x),\, g^\mu(\gamma_5\lambda^b_;\, y)]_{x^0=y^0} \\
&\qquad = if^{ab}{}_c\, g^\mu(\lambda^c_;\, x)\, \delta^3(\mathbf{x}-\mathbf{y})
\end{aligned}$$

We could also use "semi-integrated" commutators, in which the $g^{0a}(x)$ is integrated over 3-space, i.e., these would be commutators between generators and densities. They then consist in a definition of the $[U(3)\times U(3)]_\chi$ properties of $g^{\mu a}$, leading to (7.34).

Various authors[22-27] have used the following algorithm

for the evaluation of such commutators by transforming them into scattering problems. We shall give here a brief review of the essentials of the method. Write the simulated scattering amplitude

$$T^{\nu\mu} = (2\pi)^4 \delta_4 (p_A - q - p_B + q')t^{\nu\mu}$$
$$t^{\nu\mu} = i \int d^4 x e^{iqx} \langle p_A | [g^{\nu a}(x), g^{\mu b}(0)] | p_B \rangle \theta(x^0) \tag{7.35}$$

and integrate by parts,

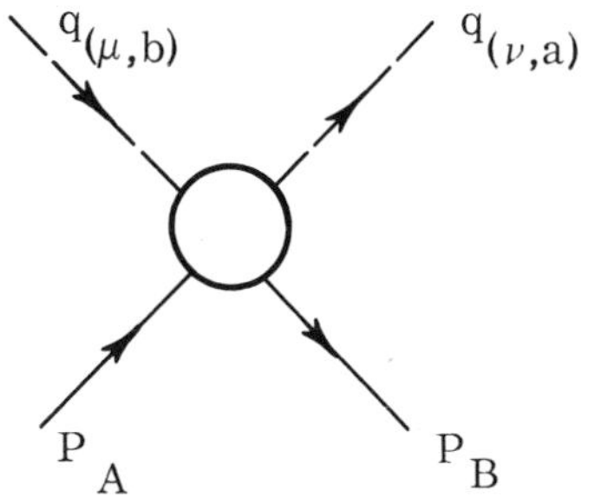

$$q_\nu t^{\nu\mu} = -\int d^4 x\, e^{iqx} \langle p_A | [\partial_\nu g^{\nu a}(x), g^{\mu b}(0)] | p_B \rangle \theta(x^0) + i \int d^4 x\, e^{iqx} \times \langle p_A | [g^{oa}(x), g^{\mu b}(0)] | p_B \rangle \delta(x^0) \tag{7.36}$$

The first term on the right-hand side is again a simulated scattering amplitude t^μ; it exists only for $\partial_\nu g^{\nu a} \neq 0$, i.e., it will be very useful for $g^\nu(\gamma_5 \lambda^a)$, although it could also apply to vector densities for the $|\Delta S| = 1$ case or even for $\Delta S = 0$ if we plan to evaluate electromagnetic corrections. The second term on the right hand side has a commutator of the type given by our equations (7.34); it can thus be rewritten after integrating over $\delta(x^0)$ and $\delta^3(\mathbf{x})$ as

$$if^{abc} \langle p_A | g^{\mu c}(0) | p_B \rangle = F^{\mu}(p_A, p_B)$$

i.e., a form factor, which is easily worked out from Lorentz invariance and U(3). We thus have a basic relationship,

$$q_{\nu} t^{\nu\mu}(s, t, q^2, q'^2) - t^{\mu}(s, t, q^2, q'^2) = -F^{\mu}(t) \qquad (7.37)$$

where $s = -(p_A + q)^2$, $t = -(p_A - p_B)^2$. Clearly, the use of (7.34) has cancelled s, q^2, q'^2 dependence on the right-hand side, and we can exploit this fact to discover relations between amplitudes on the left-hand side.

APPLYING THE ALGEBRA AS A TOA

The results we got from $[U(3) \times U(3)]_{\chi}$ used as an ASA were certainly not spectacular. The best choice of representations for the baryons yielded $-G_A/G_V = \frac{5}{3}$ or 1, with $\frac{5}{3}$ providing a D/F ratio of $\frac{3}{2}$ for the axial coupling, and thus for the pseudoscalar couplings by the Goldberger-Treiman relation. We shall now see that using the algebra as a TOA—i. e., without forcing the spectrum of one particle states to fit in some simple representations—yields extremely beautiful results. These can be grouped roughly into

1. Sum rules of the type we discussed in Chapter 5, Eqs. (5.23), (5.25) or (5.29)

$$\{K_{i,a,m}(p_a, p_m)\, t^{i}_{am}\}^2 - \sum{}'\{\text{leakage terms}\} = 1 \qquad (5.23)$$

from which we derived a value for the renormalized transitions $K^{i}_{a,m}$

$$(t^{i}_{a,m})^2 \beta K^2 = 1 + \beta \sum_{n,n'} \left\{ \left(\frac{R^{i}_{an}}{\Delta E_{na}}\right)^2 - \left(\frac{R^{i}_{an'}}{\Delta E_{n'a}}\right)^2 \right\} \qquad (5.25)$$

or the alternative normalization producing (5.29).

The leakage terms involve as we saw the integrals R^i of $\partial_\mu g^\mu$; to evaluate them, one has to use the various devices due mostly to Fubini and collaborators, some examples of which we received in Chapter 5 and in this chapter.

This group of results includes the calculation of G_A/G_V for both $\Delta S = 0$ and $|\Delta S| = 1$, relations between leptonic decays of K mesons (these involve soft pion emission relations), relations between various electromagnetic transition matrix elements.

2. Strong interactions sum rules, such as low-energy theorems, soft-pion relations, etc. These may involve some more drastic assumptions about the convergence properties of some strong amplitudes.

ADLER-WEISBERGER SUM RULE[22, 28-30]

Using equations (7.35) through (7.37) (P is a proton state)

$$t^{\nu\mu} = i \int d^4x\, e^{iqx} \langle P|[g^\nu(\gamma_5 \tau^+; x), g^\mu(\gamma_5 \tau^-; 0)]|P\rangle \theta(x^0) \tag{7.38}$$

and then going over to (7.36) contracting again with q_μ and integrating the $q_\nu t^{\mu\nu}$ term by parts, we find

$$\begin{aligned} q_\nu q_\mu t^{\nu\mu} = {} & +i \int d^4x\, e^{-iqx} \langle P|[\partial_\nu g^\nu(\gamma_5 \tau^+; 0), \\ & \partial_\mu g^\mu(\gamma_5 \tau^-; x)]|P > \theta(-x^0) \\ & - \int d^4x\, e^{-iqx} \langle P|[\partial_\nu g^\nu(\gamma_5 \tau^+; 0), \\ & g^0(\gamma_5 \tau^-; x)]|P\rangle \delta(x^0) + i \int d^4x\, e^{-iqx} q_\mu \\ & \times \langle P|[g^0(\gamma_5 \tau^+; 0), g^\mu(\gamma_5 \tau^-; x)]|P\rangle \delta(x^0) \end{aligned} \tag{7.39}$$

where we have $p^2 = m_N^2$ and use $\nu = (p \cdot q)/m_N$ as the energy variable. Weisberger obtains the G_A/G_V sum rule from (7.39), as a low-energy theorem in the limit $q^2 \to 0$, $\nu \to 0$. He evaluates the terms in (7.39) to first order in ν. For $t^{\nu\mu}$, we can use dispersion relations in ν, for any value of q^2; looking at the diagram, we observe that singularities will include the neutron pole

$$(p + q)^2 = m_N^2$$

and a cut starting from $(m_N + m_\pi)^2$

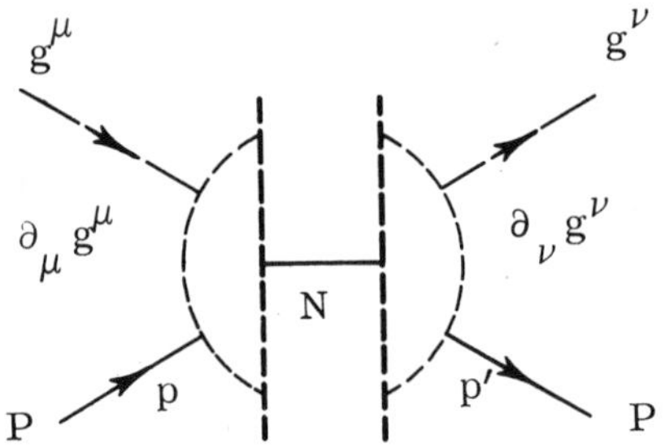

in $(p + q)^2$ terms. For ν this yields a pole at $\nu = -q^2/2m_N$ and a cut starting at $\nu = (-q^2 + m_\pi^2 + 2m_N m_\pi)/2m_N$. Clearly, for $q^2 \to 0$ only the pole contributes a singular term. This term is $\alpha |\langle N | g^\mu (\gamma_5 \tau^-; 0) | P \rangle|^2$ and thus represents g_A^2, $g_A = -G_A/G_V$ since we normalize to $G_V = 1$. The first term on the right-hand side which we denote by $R(q^2, \nu)$ and which contains a time-ordered product, represents a forward scattering amplitude for πP [as the $\partial_\nu g^\nu$ are dominated by the pion field (7.21)] on mass shell; this results from analyticity in q^2. The second term will be seen to cancel with a constant extracted from the first term; and the last term on the right-hand side will be seen to yield the identity. The result is the sum rule

$$\left(\frac{G_A}{G_V}\right)^2 = 1 + \frac{2}{\pi}\left(\frac{m_N}{g_{\overline{NN}\pi}}\right)^2 \int_{m_\pi}^{\infty} \frac{k\,dv}{\nu^2}$$

$$\times \left\{ \sigma_{tot}^{\pi^- p}(\nu) - \sigma_{tot}^{\pi^+ p}(\nu) \right\} \qquad (7.40)$$

which yields $|G_A/G_V| = 1.15$ to 1.24 in the various calculations, as against the experimental value

$$\frac{G_A}{G_V} = -1.18 \pm 0.025 \qquad (7.40')$$

We shall now follow roughly the evaluation of the various terms in (7.39), leading to (7.40).

We take first the last term on the right-hand side of (7.39). From (7.34) we know that

$$\delta(x^0)[g^0(\gamma_5\,\tau^+;\,0),\, g^\mu(\gamma_5\,\tau^-;\,x)] = 2g^\mu(\tau_3\,;\,x)\,\delta^4(x)$$

$$+ \text{ Schwinger terms}^{21} \qquad (7.41)$$

The Schwinger terms consist of derivatives of δ functions; when Fourier-transformed in (7.39), these terms yield polynomials in q_0, which vanish in the limit $q_0 \to 0$ which we shall have to use anyhow. We are thus left with

$$2i \int d^4x\, q_\mu\, e^{-iqx} \langle P|g^\mu(\tau_3\,;\,x)|P\rangle\, \delta^4(x)$$

$$= \frac{i}{(2\pi)^3}\,\frac{m_N}{E_P}\,\nu \qquad (7.42)$$

where we replace q_0 by $\nu m_n/E_p$, and we use the fact that $I_z|P\rangle = \frac{1}{2}|P\rangle$.

This then has yielded a first order term in ν.

To evaluate all other terms, we use the explicit expressions for the matrix elements, (here $q^\mu = p_1{}^\mu - p_2{}^\mu$)

$$\langle P(p_1)|g^\mu(\gamma_5\tau^+;x)|N(p_2)\rangle$$

$$= (2\pi)^{-3}\{m_N^2/E_n E_p\}^{1/2} e^{iqx}\frac{G_A}{G_V}\bar{u}(p_1)[\gamma^\mu\gamma_5 F_1(q^2)$$

$$- q^\mu\gamma_5 F_2(q^2)]\tau^+ u(p_2) \qquad (7.43)$$

and

$$\langle P(p_1)|\partial_\mu g^\mu(\gamma_5\tau^+;x)|N(p_2)\rangle$$

$$= i(2\pi)^{-3}\left\{\frac{m_N^2}{E_n E_p}\right\}^{1/2} e^{iqx}\frac{G_A}{G_V} D(q^2)\,\bar{u}(p_1)\gamma_5\tau^+ u(p_2) \qquad (7.44)$$

with

$$D(q^2) = 2m_N F_1(q^2) - q^2 F_2(q^2) \qquad (7.45)$$

and the pole-dominance postulate corresponds to $D(q^2)$ obeying unsubtracted dispersion relations and $D(0)$ being dominated by the π pole at $q^2 = \mu^2$. [The normalization in (7.44) differs by $(2\pi)^{-3/2}$ from (7.23)].

Computing the left-hand side of (7.39) from (7.43) we find, using only the one-neutron (Born) term,

$$q_\nu q_\mu t^{\nu\mu} = (2\pi)^{-3}\frac{m_N}{E_p}\left(\frac{G_A}{G_V}\right)^2 \bar{u}(p_1)\{(2m_N+\nu)F_1^2(q^2)$$

$$- 2F_1(q^2)D(q^2)\}\tau^+ u(p_2) + \text{a singular term} \qquad (7.46)$$

The singular term here arises from $m_N = m_p = m_n$,

when assuming isospin conservation, as we have assumed throughout [the calculation can be done with the exact masses, with a proper study of the effect of the electromagnetic difference; it does not affect (7.40)]. This singular term is cancelled by a piece of the first term on the right-hand side, $R(q^2, \nu)$, which has the same neutron pole in ν (to which the above singularity is due) as on the left-hand side.

Evaluating the second term on the right-hand side of (7.39), one finds it does not contain q and cancels exactly against the contribution of the first term on the right-hand side $R(q^2, \nu)$ when this is taken at $q^2 = 0, \nu = 0$. One is then only left with the contribution of the latter which is of first order in ν. This results from the part of $R(q^2, \nu)$ where the neutron pole does not appear; it has to obey an unsubtracted dispersion relation in q^2, and has double and single one-pion poles at $q^2 = m_\pi^2$, and a cut starting at $q^2 = 8m_\pi^2$. The poles are assumed to dominate [from the pole-dominance postulate for $\partial_\mu g^\mu(\gamma_5 \tau)$]; the single poles turn out to have very small contributions, and the double pole yields an elastic π-N amplitude. Using unitarity and crossing symmetry, one ends up by getting an expression which, when combined with (7.42) and (7.46) yields the Adler-Weisberger sum rule (7.40), upon equating terms $0(\nu)$ as $\nu \to 0$.

The above derivation displays the role of simulated scattering amplitudes allowing a direct application of dispersion relations; and of the pole-dominance postulate for $\partial_\mu a^\mu$, which enables us to use, as input, data from the strong-interactions entirely.

An alternative derivation, used by Adler[30] is more transparent as to the role of the $[U(3) \times U(3)]_\chi$ algebra and its representations. One starts from

$$\langle P(q)|[G(\gamma_5 \tau^+; x^0), G(\gamma_5 \tau^-; x^0)]|P(q')\rangle$$

$$= 2\langle P(q)|G(\tau_3)|P(q')\rangle = (2\pi)^3 \delta(\mathbf{q} - \mathbf{q}') \qquad (7.47)$$

One then inserts intermediate states in the commutator and

separates out the neutron term (this is the Fubini-Furlan analysis which we discussed in Chapter 5), this being assumed to represent the only one-particle intermediate state.

$$= \sum_{\text{spins}} \int \frac{d^3 k}{(2\pi)^3} \Big[\langle P(q)| G(\gamma_5 \tau^+ ; x^0)| N(k)\rangle$$

$$\times \langle N(k)| G(\gamma_5 \tau^- ; x^0)| P(q')\rangle$$

$$+ \sum_{j \neq N} \langle P(q)| G(\gamma_5 \tau^+ ; x^0)| j\rangle \langle j| G|\gamma_5 \tau^- ; x^0)| P(q')\rangle$$

$$- \text{ the commuted terms}\Big] \qquad (7.48)$$

The neutron term is easily evaluated, yielding $(2\pi)^3 \times \delta(\mathbf{q} - \mathbf{q}')(G_A/G_V)^2 \{1 - (m_N^2/q_0^2)\}$. To evaluate the remainder (a "leakage") one uses formula (5.22) of Chapter 5

$$\langle a| G^i | n\rangle = \frac{\langle a| R^i | n\rangle}{E_n - E_a} \qquad (7.49)$$

where

$$R^i = i \int \partial_\mu \, g^{\mu i} (\mathbf{x}, x^0) \, d^3x \qquad (7.50)$$

and using the pole dominance postulate (7.21) or (7.29)

$$\partial_\mu \, g^\mu (\gamma_5 \tau^\pm ; x) = C \, \phi_\pi (x)$$

one ends up with the π-N cross-sections on the right-hand side of equation (7.40). However, this calculation requires setting $q^0 \to \infty$, i.e., taking the matrix elements between protons moving at light velocity. This is similar to $m_N \ll q^0$ in the chiral symmetry limit, and we can compare with (7.18). Indeed, using the representation **(6, 3)** + **(3, 6)** of $[U(3) \times U(3)]_\chi$ we would get[31] instead of (7.40),

$$(\tfrac{5}{3})^2 = 1 + (\tfrac{4}{3})^2 \qquad (7.51)$$

where the $\frac{4}{3}$ term corresponds to the contribution of a single $I = \frac{3}{2}$ baryon, perhaps $\Delta(1670;\frac{1}{2}^-)$. However, using $q^0 \to \infty$ in fact allows for the appearance of states with higher spins; there is a large contribution from $\Delta(1238;\frac{3}{2}^+)$, and the overall repartition of contributions to (7.40) is more like,

$$\left(\frac{G_A}{G_V}\right)^2 = \frac{3}{2} = 1 + 1 \text{ (from } \Delta(1238)) - \tfrac{1}{2} \text{ (other states)} \qquad (7.51')$$

Adler[30] also gave an alternative sum rule to (7.40), in which one does not assume (7.21)-(7.29) pole dominance, and G_A/G_V is then given in terms of high-energy neutrino reactions.

One finds,

$$\left(\frac{G_A}{G_V}\right)^2 = 1 - \int_{m_N+m_\pi}^{\infty} \frac{4m_N W dW}{(W^2 - m_N^2)^2} \left[N_p^-(W) - N_p^+(W)\right] \qquad (7.52)$$

with

$$N^{\pm}(W) = \sum_{j \neq N} \delta(W - m_j) |\mathfrak{D}^{\pm}|^2_{(q-q_j)^2=0}$$

and (j stands for the intermediate states other than the neutron)

$$\mathfrak{D}_j^{\pm} = \left(\frac{m_N}{q_0}\frac{m_j}{q_{j0}}\right)^{-1/2} \langle j | \partial_\mu g^\mu (\gamma_5 \tau^{\pm}) | P(q) \rangle$$

We see that $\mathfrak{D}_j^{\pm}$ appears in (7.52) only at zero momentum transfer; it can be measured directly in high energy reactions of the type

$$\nu_\ell + N \to \ell + N'$$

as discussed[13] in equation (7.30).

THE STRANGENESS-CHANGING CURRENT AND THE D/F RATIO

The Adler-Weisberger calculation can be generalized to the $|\Delta S| = 1$ axial current. Cabibbo's identification of the atonous hadron currents as components of SU(3) corresponding to a particular SU(2) subgroup and the closure of its $U(2) \times U(2)$ algebra imply that one should not expect to get the "suppression" of $|\Delta S| = 1$ currents relatively to $\Delta S = 0$ as a renormalization result even for the nonconserved axial part; indeed, actual calculation shows it can't be done,[34] and reproduces[32] equal θ angles for vector and axial currents. However, one may expect renormalization effects that would further modify the strength of the coupling; this is indeed G_A/G_V again, a renormalization that should be common to the entire SU(3) multiplet, i.e., to the complete Cabibbo component. However, there is no a-priori prescription for a D/F ratio, as long as we have not made a choice of representations for the hadrons under $[U(3) \times U(3)]_\chi$; this is then the new unknown $\alpha = D/F$, although one could also solve for the particular values[33, 34, 36] $G_A^{P-\Sigma^0}$, $G_A^{P-\Lambda}$, $G_A^{n-\Sigma^+}$ with α as input, taken from the pseudoscalar coupling in the strong interactions. Using the sum rules to compute the overall G_A/G_V (this is the Adler-Weisberger value, since $\cos\theta \sim 1$) and α, one has[35,22] three sum rules from [we denote $G(\gamma_5\lambda^a)$ by A^ϕ, ϕ the meson with λ^a quantum numbers] the commutators

$$\langle P|[A^{\pi^+}, A^{\pi^-}]|P\rangle, \langle P|[A^{K^+}, A^{K^-}]|P\rangle,$$

$$\langle n|[A^{K^0}, A^{\overline{K}^0}]|n\rangle$$

yielding [we denote by T_ϕ the cross-sections term for $\phi - N$ scattering in equation (7.40)].

$$1 = (r_{pn}^{\pi+})^2 + T_{\pi^-} = (r_F + r_D)^2 + T_{\pi^-}$$

$$2 = (r_{p\Lambda}^{K+})^2 + (r_{p\Sigma^-}^{K+})^2 + T_{K^-} = 2(r_F^2 + \tfrac{1}{3} r_D^2) + T_{K^-}$$

$$1 = (r_{p\Sigma^+}^{K^0})^2 + T_{\overline{K}^0} = (r_F - r_D)^2 + T_{\overline{K}^0} \qquad (7.53)$$

with

$$r_{BB'}^{\phi i} = \lim_{p \to p'} \frac{\langle B'|a^{\mu i}(0)|B\rangle}{\bar{u}(p')\gamma^{\mu}\gamma_5 u(p)} \qquad (7.54)$$

and

$$T_{\phi i} = \frac{2\pi^3}{m_\phi} g_\phi^{-2} \int \sum_j \Big(|A_{B+\phi_i \to j}(\nu)|^2$$

$$- |A_{B+\overline{\phi}_i \to j}(\nu)|^2 \Big) \frac{d\nu}{\nu^2} \qquad (7.55)$$

where g_ϕ^{-1} is proportional to the C of (7.21) as in (7.24) and common to the entire ϕ multiplet,

$$\partial_\mu a^{\mu i} = m_i^2 g_\phi^{-1} \phi^i \qquad (7.56)$$

The result is $\alpha = 2.7$, which is in fair agreement with the experimental estimate of $1.6 < \alpha < 3$. Having 3 equations, we are still left with one consistency relation between the T_ϕ,

$$(T_{\overline{K}^0} - T_{\pi^-})^2 = 3(4 - 3\,T_{K^-} + T_{\overline{K}^0} + T_{\pi^-})$$

$$\times (T_{K^-} - T_{\overline{K}^0} - T_{\pi^-}) \qquad (7.57)$$

Evaluating these expressions from the experimental data gives 1.21 for the left-hand side and 2.16 for the right-hand side, which is not too good; however, solving (7.57) as an equation for T_{K^-}, with T_{π^-} and $T_{\overline{K}^0}$ as input, we find T_{K^-} = 1.3, to be compared with 1.15, the experimental estimate.

K AND π MESON LEPTONIC DECAYS

Using the soft-pion emission relations[12,16,18] derived from the pole-dominance interpretation of the Goldberger-Treiman relation, Callan and Treiman derived a series of relations connecting the three leptonic decay modes $K \to \ell + \overline{\nu}_\ell$, $K \to \pi + \ell + \overline{\nu}_\ell$, $K \to \pi + \pi + \ell + \overline{\nu}_\ell$, i.e., $K_{\ell 2}$, $K_{\ell 3}$, $K_{\ell 4}$; similarly, $\pi^+ \to e^+ + \nu_e$ and $\pi^+ \to \pi^0 + e^+ + \nu_e$

The technique used is similar to the method we discussed for the evaluation of commutators between densities. In equation (7.35), insert $g^{\nu a} \to a^{03}(x)$; $g^{\mu b} \to (v^{\mu 4} - iv^{\mu 5} + a^{\mu 4} - ia^{\mu 5})/2$ or j^μ_A ($|\Delta S| = 1)/\sin\theta$, or $j^{\mu K^-}_A$. Then take $q \to 0$; the left-hand side of equation (7.36) vanishes and we equate the two right-hand side terms. We find,

$$\int d^4x\, \delta(x^0) \langle A|[a^{03}(x), j^{\mu K^-}_A(0)]|B\rangle$$

$$= -\frac{G_A}{G_V}\frac{m_N}{g_{\overline{N}N\pi}} \int d^4x (m^2_\pi + \Box)\, \theta(x^0)$$

$$\times \langle A|[\phi_{\pi^0}(x), j^{\mu K^-}_A(0)]|B\rangle \qquad (7.58)$$

where we have used (7.21)-(7.29) to replace $\partial_\nu a^{\nu 3}$ by ϕ_{π^0}. Taking a K^+ meson as $|B\rangle$, we have now on the left-hand side the hadron atonous transition matrix element for $K^+ \to A + \ell^+ + \nu$, since

$$[a^{03}(x), j^{\mu K^-}_A(0)]_{x_0=0} = \tfrac{1}{2}\, \delta^3(\mathbf{x})\, j^{\mu K^-}_A(0)$$

On the right-hand side we find a term proportional to the decay $K^+ \to A + \pi^0 + \ell^+ + \nu$ evaluated at $q^\mu = 0$ for the π^0. Thus

$$\langle A | j_A^{\mu K^-} | K^+ \rangle = -\left(2i \frac{G_A}{G_V} \frac{m_N}{g_{\overline{NN}\pi}}\right)$$

$$\times \langle A\pi^0 | j_A^{\mu K^-} | K^+ \rangle (2q^0)^{1/2}$$

$$\text{for } q^\mu(\pi^0) \to 0 \qquad (7.59)$$

With A as the vacuum, this relates $K_{\ell 2}$ to off mass shell $K_{\ell 3}$; a similar relation holds for $\pi_{\ell 2}$ and $\pi_{\ell 3}$. Taking A as π^0, we get a relation between $K_{\ell 3}$ and $K_{\ell 4}$ in the modes with only neutral π and off mass shell.

Replacing a^{03} in (7.58) by $a^{0\pi^-}$, we find

$$[a^{0\pi^-}(x), j_A^{\mu K^-}(0)]_{x^0=0} = 0$$

implying, taking for example π^- for $\langle A|$,

$$(2q^0)^{1/2} \langle \pi^+ \pi^- | j_A^{\mu K^-}(0) | K^+ \rangle \to 0 \qquad q(\pi^+) \to 0 \quad (7.60)$$

The actual relation $(K_{\ell 2}, K_{\ell 3})$ requires us to compare the matrix elements, (k^μ is the K meson momentum, f_K a dimensionless constant)

$$K_{\ell 2} : (2K^0)^{1/2} \langle 0 | j_A^{\mu K^-} | K^+ \rangle = G_V\, m_K\, f_K\, K^\mu$$

$$K_{\ell 3} : (2k^0)^{1/2} (2q^0)^{1/2} \langle \pi^0 | j_A^{\mu K^-} | K^+ \rangle$$

$$= G_V [f_+ (k + q)^\mu + f_- (k - q)^\mu] \qquad (7.61)$$

The f_+ and f_- form factors depend on $K \cdot q$ and q^2. Inserting (7.61) in (7.59), we find

$$|f_K| = \left| 2 \frac{G_A}{G_V} \frac{m_N}{m_K g_{\overline{N}N\pi}} \right| |f_+(0, 0) + f_-(0, 0)|$$

$$= 0.32\, |f_+(0, 0) + f_-(0, 0)| \tag{7.62}$$

Ignoring off-mass shell corrections, the right-hand side comes out to be 0.074 ± 0.014; the left-hand side, also from experiment, is $|f_K| = 0.070 \pm 0.001$.

In the $(\pi_{\ell 2}, \pi_{\ell 3})$ relation, $f_- = 0$ and we get

$$|f_\pi| = \left| \frac{G_A}{G_V} \frac{m_N}{m_\pi G_{\overline{N}N\pi}} \right| |f_+(\pi)| \tag{7.63}$$

Here the left-hand side is 0.94, the right-hand side 0.85; again experiment seems to bear out these algebraic relations.

For $K_{\ell 3}$ to $K_{\ell 4}$, we need (p^μ and q^μ relate to π^- and π^+)

$$K_{\ell 4}: (2k^0)^{1/2} (2p^0)^{1/2} (2q^0)^{1/2} \langle \pi^+ \pi^- | j_A^{\mu K^-} | K^+ \rangle$$

$$= G_V \frac{1}{m_K} \{(q + p)^\mu F_1 + (q - p)^\mu F_2$$

$$+ (k - q - p)^\mu F_3 + m_K^{-2} \epsilon_{\mu\nu\rho\sigma} k^\nu p^\rho q^\sigma F_4\} \tag{7.64}$$

with the form factors $F_i(k \cdot p, k \cdot q, p \cdot q, k^2, p^2, q^2)$. For $q^2 = 0$, we must have

$$(F_1/F_2) = 1, \quad F_3 = 0 \tag{7.65}$$

so as to satisfy (7.60). These are off mass shell predictions at $q^{\mu} = 0$; experimentally $(F_1/F_2) = 0.8 \pm 0.3$ on mass shell, F_3 is difficult to measure.

If we now set $p^{\mu} = 0$, we find the predictions,

$$2|f_+| = \left|\frac{G_A}{G_V}\,\frac{m_N}{m_K g}\right| |F_1 + F_2|$$
$$|f_+ + f_-| = \left|\frac{G_A}{G_V}\,\frac{m_N}{m_K g}\right| |F_3| \qquad (7.66)$$

Had it not been for the form factors momentum dependence, the last relation would have been in contradiction to (7.65) and (7.62). Clearly we are faced with a difficulty— how do we know which meson should be "softened"?

The paradox was solved by Weinberg[39] who showed that we really have to take *both* pions off the mass shell, in accordance with his generalization of soft-pion production relations to the case of multiple production,[18] which we discussed above. To define the F_i off the mass shell here, we have to use the reduction formula of field theory, then use the pole dominance hypothesis to replace $(q^2 - m_\pi^2)\phi_\pi$ by $(q^2 - m_\pi^2) C^{-1} \partial_\alpha a^\alpha$. The amplitude for (7.64) is then,

$$g_\pi^2 m_\pi^{-4} (q^2 - m_\pi^2)(p^2 - m_\pi^2) \int d^4x\, d^4y\, e^{-iqx} e^{ipy}$$
$$\times \langle 0 | T\{\partial_\alpha a^{\alpha\pi^+}(x), \partial_\beta a^{\beta\pi^-}(y), a^{\mu K^-}(0)\} | K^+\rangle$$
$$= i(2\pi)^{-3/2} (2k^0)^{-1/2} \frac{G_V}{m_K} \{(q + p)^\mu F_1$$
$$+ (q - p)^\mu F_2 + (k - p - q)^\mu F_3$$
$$+ \epsilon^\mu{}_{\nu\rho\sigma} k^\nu p^\rho q^\sigma m_K^{-2} F_4\} \qquad (7.67)$$

where we have used (7.24) with the normalization

$$\langle 0 | \partial_\alpha a^{\alpha i} | \pi j \rangle = g_\pi^{-1} m_\pi^2 (2\pi)^{-3/2} (2q^0)^{-1/2} \delta^{ij} \tag{7.24'}$$

The pole dominance hypothesis requires the F_i in (7.67) to vary slowly with q^α and p^β, i.e., we can replace the F_i by first order terms in an expansion in q^α and p^β. As to F_3, its contribution to the decay is small, as it multiplies $(k - p - q)$, the leptons' four momentum, and $m_\ell < m_\pi$. We thus take only the zeroth order term in the expansion of F_3. Rewriting the time-ordered product on the left-hand side of (7.67) as,

$$T\{\partial_\alpha a^{\alpha a}(x), \partial_\beta a^{\beta b}(y), a^{\mu n}(0)\}$$

$$= \partial_\alpha \partial_\beta T\{a^{\alpha a}(x), a^{\beta b}(y), a^{\mu n}(0)\}$$

$$- \text{all compensating terms} \tag{7.67'}$$

we can discard all higher order terms (such as the first one, which is in $q_\alpha p_\beta$, plus a part with a first order K pole contributing to F_3) and collect the effective terms[39]; in so doing we make use of (7.34).

The resulting expression involves the $K_{\ell 2}$ and $K_{\ell 3}$ form factors. We insert the expressions previously derived for these, and after a somewhat laborious computation, we find,

$$F_1 = (2f_+(0)\, m_K\, g_\pi)\, \delta_{ab}\, \delta_{nd} \tag{7.68'}$$

$$F_2 = (2f_+(0)\, m_K\, g_\pi)\, \epsilon_{abc} (\tau^c)_{nd} \tag{7.68''}$$

$$F_3 = [(f_+(0) + f_-(0)) m_K\, g_\pi]$$

$$\times \left\{\delta_{ab}\, \delta_{nd} + i\epsilon_{abc} (\tau^c)_{nd} \frac{k \cdot (p - q)}{k \cdot (p + q)}\right\} \tag{7.68'''}$$

where d is the SU(3) index in the structure constant f_{and}. Inserting the experimental values for f_+ etc..., we find $A = |2f_+(0)\, m_K g_\pi| = 1.20 \pm 0.07$ and $B = |(f_+(0) + f_-(0))\, m_K g_\pi| = 1.75 \pm 0.03$. The soft pion relations predict

$$F_1 = F_2 = A\,,\; F_3 = B\left[1 - \frac{k(p-q)}{k(p+q)}\right]$$

$$\text{for } K^+ \to \pi^+ + \pi^- + e^+ + \nu_e \tag{7.69}$$

$$F_1 = A,\; F_2 = 0,\; F_3 = B \text{ for } K^+ \to \pi^0 + \pi^0 + e^+ + \nu_e \tag{7.70}$$

$$F_1 = A,\; F_2 = -A\,,\; F_3 = -B\left[\frac{k(p-q)}{k(p+q)}\right]$$

$$\text{for } K_2^0 \to \pi^- + \pi^0 + e^+ + \nu_e$$

(here q relates to π^-, p to π^0) (7.71)

The measured averages' ratio $(\langle F_1\rangle/\langle F_2\rangle)$ in (7.69) is 0.8 ± 0.3; using their predicted absolute value A, we obtain

$$\Gamma_{th}(K^+ \to \pi^+ + \pi^- + e^+ + \nu_e)$$

$$= (2.87 \pm 0.33) \times 10^3\ \text{sec}^{-1}$$

to be compared with

$$\Gamma_{ex} = (2.9 \pm 0.6) \times 10^3\ \text{sec}^{-1}$$

The agreement is remarkable.

For the other K_{e4} decays the predictions are,

$$\frac{\Gamma(K^+ \to 2\pi^0 + e^+ + \nu)}{\Gamma(K^+ \to \pi^+ + \pi^- + e^+ + \nu)} = 0.84$$

$$\frac{\Gamma(K_2^0 \to \pi^- + \pi^0 + e^+ + \nu)}{\Gamma(K^+ \to \pi^+ + \pi^- + e^+ + \nu)} = 0.16$$

There are as yet no experimental numbers testing these predictions. With this analysis, one now has also an understanding of the rapid increase between

$$F_3(q = 0) = 0 \text{ in } (7.65) \text{ and } F_3(p = 0) = 2|B| \text{ in } (7.66)$$

From Equation (7.68‴), one sees that F_3 has a K pole which does not appear in F_1, or F_2, so that the latter do not have this rapid variation. The pole corresponds to soft emission of the 2π by the K, which then undergoes $K \to \ell + \nu$ (this decay is then proportional to $k - p - q$, i.e., it contributes only to F_3). The residue has been computed and is in agreement with the required rise in (7.66).

APPLYING THE ALGEBRA TO MOMENTS

By studying the commutator between two electric dipole moment operators, a number of authors[40,41] have derived the sum rule,

$$\left(\frac{\mu_p - \mu_n}{2m_N}\right)^2 + \frac{1}{2\pi^2\alpha}\int \frac{d\nu}{\nu}\,(2\sigma^V_{1/2} - \sigma^V_{3/2})$$

$$= \left\langle \frac{r^2}{3} \right\rangle^V_{(F_E)P} \tag{7.72}$$

where μ_p and μ_n are the proton and neutron magnetic moments, σ^V_I is the total photoproduction cross-section of $I = \frac{1}{2}$ or $\frac{3}{2}$ states by isovector photons on protons, ν is the laboratory energy variable and r is the Dirac (F_E) charge radius of the proton. One uses

$$\mathbf{D}^i = \int d^3\mathbf{x}\, \mathbf{x}\, v^{0i}(x) \tag{7.73}$$

which yields (D_1 is in the x_1 direction)

$$[D_1(\tau^+),\ D_1(\tau^-)] = 2 \int d^3x\, v^0(x, \tau^3)\,(x_1)^2 \tag{7.74}$$

and between two proton states with momenta $\mathbf{q}$, $\mathbf{q}'$ in the z direction, we can separate out the neutron intermediate state from all others. The p − n dipoles are the anomalous isovector magnetic moments, producing the first term on the left-hand side of (7.72); the right-hand side is just the right-hand side of (7.74), with $\langle r^2 \rangle$ reproducing the electric F_E^V form factor charge distribution. It is related to G_E^V via

$$\frac{r^2}{6} = -\frac{d\, G_E^V}{d\, q^2} + \frac{1}{8m_N^2} \tag{7.75}$$

The integral over cross-sections in (7.72) arises from the intermediate states other than the neutron, by a straightforward application of the Fubini-Furlan expansion we described in equation (5.23) for instance.

From $\partial_\alpha v^\alpha = 0$, we can write

$$\langle\beta|\dot{D}_1(\tau^3)|p(\mathbf{q})\rangle = \langle\beta| \int d^3\mathbf{x}\, v^{1,3}(x)|p(\mathbf{q})\rangle$$

$$= (2\pi)^3\delta^3(\mathbf{q} - \mathbf{q}_\beta)\langle\beta|v^{1,3}(0)|p(\mathbf{q})\rangle$$

and

$$\langle\beta|D_1(\tau^3)|p(\mathbf{q})\rangle = (2\pi)^3\, \delta(\mathbf{q} - \mathbf{q}_\beta)$$

$$\times \frac{\langle\beta|v^{1,3}(0)\,|\,p(\mathbf{q})\rangle}{i(E_\beta - E_9)} \tag{7.76}$$

One now considers for convenience the limit $\mathbf{q} \to \infty$. In this limit, the matrix elements of $v^{1,3}(0)$ are proportional to the amplitudes $\gamma + p \to \beta$. Separating out the $I = \frac{1}{2}$ and

$\frac{3}{2}$ contributions, and using the appropriate Clebsch Gordan coefficient, we then get for the intermediate states other than the neutron,

$$A(\mathbf{q}, \mathbf{q}') = 4 A_{1/2}(\mathbf{q}, \mathbf{q}') - 2 A_{3/2}(\mathbf{q}, \mathbf{q}')$$

and A can be expressed as integrals over total cross-sections. Note that convergence of the integral is ensured by the fact that we can assume that the isospin current matrix element is dominated by the ρ meson; $(2\sigma^V_{1/2} - \sigma^V_{3/2})$ is then proportional to $\sigma(\rho^+ + p) - \sigma(\rho^- + p)$, extrapolated to $t \neq m^2_\rho \to 0$. This is a quantity which is guaranteed to vanish at $\omega \to \infty$ by the Regge analysis. The integral then converges.

The experimental value is $\mu_p - \mu_n = 4.7$; taking only the $\sigma^V_{3/2}$ contribution (assumed to consist mainly of $\Delta(1238)$) gives a calculated value of 5.5. The $\sigma^V_{1/2}$ is presumably responsible for the difference, mainly from the near-threshold electric dipole transition and the $j = \frac{3}{2}^-$ $N^*(1518)$.

One can[38] also take (7.74) between π^+ states. There is no one-particle contribution, as π^+ has no magnetic moment; the result is

$$\frac{2}{3}\langle r^2\rangle^V_\pi = \frac{1}{2\pi^2\alpha}\int\frac{d\omega}{\omega}\left[\sigma^V(\gamma + \pi^0 \to \beta_{I=0}) + \sigma^V(\gamma + \pi^+ \to \beta_{I=1}) - \frac{5}{4}\sigma^V(\gamma + \pi^0 \to \beta_{I=2})\right] \quad (7.77)$$

If we stick to $j = 1^-$ states, we find $\beta_{I=0} \to \omega(790)$, which can be computed from $\omega \to \pi^0 + \gamma$; $\phi(1020)$ contributes very little. There is then no other state in (7.77), and we get

$$r^2_\pi = \frac{18}{\alpha}\left(\frac{m_\omega}{m^2_\omega - m^2_\pi}\right)^3 \Gamma(\omega \to \pi^0\gamma) \quad (7.77')$$

This predicts $r_\pi \sim 0.5$ fm. From ρ-dominance of the form factor one would deduce $r_\pi = \sqrt{6}/m_\rho = 0.63$ fm.

It has been noted by Dashen and Gell-Mann[39] that applying the algebra to moments is in fact equivalent to working with an algebra of Fourier-transformed densities. The local commutation relations (7.34) at equal-times,

$$[v^{oa}(\mathbf{x}_1),\ v^{ob}(\mathbf{x}_2)] = i f^{ab}{}_c\, v^{oc}(\mathbf{x}_1)\,\delta^3(\mathbf{x}_1 - \mathbf{x}_2)$$

will lead via

$$\int e^{iq_1 x_1}\, v^{oa}(\mathbf{x})\, d^3\mathbf{x} = v^{oa}(\mathbf{q}_1)$$

to

$$[v^{oa}(\mathbf{q}_1),\ v^{ob}(\mathbf{q}_2)] = i f^{ab}{}_c\, v^{oc}(\mathbf{q}_1 + \mathbf{q}_2) \tag{7.78}$$

We have always worked to first order in electromagnetism. The left-hand side of (7.78) between A and B now contains products of all multipole transitions leading to the variable intermediate states J(F is the electric monopole, E dipole, M magnetic dipole) and resulting from expanding v^{oi}_{AJ} into invariant matrix elements.

$$\sum_J F^a_{AJ}(q_1^2)\, F^b_{JB}(q_2^2) + (q_1\, q_2) \sum_J (M^a_{AJ}(q_1^2)\, M^b_{JB}(q_2^2) + E^a_{AJ}(q_1^2)\, E^b_{JB}(q_2^2)) + \cdots - (a \longleftrightarrow b) = \sum i f^{ab}{}_c\, F^c_{AB} \times ((q_1 + q_2)^2) \tag{7.79}$$

Working between states at $\mathbf{p} \to \infty$ and taking various values of q_i produces a variety of results. With $q_1^2 = q_2^2 =$

$q_1 \cdot q_2 = 0$ we have the usual commutator between generators, involving only F^i ; with $q_1^2 = q_1 \cdot q_2 = 0$, $q_2^2 \neq 0$ we have the commutators between a generator and a density which we used to derive dispersion relations. For $q_1 = -q_2$, the left-hand side looks like a cross-section and corresponds to many sum rules in which this is made use of to get at experimental quantities.

We can also expand both sides in powers of q_1^2, q_2^2, $q_1 \cdot q_2$ and equate coefficients. This is the procedure which corresponds to commutators of moments; with $q_1^2 = q_2^2 = 0$, equating first order terms in $q_1 \cdot q_2$ yields a sum rule for $(M^a_{AJ}(0))^2$ which is the same as (7.72).

Working with this method, Kawarabayashi and Suzuki[41] have shown that by taking the commutator (v^{oe} is the electric charge density)

$$[v^{oe}(\mathbf{q}_1), v^{oe}(\mathbf{q}_2)] = 0$$

between up-spinning protons, the left-hand side resembles (7.74) except that the transitions are in spin instead of I-spins. We differentiate with respect to q_{1x} and q_{2y}, and then take the limit $\mathbf{q}_1 = \mathbf{q}_2 \to 0$. In the limit of k_z (proton) $\to \infty$, the one-particle contribution to intermediate states is μ^P_A, the proton anomalous magnetic moment; and taking the two parts of the commutator will yield the differences between the squared amplitudes for the absorption of a circularly polarized photon by a proton polarized with its spin parallel and antiparallel. The result is a sum rule which was derived by Drell and Hearn[42] from different assumptions,

$$\left(\frac{\mu^P_A}{2m_N}\right)^2 + \frac{1}{2\pi^2 \alpha} \int_0^\infty (\sigma_{PAR}(\nu) - \sigma_{ANT}(\nu)) \frac{d\nu}{\nu} = 0 \tag{7.80}$$

In the original derivation, commutators played no role; instead, unsubtracted dispersion relations were assumed for the spin flip part of the forward Compton amplitude.

Using the same method for the Fourier transforms of space components appearing in (7.34), one finds[41] for

$$[v^{x}(\tau^1 + i\tau^2, \mathbf{q}_1), v^0(\tau^1 - i\tau^2, \mathbf{q}_2)]$$
$$= 2v^{x}(\tau^3, \mathbf{q}_1 + \mathbf{q}_2) + \text{singular terms}$$

inserted again between up-spinning proton states, and differentiating with respect to q_{2y}, one arrives at a sum rule for μ_T^V, the total isovector magnetic moment.

$$\frac{1}{4\pi^2\alpha}\int_0^\infty \{(2\sigma_{1/2}^V(\nu) - \sigma_{3/2}^V(\nu))_{PAR} - (2\sigma_{1/2}^V(\nu) - \sigma_{3/2}^V(\nu))_{ANT}\}\, d\nu = \frac{\mu_T^V}{2m_N} \tag{7.81}$$

This sum rule is correct provided the integral converges. Taking the first two resonances $\Delta(1238)$ and $N^*(1518)$ yields $\mu_T^V = 2.1$, which implies that one should expect important contributions higher up in the energy.

The Firenze group[43] has derived an approximate sum rule

$$\frac{1}{3}[\langle r_p^2\rangle - \langle r_n^2\rangle] = \left(\frac{\mu_p - \mu_n}{2m_N}\right)^2 \left(\frac{G_A}{G_V}\right)^2 \tag{7.82}$$

by connecting the Adler-Weisberger sum rule with (7.72). Extending the analysis to strange currents yields,

$$\langle r_n^2\rangle = 0, \ \frac{1}{3}\langle r_p^2\rangle = \left(\frac{\mu_p - \mu_n}{2m_N}\right)^2 \left(\frac{G_V}{G_A}\right)^2 \tag{7.83}$$

and

$$\left(\frac{D}{F}\right)_{\text{axial current}} = \left(\frac{D}{F}\right)_{\text{magnetic moments}} \qquad (7.83')$$

OTHER ELECTROMAGNETIC SUM RULES

Using semi-integrated commutators in a dispersion analysis, Fubini et al[44] have computed the anomalous magnetic moments in terms of meson photoproduction amplitudes. From (A is $G(\gamma_5)$)

$$[A(\tau^i, x), v^{\mu j}(x')] = 0 \qquad \text{for } i, j = 3, 8$$

taken between nucleon states, using the methods of (5.34) to (5.42) they assume for each invariant amplitude (in the transitions to intermediate states) an unsubtracted dispersion relation at fixed $\Delta^2 = 0$. The spectral functions here arise from matrix elements like

$$\langle P|\partial_\alpha a^\alpha|n\rangle\langle n|\epsilon_\mu j^\mu|P'\rangle \qquad (7.84)$$

where ϵ_μ is a polarization vector. Using pole dominance for $\partial_\alpha a^\alpha$, we get amplitudes $\gamma + p \to p + \pi^0$ etc. Inserting the values from the experimental cross-sections, one finds

$$\mu_A^V = 1.90$$

as against the experimental

$$\tfrac{1}{2}(\mu_A^P - \mu_A^n) = 1.85$$

The method can be extended to $|\Delta S| = 1$ currents and used[45] to compute hyperon magnetic moments. The results are

$\mu_\Lambda = -0.84$ (experimental value -0.77 ± 0.27; SU(3) value : -0.96)

$\mu_{\Sigma^+} = 4.6$ (experimental value 2.3 to 4.3; SU(3) value : 2.79)

Another example of such a low-energy $\pi - \gamma$ relation is the Kroll-Ruderman theorem[47,48] for pion photoproduction, which Okubo[49] proved using the commutator (7.34)

$$[a^{0i}(x), v^{\mu e}(y)]_{x^0 = y^0} = i f^{i3j} a^\mu_j (x) \delta^3(\mathbf{x} - \mathbf{y})$$

with "i" as an I-spin index, "e" represents the electric charge component of SU(3). Okubo in fact uses integrated operators in these commutation relations, and derives the theorem by using the method of Fubini and Furlan we described in chapter V, though with a more careful handling of surface terms $G(\pm\infty)$. This is essential in the derivation of

$$\int d^4x\, \theta(x^0) \langle \mathbf{p} | [v^{\nu e}(0), \partial_\alpha a^{\alpha i}(x)] | \mathbf{p} \rangle$$

$$= i\left(\frac{-G_A}{G_V}\right) (2\pi)^{-3} \epsilon^{3ij}\, \bar{u}(p) \gamma^4 \gamma^\nu \gamma_5 \tau_j u(p) \qquad (7.85)$$

where part of the right-hand side arises from

$$\left[\int_{t=0} d^3x\, v^\nu(x, t), \int_{t'=\infty} d^3y\, a^0(y, t')\right]$$

The resulting matrix element $M^\nu(k, q)$ in (ϵ_ν is the polarization vector) becomes, with $k \to 0$, $q \to 0$ and

$$T(\gamma_{(e)} + N \rightarrow \pi_{(j)} + N) = (4k^0 q^0)^{-1/2}\, e\, \epsilon_\nu(k)\, M^\nu_{(ei)}(k, q)$$

$$M^\nu_{(ei)}(0, 0) = (2\pi)^{-6} \frac{g_{\overline{N}N\pi}}{2m_N} K_{\overline{N}N\pi}(0) \left(\frac{m_N}{P^0}\right)^2 \qquad (7.86)$$

$$\times\ \epsilon_{3ij}\, \bar{u}(p)\gamma^\nu \gamma_5 \tau^i u(p)$$

which exists only for $\nu \neq 4$. This is the Kroll-Ruderman theorem, which gives M^ν in the $k \rightarrow 0$, $q \rightarrow 0$ limit as equal to the Born term, except for the new correction $K_{\overline{N}N\pi}(0)$ due to $q^2 = 0$.

NONLEPTONIC ATONOUS HAMILTONIAN

When the explicit structure of a Hamiltonian density is known to consist of products of currents, we can use the $[U(3) \times U(3)]_\chi$ commutation relations to determine

$$[G(\gamma_5 \lambda^i), \mathcal{H}_{NL}(x)]$$

The results we shall now review, due to Suzuki and Sugawara[49,50] rest upon the assumption of a structure,

$$\mathcal{H}_{NL} = (G/\sqrt{2}) \{(j_A^{\mu 1} + i\, j_A^{\mu 2}) \cos\theta$$

$$+ (j_A^{\mu 4} + j_A^{\mu 5}) \sin\theta\} \times \{(j^1_\mu - i\, j^2_\mu) \cos\theta$$

$$+ (j^4_\mu - i\, j^5_\mu) \sin\theta\} \qquad (7.87)$$

We also decompose $\mathcal{H}_{NL}$ into parity conserving and parity violating parts,

$$\mathcal{H}_{NL} = \mathcal{H}_{PC} + \mathcal{H}_{PV} \tag{7.88}$$

With CP conserved, $C(\mathcal{H}_{PC}) = 1$, $C(\mathcal{H}_{PV}) = -1$. Using the commutation relations (7.16′) we find (A^i is $G(\gamma_5 \lambda^i)$, V^i is $G(\lambda^i)$)

$$[\mathcal{H}_{PC}, A^3] = -\tfrac{1}{2}\mathcal{H}_{PV}$$

$$[\mathcal{H}_{PV}, A^3] = -\tfrac{1}{2}\mathcal{H}_{PC}$$

$$\begin{aligned}[\mathcal{H}_{PC}, A^1] = (G/\sqrt{2}) \cos\theta \sin\theta \{ & a^{\mu 3}(v^4_\mu - i\, v^5_\mu) \\ & + \tfrac{1}{2}(v^{\mu 1} + i\, v^{\mu 2})(a^6_\mu - i\, a^7_\mu) \\ & + (v_\mu \longleftrightarrow a_\mu)\} + \text{h.c.}\end{aligned}$$

$$\begin{aligned}[\mathcal{H}_{PC}, -iA^2] = (G/\sqrt{2}) \cos\theta \sin\theta \{ & a^{\mu 3}(v^4_\mu - i\, v^5_\mu) \\ & - \tfrac{1}{2}(v^{\mu 1} + i\, v^{\mu 2})(a^6_\mu - i\, a^7_\mu) \\ & + (v_\mu \longleftrightarrow a_\mu)\} + \text{h.c.}\end{aligned}$$

$$\begin{aligned}[\mathcal{H}_{PV}, A^1] = (G/\sqrt{2}) \cos\theta \sin\theta \{ & v^{\mu 3}(v^4_\mu - i\, v^5_\mu) \\ & + \tfrac{1}{2}(v^{\mu 1} + i\, v^{\mu 2})(v^6_\mu - i\, v^7_\mu) \\ & + (v_\mu \longleftrightarrow a_\mu)\} + \text{h.c.}\end{aligned}$$

$$[\mathcal{H}_{PV}, -iA^2] = (G/\sqrt{2}) \cos\theta \sin\theta \{v^{\mu 3}(v^4_\mu - i v^5_\mu) - \tfrac{1}{2}(v^{\mu 1} + i v^{\mu 2})(v^6_\mu - i v^7_\mu) + (v_\mu \longleftrightarrow a_\mu)\} + \text{h.c.} \tag{7.89}$$

These commutators are directly connected with the hyperon decay amplitudes of the type $B^i \to B^f + \pi^2$ (such as $\Sigma^+ \to n + \pi^+$ etc.) Such an amplitude is written, according to the reduction formula, as

$$\langle B^f(q)\,\pi^\ell(k)\,|\int d^3\mathbf{x}\,\mathcal{H}_{NL}(\mathbf{x},0)\,|B^i(p)\rangle = -i\int d^4y\,\langle B^f|[j^\ell_\pi(y), \int d^3x\, H_{NL}(\mathbf{x},0)] \times \theta(y)|B^i\rangle\, e^{+iky} \tag{7.90}$$

where j^ℓ_π stands for

$$(\Box + m^2_\pi)\,\phi^\ell_\pi(y) = j^\ell_\pi(y) \tag{7.90'}$$

Using the covariant normalization $\langle B^f|B^i\rangle = 2q^0\delta_4(q-p)$, and $p^0 = q^0 + k^0$ we find (n denotes the intermediate states and their momenta)

$$(2\pi)^3\,\delta(\mathbf{k} + \mathbf{q} - \mathbf{p}) \sum_n \Big\{\langle B^f|\mathcal{H}_{NL}(0)|n\rangle\langle n|j^1_\pi(0)|B^i\rangle \times \frac{\delta^3(\mathbf{n}-\mathbf{q})}{2n^0(q^0 - n^0)} - \langle B^f|j^\ell_\pi(0)|n\rangle\langle n|\mathcal{H}_{NL}(0)|B^i\rangle \times \frac{\delta^3(\mathbf{n}-\mathbf{q})}{2n^0(n^0 - p^0)}\Big\} \tag{7.90''}$$

to be compared with the commutator [using (7.29)] and integrating by parts, and replacing ϕ_π^2 by $(\Box + m_\pi^2)^{-1} j_\pi^1$

$$\langle B^f | [\int d^3x\, \mathcal{H}_{NL}(\mathbf{x}, 0), A^\ell] | B^i \rangle$$

$$= (2\pi)^3 \frac{2m_N m_\pi^2 (-G_A/G_V)}{g_{\overline{N}N\pi} K_{\overline{N}N\pi}(0)}$$

$$\times \delta^3(\mathbf{q} - \mathbf{p}) \sum_n \Big\{ \langle B^f | \mathcal{H}_{NL}(0) | n \rangle$$

$$\times \langle n | j_\pi^\ell(0) | B^i \rangle \frac{\delta^3(\mathbf{n} - \mathbf{g})}{2n_0 (p_0 - n_0)[m_\pi^\ell - (n_0 - p_0)^2]}$$

$$- \langle B^f | j_\pi^\ell(0) | n \rangle \langle n | \mathcal{H}_{NL}(0) | B^i \rangle$$

$$\times \frac{\delta^3(\mathbf{n} - \mathbf{p})}{2n_0(n_0 - q_0)[m_\pi^2 - (n^0 - q^0)^2]} \Big\} \qquad (7.91)$$

and one more term to which we shall later return. Using the identity (5.26′) we note that taking $\mathbf{p} = \mathbf{q} \to \infty$, and assuming $m_{Bi} = m_{Bf}$, $q^0 \to p^0$, equalizing the kinematical factor in both terms. Assuming rapid convergence in the sum over $|n\rangle$, such that one may interchange the order of Σ_n and $\mathbf{q} \to \infty$, $(n^0 - q^0)^2 \to 0$,

$$\lim_{\mathbf{q} \to \infty} \langle B^f | [A^\ell, \int d^3x\, \mathcal{H}_{NL}(\mathbf{x}, 0)] | B^i \rangle / \delta^3(\mathbf{q} - \mathbf{p})$$

$$\approx \frac{2m_N(-G_A/G_V)}{g_{\overline{N}N\pi} K_{\overline{N}N\pi}(0)} \lim_{\mathbf{q} \to \infty} \frac{\langle B^f \pi^\ell | \int d^3x\, \mathcal{H}_{NL}(\mathbf{x}, 0) | B^i \rangle}{\delta^3(\mathbf{q} + \mathbf{k} - \mathbf{p})}$$

$$(7.92)$$

Equations (7.89) can now be used on the left-hand side; they "rotate" $\mathcal{H}_{NL}$ into other components. $\mathcal{H}_{NL}$ being a symmetrized product, it is part of the $\mathbf{8}_D$ and **27** in the $\mathbf{8} \times \mathbf{8}$ product $j_A^{\mu} j_A^{\nu t} g_{\mu\nu}$. From unitary parity (chapter IV) we know that $\langle B^f | \mathbf{8}_D | B^i \rangle$ has $C_u = 1$; on the other hand, we noted that $C(\mathcal{H}_{PV}) = -1$, and as $C_u(\mathcal{H}_{PV}) = C(\mathcal{H}_{PV}) C_u(\mathbf{8}_D) = -1$, we find

$$\langle B^f | [\mathcal{H}_{PC}, A^{\ell}] | B^i \rangle = 0 \tag{7.93}$$

We thus get no contribution for the $\mathcal{H}_{PC}$ decays from (7.92). For $\mathcal{H}_{PV}$, as $\langle B^f | [\mathcal{H}_{PV}, A^{\ell}] | B^i \rangle$ does not vanish, (7.92) provides us with a set of 7 equations for the parity-violating transitions, in terms of 3 amplitudes a(**27**), a($\mathbf{8}_{ss}$), a($\mathbf{8}_{as}$).

We thus find (for s-waves)

$$\sqrt{2}\,(\Xi^0 \to \Lambda\pi^0) + (\Xi^- \to \Lambda\pi^-) = 0 \tag{7.94}$$

$$\sqrt{2}\,(\Lambda \to n\pi^0) + (\Lambda \to P\pi^-) = 0 \tag{7.95}$$

$$(\Sigma^- \to n\pi^-) - \sqrt{2}\,(\Sigma^+ \to P\pi^0) - (\Sigma^+ \to n\pi^+) = 0 \tag{7.96}$$

(7.94) and (7.95) reproduce the $|\Delta I| = \frac{1}{2}$ rules for Ξ and Λ decays. Equation (7.96) reproduces effectively the $|\Delta I| = \frac{1}{2}$ rule for Σ decay, but the Σ_+^+ amplitude has a different sign in the equation. However, Σ_+^+ being experimentally pure S or pure P wave, this sign is meaningless. One also finds

$$2(\Xi^- \to \Lambda\pi^-) + (\Lambda \to p\pi^-)$$

$$= (\sqrt{\tfrac{3}{2}})(\Sigma^+ \to n\pi^+) + \sqrt{3}\,(\Sigma^+ \to p\pi^0) \qquad (7.97)$$

which is also experimentally validated if Σ_+^+ is p-wave.

If one assumes octet dominance (or adds neutral currents so as to cancel **27** one gets for the s-wave,

$$(\Sigma^+ \to n\pi^+) = 0 \qquad (7.98)$$

so that

$$2(\Xi^- \to \Lambda\pi^-) + (\Lambda \to p\pi^-) - \sqrt{3}\,(\Sigma^+ \to p\pi^0) \qquad (7.97')$$

which had been derived by Gell-Mann from SU(3), the structure of $\mathcal{H}_{NL}$ and octet dominance (see Chapter 6). All the above results are satisfied by the experimental values within the present errors. Note that $|\Delta I| = \frac{1}{2}$ emerges without an octet dominance assumption.

The P-wave decays have been somewhat more difficult to evaluate. They arise[51,52,53] through a surface term omitted in equation (7.92), and consisting in the limit of SU(3) symmetry of a baryon pole term. It is easiest to understand the role of this term by looking[52] at the method of equation (7.36). Taking for $t^{\nu\mu}$ of (7.36) an amplitude

$$M^{\mu\ell}(q, p, k) = \int d^4x\, e^{ikx} \langle B^f \,|\, T(a^{\mu\ell}(x), \mathcal{H}_{NL}(0)|B^i\rangle \qquad (7.99)$$

we get in (7.36)

$$-ik_\mu M^{\mu\ell} - \int d^3x \langle B^f | [a^{o\ell}(\mathbf{x}, 0), \mathcal{H}_{NL}(0)] | B^i \rangle e^{-i\mathbf{kx}}$$

$$= \int d^4x \, e^{ikx} \langle B^f | T(\partial_\mu a^{\mu\ell}(x), \mathcal{H}_{NL}(0) | B^i \rangle \tag{7.100}$$

The right-hand side represents our $B^i \to B^f + \pi(k^2 = 0)$ amplitude (7.90). On the left-hand side we have seen that

$$\langle B^f | \mathcal{H}_{PV} | B^i \rangle \to 0$$

in the SU(3) limit, so that if we take $\mathcal{H}_{PV}$ in (7.99) and insert intermediate states, $M^{\mu\ell}$ does not contribute in (7.100); on the other hand, $\mathcal{H}_{PV}$ in (7.100) gives a finite contribution from the commutator term, which has $C_u = 1$ in this case. This was our result (7.92).

For $\mathcal{H}_{PC}$, the commutator in (7.100) vanishes in the SU(3) limit; but we now have a finite contribution from the baryon pole term in X of (7.99). The denominator will look like a strong interaction form factor for the coupling $\overline{B}^f \cdot B^i$ (j is an intermediate state) to an "a^μ" meson, with a denominator Δm_{fj}^2. When B^i belongs to the baryon octet, $k_\mu M^{\mu(\ell)}$ does not vanish for $k_\mu \to 0$; however, its contribution is limited to pole terms in the SU(3) limit.

The structure of M^μ shows that these pole terms represent a situation in which the reaction occurs in two stages, a strong interaction in which the pion is produced (this is the Born term resulting from the action of $a^{\mu\ell}$, say between B_f and B_j); and a direct weak transition with $|\Delta S| = 1$ enacted by $\mathcal{H}_{NL}$ between B_j and B_i, for instance.

There are in fact two such diagrams,

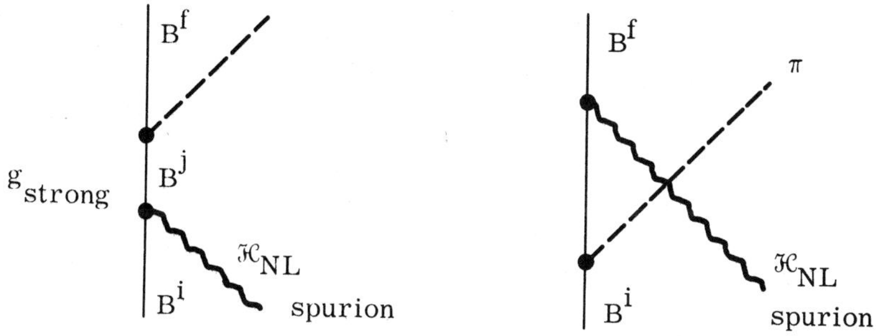

The results reproduce[51-53] roughly the sequence of P-wave decays, but they all come out too small[53] by 50%. Itzykson and Jacob[54] have reanalyzed the various contributions and corrected some omissions, with good results. Their analysis showed the existence of an additional term in M^{μ}, contributing to the P-wave. This arises in part via a pole corresponding to the emission of a K meson which then connects to the π via $\mathcal{H}_{NL}$. In any case, the P-wave decays involve assumptions of an SU(3) limit.

Using similar methods and some plausible assumptions with respect to the amplitudes' momentum dependence, Hara and Nambu[55] have studied $K \to 3\pi$ and $K \to 2\pi$. The two processes are connected by soft-pion emission relations; the results display very good agreement with experiment. However, some of the predictions based upon an assumption of full SU(3) symmetry do not seem to fit the picture well. There is also not enough evidence from this calculation for the $j_A^{\mu}(j_A^{\dagger})_{\mu}$ structure of $\mathcal{H}_{NL}$, as against $\mathcal{H}'_{NL} = v^{\mu 6} + a^{\mu 7}$ for instance.

In a study of the $K \to 2\pi$ decay modes, without imposing an **8** behavior of $\mathcal{H}_{NL}$, the Rochester group[56] has used $K_{\ell 2}$, $\pi_{\ell 2}$, the form factors of $K_{\ell 3}$, F_1 and F_2 (the electromagnetic form factors); these provide a knowledge of the matrix elements of v^{μ} and a^{μ} appearing in the $\mathcal{H}_{NL}$ product, which can thus be computed directly. The results for the rates (CP conserving) in $\sec^{-1}$ are

	Theory	Experiment
$R(K_1^0 \to \pi^+ \pi^-)$	7.4×10^9	7.91×10^9
$R(K_1^0 \to \pi^+ \pi^0)$	3.6×10^9	3.57×10^9
$R(K^+ \to \pi^+ \pi^0)$	0.4×10^7	1.74×10^7

It is interesting that without assuming $|\Delta I| = \frac{1}{2}$ (or the equivalent octet dominance of $\mathcal{H}_{NL}$) one gets a suppression of the $K^+ \to \pi^+ \pi^0$ decay mode. Similarly, Chiu and Schechter[57] found an "effective" octet dominance emerging for the hyperon decays, using the same type of direct evaluation of the matrix elements of $\mathcal{H}_{NL}$. They also found a reasonable F/D ratio for this weak spurion.

An extension of this idea led the same authors[58] to the evaluation of the electromagnetic and medium-strong mass-splittings, using in both cases a current-current Hamiltonian. They were able to reproduce a fit to the entire set of splittings with one single parameter in each case. It is interesting that the current-current nature of $\mathcal{H}_{\Delta m}$ would fit with the conjectures about the 5th interaction[59] which we described in Chapter 5.

STRONG INTERACTIONS SUM RULES

We have seen how the algebra of atonous and electromagnetic currents may be used to derive sum rules relating to strong couplings. We used vector meson dominance of the vector current form factors (5.20) to derive Sakurai's universal coupling in (5.21).

Similarly, we used pion dominance of the form factor (7.26) of the axial vector current's divergence to derive the Goldberger-Treiman relation, a sum rule (7.28) for the $g_{\overline{N}N\pi}$ strong coupling.

This approach can be extended via assumptions such as vector-meson dominance of the tensor currents (PCTC) in the frame of a larger algebra which we shall discuss in Chapter VIII. The results of Chapter IX may in part[46] be due to a 2^+ meson dominance of a piece of the $\theta^{\mu\nu}$ stress-energy tensor "current".

We shall now discuss an example in which further conditions are derived for the ρ-meson coupling to pions. The sum rule,[60-61]

$$\left(\frac{m_N}{m_\rho}\right)^2 \simeq \frac{1}{2(G_A/G_V)^2}\left(\frac{g_{\bar{N}N\pi}}{g_{\rho\pi\pi}}\right)^2 \tag{7.101}$$

yields $(g^2_{\rho\pi\pi}/4\pi) \sim 3.3$, as against an experimental estimate of 2.1. The following should be borne in mind:

(a) to derive (7.101), Gilman and Schnitzer use the fact that both axial vector currents and vector currents yield the same result upon commutation in (7.16′). By inserting the axial currents commutator between ρ-meson states on the one hand, and on the other hand inserting the vector currents commutator between π-mesons, something like a self-consistency argument is derived. The algebra is used as a TOA throughout; the technique is that of (7.38). The second commutator is related to the Cabibbo-Radicati sum rule (7.72). ρ-meson dominance of the vector form factor is given a field theory formulation, which may be stronger than (5.20). One assumes for the ρ^a_μ field,

$$\rho^a_\mu = \frac{g_\rho}{m^2_\rho} V^a_\mu \tag{7.102}$$

an expression similar to (7.21).

Soft pion relations have been applied to appropriate strong interaction processes. We shall give one example of this approach.

Using the reduction formula, pion dominance and an analysis of the various contributions to $\pi + A^i \rightarrow \pi + A^f$, several authors have evaluated pion scattering lengths. Weinberg[62] finds that for targets A much heavier than the pion, (T is the total isospin, T is the target isospin)

$$a_T = -L(1 + m_\pi/m_A)^{-1}[T(T+1) - T_A(T_A+1) - 2] \tag{7.103}$$

$$L = 0.11\ m_\pi^{-1} \tag{7.103'}$$

This gives for $\pi - N$ scattering

$$a_{1/2} = 0.20\ m_\pi^{-1}\ (\text{experimental value } 0.171 \pm 0.005\ m_\pi^{-1})$$

$$a_{3/2} = -0.10\ m_\pi^{-1}\ (\text{experimental value } -0.088 \pm 0.004\ m_\pi^{-1})$$

Among the other things these results seem to rule out the presence of any strong low-energy π-π interaction, as the derivation would have failed if such a singularity at $M \sim 2m_\pi$ should have been considered. For π-π scattering, the analysis is quite different, as one has to deal with terms which could be considered small in the former case. Weinberg finds the relation,

$$2a_0 - 5a_2 = 6L = 0.6q\ m_\pi^{-1}$$

Adding a specific assumption involving the existence of a "σ'" meson with $j = 0^+$ and $I = 0$ produces a second relation

$$(a_0/a_2) = -\tfrac{7}{2}$$

which implies $a_0 = 0.20\ m_\pi^{-1}$, $a_2 = -0.06\ m_\pi^{-1}$ and corresponds to relatively small π-π scattering lengths.

SUPERCONVERGENCE

Let us return to the identity (7.36). Taking for the indices a and b some canonical set of raising or lowering generator densities (such as I^+, I^- or U^+, U^- etc.), the last term of (7.36) is a form factor; if we pick for instance in (7.35) space components of vector densities, we find for that term

$$\langle p_1 [|v^0(\tau^+, x), v^\mu(\tau^-, 0)] | p_2 \rangle$$

$$= 2\langle p_1 | v^{\mu 3}(0) | p_2 \rangle \, \delta^3(\mathbf{x}) = 2\lambda_3 F(t) P^\mu \, \delta^3(\mathbf{x}) \tag{7.104'}$$

where λ_3 is the I_3 eigenvalue for the A(= B since $v^{\mu 3}$ is I-spin diagonal) states, and we now denote by p_1 and p_2 their momenta with $P^\mu = (p_1 + p_2)/2$.

Equation (7.36) or (7.37) is now

$$q_{i\nu} t^{\nu\mu} = t^\mu + 2F(t)P^\mu \tag{7.104}$$

where P^μ has now been extracted from $F^\mu(p_1, p_2)$, and we have denoted the momentum of the simulated meson a by q_1. Fubini[23] has also defined the inverse Hilbert transforms $u^{\nu\mu}$ and u^μ of $t^{\nu\mu}$ and t^μ; these are given by the (7.35) and (7.36) definitions of $t^{\nu\mu}$ and t^μ, without the $\theta(x^0)$ term. All invariant components of $t^{\nu\mu}$ and t^μ are then Hilbert transforms of the corresponding components of $u^{\nu\mu}$ and u^μ. With $p_1 - p_2 = \Delta$, $(q_1 + q_2)/2 = Q$, $P \cdot Q = \nu$, $\Delta^2 = t$ and $q_2 = p_1 + q_1 - p_2$ we have decompositions

$$t^{\nu\mu} = AP^\nu P^\mu + B_1 P^\nu Q^\mu + B_2 P^\nu \Delta^\mu + B_3 P^\mu Q^\nu$$
$$+ B_4 P^\mu \Delta^\nu + C_1 Q^\nu Q^\mu + C_2 Q^\nu \Delta^\mu + C_3 Q^\mu \Delta^\nu$$
$$+ C_4 \Delta^\nu \Delta^\mu + C_5 \delta^{\nu\mu} \tag{7.104''}$$

$$t^\mu = LP^\mu + N_1 Q^\mu + N_2 \Delta^\mu \tag{7.104'''}$$

and we use a, b_i, c_i, ℓ, n_i respectively for the corresponding components in the tensor decomposition of $u^{\nu\mu}$ and u^{μ}. We can now write dispersion relations in ν,

$$A(\nu) = \frac{1}{\pi} \int \frac{a(\nu')}{\nu' - \nu} d\nu'$$

$$L(\nu) = \frac{1}{\pi} \int \frac{\ell(\nu')}{\nu' - \nu} d\nu' \qquad \text{etc.} \tag{7.105}$$

In addition, crossing symmetry fixes,

$$a(\nu) = a(-\nu) \qquad b_i(\nu) = -b_i(-\nu) \qquad c_i(\nu) = c_i(-\nu)$$

$$\ell(\nu) = -\ell(-\nu) \qquad n_i(\nu) = n_i(-\nu) \tag{7.105'}$$

Inserting the decompositions (7.104″) and (7.104‴) in (7.104) and equating coefficients of P^{μ} we find,

$$A\nu + B_3(Q \cdot q_1) + B_4(\Delta \cdot q_1) - L = 2F(t) \tag{7.107}$$

As to the inverse Hilbert transforms, we note that the second term on the right-hand side of (7.36) arose in the integration by parts only because of the existence of $\theta(x^0)$ in (7.35), yielding $\delta(x^0)$ in that term. The equivalent of (7.36) or (7.104) for $u^{\nu\mu}$ and u^{μ} is thus

$$q_{1\nu}\, u^{\nu\mu} = u^{\mu} \tag{7.106}$$

Fubini has indeed noted that (7.36) (or (7.104)) and (7.106) reduce to a Poisson-bracket operation, (h denotes the Hilbert transform)

$$(q_\nu h - h q_\nu)\, u^{\nu\mu} = 2F(t) \tag{7.106'}$$

and we have

$$a\nu + b_3(Q \cdot q_1) + b_4(\Delta \cdot q_1) - \ell = 0 \tag{7.107'}$$

But inserting (7.105), (7.105′) and (7.107′) in (7.107) reduces it to

$$\frac{1}{\pi}\int_0^\infty a(\nu', q_1^2, q_2^2, t)\, d\nu' = F(t) \tag{7.108}$$

Taking for the simulated meson momenta $q_1^2 = q_2^2 = 0$ this becomes

$$\frac{1}{\pi}\int_0^\infty a(\nu', t)\, d\nu' = F(t) \tag{7.108′}$$

which gives an off-mass-shell form factor F(t) in terms of an on-mass-shell amplitude $a(\nu, t)$.

More generally, we note that the dependence on the simulated masses q_1^2 and q_2^2 in (7.108) cancels out in the ν' integration; this implies a cancellation of the residues of all singularities. Multiplying both sides of (7.108) by $(q_1^2 - m_1^2)(q_2^2 - m_2^2)$ so as to extract the q_1^2, q_2^2 dependence of the left-hand side, we note that for $q_1^2 \to m_1^2$ and $q_2^2 \to m_2^2$, the right-hand side cancels out altogether. Remembering (7.105) we have,

$$\int \text{Im } A(\nu, t)\, d\nu = 0 \tag{7.109}$$

which is in fact a strong-interactions sum rule. For ρ-π scattering, which is the reaction corresponding to (7.104′), with m_1^2 and m_2^2 representing the ρ-meson, whose pole is supposed to dominate the vector currents, we find

$$\int \text{Im } A_1(\nu, 0)\, d\nu = 0 \qquad \int \text{Im } B_2(\nu, 0)\, d\nu = 0$$

Supposing that the 0^- and 1^- states saturate the sum rule, one finds,

$$(g^2_{\omega\rho\pi} + g^2_{\phi\rho\pi})\, m^2_\rho - 4g^2_{\rho\pi\pi} = 0 \tag{7.110′}$$

$$(\nu_\omega + m^2_\rho)\, g^2_{\omega\rho\pi} + (\nu_\phi + m^2_\rho)\, g^2_{\phi\rho\pi} - 4g^2_{\rho\pi\pi} = 0 \tag{7.110″}$$

with

$$\nu_{\phi,\omega} = \tfrac{1}{2}(m^2_{\phi,\omega} - m^2_\rho - m^2_\pi)$$

Subtracting (7.110′) from (7.110″), we find

$$\nu_\omega \, g^2_{\omega\rho\pi} + \nu_\phi \, g^2_{\phi\rho\pi} = 0 \tag{7.111}$$

with $\nu_\omega \sim 0$, this implies $g^2_{\omega\rho\pi} >> g^2_{\phi\rho\pi}$, a well-known fact which corresponds to the identification of ω and ϕ with $(u\bar{u} + d\bar{d})/\sqrt{2}$ and $s\bar{s}$ respectively in U(3) and U(6), and to a quantum number of U(6) as we shall see below. The equations (7.109) represent, as we see in (7.110) relations between couplings and masses. They are identical in this case with equations which would be derived from the bootstrap idea; if indeed it should turn out that this is always so, one would have here a formulation leading to the bootstrap's self-consistency equations, without the actual dynamical model. These relations have been proposed by Fubini and collaborators[63] and Soloviev[64] to be closely related to unitary bounds on strong interaction amplitudes involving higher spins. If an analytic function $A(\nu)$ satisfying the dispersion relation

$$A(\nu) = \frac{1}{\pi}\int \frac{\operatorname{Im} A(\nu')\, d\nu'}{\nu' - \nu}$$

is subject to an asymptotic bound for

$$|A(\nu)| < \nu^\beta \qquad \beta < -1 \tag{7.112}$$

it also satisfies

$$\int \operatorname{Im} A(\nu)\, d\nu = 0 \tag{7.112′}$$

which explains why we should consider sum rules of that type as superconvergence relations. The subject has not yet been fully investigated; it seems to hold much promise of further developments in our understanding of the connections between algebraic and analytic structures.

REFERENCES

1. S. Coleman and S. Glashow, *Ann. Phys.* **17**, 41 (1962); **24**, 37 (1963).
2. M. Gell-Mann and M. Levy, *Nuovo Cimento* **16**, 705 (1960).
3. Y. Nambu, *Phys. Rev. Letters* **4**, 380 (1960); Y. Nambu and and G. Jona-Lasinio, *Phys. Rev.* **122**, 345 (1961) and **124**, 246 (1961); Chou Kuang-Chao, *JETP* **12**, 492 (1961).
4. N. Cabibbo, *Phys. Rev. Letters* **10**, 531 (1963).
5. M. Gell-Mann and Y. Ne'eman, *Annals of Phys.* **30**, 360 (1965).
6. M. Gell-Mann, *Physics* **1**, 63 (1964).
7. H. Goldberg and Y. Ne'eman, *Nuovo Cimento* **27**, 1 (1963).
8. Y. Hara, *Phys. Rev.* **139**, B134 (1965).
9. A. H. Rosenfeld, A. Barbaro-Galtieri, J. Kirz, W. J. Podolsky, M. Roos, W. J. Willis, and C. G. Wohl, UCRL 8030 (1966) and *Proc. Intern. Conf. High Energy Physics*, Berkeley (1966), to be published.
10. M. L. Goldberger and S. B. Treiman, *Phys. Rev.* **110**, 1178 (1958).
11. Y. Nambu and J. J. Sakurai, *Phys. Rev. Letters* **11**, 42 (1963); D. Horn, *Nuovo Cimento*, **29**, 571 (1963).
12. S. Adler, *Phys. Rev.* **137**, B1022 (1965).
13. S. Adler, *Phys. Rev.* **135**, B963 (1964).
14. S. Adler, *Phys. Rev.* **139**, B1638 (1965).
15. Y. Nambu and D. Lurie, *Phys. Rev.* **125**, 1429 (1962).
16. Y. Nambu and E. Shrauner, *Phys. Rev.* **128**, 862 (1962).
17. E. Shrauner, *Phys. Rev.* **131**, 1847 (1963).
18. S. Weinberg, *Phys. Rev. Letters* **16**, 879 (1966).
19. S. Fubini and G. Furlan, *Physics* **1**, 229 (1965).
20. S. Fubini, G. Furlan, and G. Rossetti, *Nuovo Cimento* **40**, 1171 (1965).
21. J. Schwinger, *Phys. Rev. Letters* **3**, 296 (1959); *Phys. Rev.* **130**, 406 (1963).
22. W. I. Weisberger, *Phys. Rev.* **143**, 1302 (1966).
23. S. Fubini, *Nuovo Cimento* **43**, 475 (1966).
24. V. Alessandrini, M. A. B. Beg, and L. S. Brown, *Phys. Rev.* **144**, 1122 (1966).

25. C. Bouchiat and P. Meyer, *Phys. Letters* **22**, 198 (1966).
26. J. D. Björken, *Phys. Rev.* **148**, 1467 (1966).
27. M. Jacob has reviewed the method in a Saclay report.
28. S. L. Adler, *Phys. Rev. Letters* **14**, 1051 (1965).
29. W. I. Weisberger, *Phys. Rev. Letters* **14**, 1047 (1965).
30. S. Adler, *Phys. Rev.* **140**, B736.
31. See Ref. 4, and M. Gell-Mann, *Proc. Intern. Conf. High Energy Phys.* (Rochester, 1960), pp. 508-513.
32. M. Ademollo and R. Gatto, *Phys. Rev. Letters* **13**, 264 (1964).
33. C. A. Levinson and I. J. Muzinich, *Phys. Rev. Letters* **15**, 715 (1965).
34. L. K. Pandit and J. Schechter, *Phys. Letters* **19**, 56 (1965).
35. D. Amati, C. Bouchiat and J. Nuyts, *Phys. Letters* **19**, 59 (1965).
36. I. M. Bar Nir, *Phys. Rev. Letters* **16**, 473 and 927 (1966).
37. C. G. Callan and S. B. Treiman, *Phys. Rev. Letters* **16**, 153 (1966).
38. G. Furlan and B. Renner, *Nuovo Cimento* **44**, 596 (1966).
39. S. Weinberg, *Phys. Rev. Letters* **17**, 336 (1966).
40. N. Cabibbo and L. A. Radicati, *Phys. Letters* **19**, 697 (1966); R. Dashen and M. Gell-Mann, *Third Coral Gables Conf. (1966) on Symmetry at High Energy*, p. 168; J. D. Björken, unpublished.
41. K. Kawarabayashi and M. Suzuki, *Phys. Rev.* **150**, 1181 (1966).
42. S. D. Drell and A. C. Hearn, *Phys. Rev. Letters* **16**, 908 (1966).
43. F. Buccella, G. Veneziano and R. Gatto, *Nuovo Cimento* **42**, 1019 (1966).
44. S. Fubini, C. Rossetti, and G. Furlan, *Nuovo Cimento* **43**, 161 (1966).
45. V. S. Mathur and L. K. Pandit, *Phys. Letters* **20**, 308 (1966).
46. C. Frahm, Y. Ne'eman and J. Yellin, *Fourth Coral Gables Conf. (1967) on Symmetry at High Energy*, to be published by W. H. Freeman, San Francisco.
47. N. N. Kroll and M. A. Ruderman, *Phys. Rev.* **93**, 233 (1954).

48. A. Klein, *Phys. Rev.* **99**, 998 (1955).
49. M. Suzuki, *Phys. Rev. Letters* **15**, 986 (1966).
50. H. Sugawara, *Phys. Rev. Letters* **15**, 870 (1966).
51. Y. Hara, Y. Nambu, and J. Schechter, *Phys. Rev. Letters* **16**, 380 (1966).
52. S. Badier and C. Bouchiat, *Phys. Letters* **20**, 529 (1966).
53. L. S. Brown and C. M. Sommerfield, *Phys. Rev. Letters* **16**, 751 (1966).
54. C. Itzykson and M. Jacob, to be published.
55. Y. Hara and Y. Nambu, *Phys. Rev. Letters* **16**, 875 (1966).
56. E. Ferrari, V. S. Mathur, and L. K. Pandit, *Phys. Letters* **21**, 560 (1966).
57. Y. T. Chiu and J. Schechter, *Phys. Rev. Letters* **16**, 1022 (1966).
58. Y. T. Chiu and J. Schechter, report EFINS 66-61 (1966), to be published.
59. Y. Ne'eman, *Phys. Rev.* **134**, B1355 (1964).
60. F. J. Gilman and H. J. Schnitzer, *Phys. Rev.* **150**, 1362 (1966).
61. K. Kawarabayashi and M. Suzuki, *Phys. Rev. Letters* **16**, 255 and 384 (1966) have derived this result. However, their derivation involves further assumptions.
62. S. Weinberg, *Phys. Rev. Letters* **17**, 616 (1966).
63. V. de Alfaro, S. Fubini, G. Rossetti, and G. Furlan, *Phys. Letters* **21**, 576 (1966).
64. L. D. Soloviev, translation in *J. Nucl. Phys. (USSR)* **3**, 133 (1966).

8

THE U(12) TOA OF SPACE-INTEGRALS OF CURRENT COMPONENTS AND ITS ASA SUBSETS

THE U(6) ALGEBRA—ABSTRACT RESULTS

In our gradual development of the algebraic approach, we have gone from U(3) to U(3) × $U(3)_\chi$; we now embed these algebras in a larger structure fulfilling the commutation relations of A_5, the traceless 6-dimensional algebra. Together with the identity matrix, it generates the group U(6).

We shall soon see that there are several different physical systems which are isomorphic to that algebra; the ones we shall be using will generally form some generalization of the system of current-generated algebras which we have used up to this point. However, it is easier to get acquainted with this group in terms of its first interesting application to hadron systematics, the non-relativistic scheme suggested by Gursey and Radicati,[1] Sakita,[2] and Zweig.[3] We shall further see that most of the physical results obtained in such a treatment survive the obviously inadequate dynamical assumption of a spin-independent strong interaction (this is why it fits a non-relativistic hypothetical picture modelled on atomic physics where $\mathbf{S}\cdot\mathbf{L}$ coupling is very weak); they survive because there are other physical systems with the same group-theoretical properties, leading to the same results from a more plausible set of assumptions. One should thus consider the following U(6) picture mainly as a didactic introduction to the group.

The defining representation is the system $(u_+, u_-, d_+, d_-, s_+, s_-)$ of quark states, where $q_{+,-}$ denote the $\sigma_Z = \pm\frac{1}{2}$ states; it forms the representation **6** or (1, 0, 0, 0, 0). The rank of the SU(6) algebra is 5 (excluding baryon-charge or quark-number divided by 3); we have I_Z, Y, σ_Z as quantum numbers of $SU(3) \times SU(2)_\sigma$, where $SU(2)_\sigma$ is the spin angular momentum of the quarks. The larger group we introduce has 35 generators, as against $8 + 3 = 11$, for the $SU(3) \times SU(2)_\sigma$ subgroup. The two new additional quantum numbers can be picked as

$$N_\sigma^3 = 2\sigma_Z \lambda^3 \tag{8.1}$$

and

$$Y_\sigma^3 = \sigma_Z \lambda^8; \tag{8.2}$$

it is at times more convenient to take

$$Y_\sigma^5 = \sigma_Z \left(\lambda^8 - \frac{\sqrt{2}}{2}\lambda^0\right) \Big/ \sqrt{3} \tag{8.2'}$$

i.e., the z-component of the 3rd quark's spin.

Note that the spin-unitary spin identifications are only correct for **6**; if we go over to the antiquark **6*** (0, 0, 0, 0, 1) for instance, the N_3 and Z_3 eigenvalues change sign of course, whereas $(\sigma_Z) \times (\lambda^3)$ etc., would remain the same.

To remove all degeneracies in defining a state, we need aside from 5 quantum numbers defining the representation (the h_i set of the highest weight, or its I_3, Y, σ_Z, N, Z' for instance) $(p - 3r)/2 = [35 - (3 \times 5)]/2 = 10$ additional quantum numbers. The SU(3) (λ, μ) and SU(2) "j" give us 3; I^2 is a fourth natural choice. The others are more complicated and have been picked in various ways. At times it has been found useful to work with a decomposition chain which does not go through the $SU(3) \times SU(2)_\sigma$ subgroup.

The easiest chain of course, is SU(6) $\supset$ SU(5) $\supset$ SU(4) $\supset$ SU(3) $\supset$ SU(2), with the 10 required quantum numbers given by the $h'_1 \ldots h'_4$, $h''_1 \ldots h''_3$, $h'''_1 h'''_2$ and h^{IV}_1 of the chain of submultiplets; this is a chain which does not contain unitary-spin SU(3) as a step in the decomposition. At best, one can identify the SU(4) in the chain with $\mathbf{I} \times \boldsymbol{\sigma}$ and SU(2) with $\boldsymbol{\sigma}$, an identification which is convenient when dealing with the non-strange system; this SU(4) commutes with $\sigma\lambda^8 = \mathbf{Y}_\sigma$. We thus have besides SU(3) $\times$ $SU(2)_\sigma$ another useful decomposition into $SU(4)_{I\sigma}$ ($\supset SU(2)_I \times SU(2)_\sigma$) $\times$ $SU(2)_Y$. In both cases, we need to know the decomposition of SU(n) into SU(m) $\times$ SU(m′) representations, either with $n = mm'$ or $n = m + m'$. This is a straightforward tensor reduction problem, with **6** appearing as (**3**, **2**) in SU(3) $\times$ $SU(2)_\sigma$ and as (**4**, **0**) + (0, **2**) for $SU(4)_{I\sigma} \times SU(2)_Y$.

The adjoint representation **35** (1, 0, 0, 0, 1) is (**8**, **3**) $\oplus$ (**8**, **1**) $\oplus$ (**1**, **3**) in SU(3) $\times$ $SU(2)_\sigma$ (we shall be using this decomposition except if otherwise stated). It is in the product **6** $\times$ **6*** of a quark and antiquark; indeed, taken in an S-state these would then be equivalent to odd-parity states with the above quantum numbers, i.e., it can be used for the $j = 1^-$ nonet **8** + **1** and the $j = 0^-$ octet. The **6** $\times$ **6*** also contains $(\mathbf{1}, \mathbf{1})^-$ in that picture, and this could be the η(960 MeV, 0^-).

For the baryons, we have the choice of representations in **6** $\times$ **6** $\times$ **6**, if we want to keep the U(3) normalization of "making" them from 3 quarks. This product contains

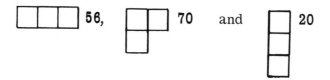

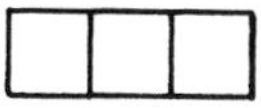 **56**, 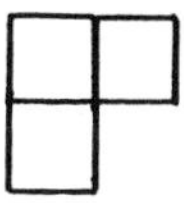 **70** and  **20**

Thinking in terms of S-states and keeping to Fermi statistics for the quarks, we would have picked **20** (0, 0, 1, 0, 0), the totally antisymmetric representation.[2] However, all useful results have come[1,3] from the choice of **56**, or (3, 0, 0, 0, 0) whose content is (**8**, **2**) +

(**10**, **4**). It can thus fit together the **8**, $j = \frac{1}{2}^+$ and **10**, $j = \frac{3}{2}^+$ and is therefore naturally related with the strong-coupling theories of the forties, the Chew-Low model and more recent reciprocal bootstrap calculations. All these had in common the emergence of the $j = \frac{3}{2}$, $I = \frac{3}{2}$ resonance [the $\Delta(1238)$] as a bound state of the baryon system together with the nucleon. The choice of **56** implies[4] that the quark be a parafermion field of order 3; if one has indeed to consider **6** as a physical representation. Alternatively, more complicated models may be considered; we shall touch this question in our last chapters.

We now note[5] that

$$\mathbf{56} \times \mathbf{35} = \mathbf{1134} + \mathbf{700} + \mathbf{70} + \mathbf{56} \tag{8.3}$$

with the $SU(3) \times SU(2)_\sigma$ contents,[5,6]

$$\mathbf{70}(1,1,0,0,0): (\mathbf{10},\mathbf{2}) + (\mathbf{8},\mathbf{4}) + (\mathbf{8},\mathbf{2}) + (\mathbf{1},\mathbf{2})$$

$$\begin{aligned}\mathbf{700}(4,0,0,0,1): (\mathbf{35},\mathbf{6}) &+ (\mathbf{10},\mathbf{6}) + (\mathbf{35},\mathbf{4}) + (\mathbf{27},\mathbf{4})\\ &+ (\mathbf{10},\mathbf{4}) + (\mathbf{8},\mathbf{4}) + (\mathbf{27},\mathbf{2})\\ &+ (\mathbf{10},\mathbf{2}) + (\mathbf{10}^*,\mathbf{2}) + (\mathbf{8},\mathbf{2})\end{aligned}$$

$$\begin{aligned}\mathbf{1134}(2,1,0,0,1): (\mathbf{27},\mathbf{6}) &+ (\mathbf{10},\mathbf{6}) + (\mathbf{8},\mathbf{6}) + (\mathbf{35},\mathbf{4})\\ &+ (\mathbf{27},\mathbf{4})_A + (\mathbf{27},\mathbf{4})_B\\ &+ (\mathbf{10},\mathbf{4})_A + (\mathbf{10},\mathbf{4})_B\\ &+ (\mathbf{10}^*,\mathbf{4}) + (\mathbf{8},\mathbf{4})_A\\ &+ (\mathbf{8},\mathbf{4})_B + (\mathbf{8},\mathbf{4})_C + (\mathbf{1},\mathbf{4})\\ &+ (\mathbf{35},\mathbf{2}) + (\mathbf{27},\mathbf{2})_A\\ &+ (\mathbf{27},\mathbf{2})_B + (\mathbf{10},\mathbf{2})_A\\ &+ (\mathbf{10},\mathbf{2})_B + (\mathbf{10}^*,\mathbf{2})\\ &+ (\mathbf{8},\mathbf{2})_A + (\mathbf{8},\mathbf{2})_B\\ &+ (\mathbf{8},\mathbf{2})_C + (\mathbf{1},\mathbf{2})\end{aligned}$$

These representations can thus be considered as candidates for baryon resonances. In particular, a **70**$^-$ has been considered[5]; the **700**$^-$ is an alternative in some schemes,[7] and the **1134**$^-$ has recently been studied[8] as it is the only one of the three that could accommodate a $j = 5^-/2$ octet. Of course, in a nonrelativistic system of bound quarks one could also have **56** with $L = 1, 2 \ldots.$ We shall see that this can be done in the current-algebra classifications too. For some higher spin and I-spin even-parity resonances, a **700**$^+$ has been suggested.[9]

For meson resonances, one can use the states in the product

$$\mathbf{35} \times \mathbf{35} = \mathbf{1} + \mathbf{35}_A + \mathbf{35}_S + \mathbf{189} + \mathbf{280} + \mathbf{280^*} + \mathbf{405} \tag{8.4}$$

In particular, the **189** and **405** have been considered[10] for the $j = 2^+$ nonet,

$$\begin{aligned}\mathbf{189}(0, 1, 0, 1, 0){:}\ & (\mathbf{1}, \mathbf{1}) + (\mathbf{8}, \mathbf{1}) + (\mathbf{27}, \mathbf{1}) + (\mathbf{8}, \mathbf{3})_A \\ & + (\mathbf{8}, \mathbf{3})_B + (\mathbf{10}, \mathbf{3}) + (\mathbf{10^*}, \mathbf{3}) \\ & + (\mathbf{1}, \mathbf{5}) + (\mathbf{8}, \mathbf{5}) \\ \mathbf{405}(2, 0, 0, 0, 2){:}\ & (\mathbf{1}, \mathbf{1}) + (\mathbf{8}, \mathbf{1}) + \mathbf{27}, \mathbf{1}) + (\mathbf{8}, \mathbf{3})_A \\ & + (\mathbf{8}, \mathbf{3})_B + (\mathbf{10}, \mathbf{3}) + (\mathbf{10^*}, \mathbf{3}) \\ & + (\mathbf{27}, \mathbf{3}) + (\mathbf{1}, \mathbf{5}) + (\mathbf{8}, \mathbf{5}) \\ & + (\mathbf{27}, \mathbf{5})\end{aligned}$$

Mass formulae are one type of application of U(6) whose interpretation has not varied much; indeed, the next ASA we shall derive from the currents contains a U(6) subgroup which coincides at the quark level with the non relativistic generators we have used to introduce the group. An important point to remember here is that in a U(6) multiplet, several U(3) mixings [due to the SU(3)-breaking interaction] may occur. An assumption of U(6) is that physical states are eigenstates of Y^3_σ and $(\mathbf{Y}_\sigma)^2$; this then fixes mixing ratios between different (λ, μ) of SU(3).

For example, ϕ is considered to represent $s^\dagger s$, with $(\mathbf{Y}_\sigma)^2 = 2$ and $Y^3_\sigma = 1, 0, -1$, whereas ω has $\mathbf{Y}_\sigma = 0$. This fixes the mixing to be

$$\begin{aligned} \phi &= (1/\sqrt{3})(\omega^0\sqrt{2} - \phi^0) \\ \omega &= (1/\sqrt{3})(\omega^0 + \phi^0\sqrt{2}) \end{aligned} \tag{8.5}$$

If one chooses to assume that SU(3)-breaking transforms like the mass of s, the third quark, the above identification corresponds to taking

$$m(\rho) = m(\omega) \tag{8.6'}$$

which is correct to within some 20 MeV.

For the 0^- mesons, $\mathbf{Y}_\sigma = 0$ and the scheme does not impose a mixing; on the other hand, requiring states to be unmixed SU(6) representations would forbid it altogether in this case.

Conservation of $\mathbf{Y}_\sigma$ forbids $\phi \to \rho + \pi$; it is indeed experimentally suppressed by a full order of magnitude relative to $K + \bar{K}$. One also derives,

$$2m^2(K^*) - m^2(\phi) = m^2(\rho) \tag{8.6''}$$

from counting "Δm_s" increments. Note that these formulae fit any model in which mesons are made of two triplets and ϕ and ω are recombined so that ϕ is ss'. Indeed we also get here the Schwinger formulae,[11] derived in a different context,

$$m^2(K^*) - m^2(\rho) = m^2(K) - m^2(\pi) \tag{8.7}$$

$$[m^2(\omega) - m^2(\rho)][m^2(\phi) - m^2(\rho)]$$

$$- \tfrac{4}{3}[m^2(K^*) - m^2(\rho)][m^2(\omega) + m^2(\phi) - 2m^2(K^*)]$$

$$= \tfrac{8}{9}[m^2(K^*) - m^2(\rho)]^2(1 - \zeta^2) \qquad (8.7')$$

ζ denotes the spin-space overlap integral between **1** and **8** non-relativistically. For the 1^- nonet, $\zeta \sim 1$. If this were always true, we would be relating SU(3) splitting with "Δm_S" counting, thus excluding spin-dependent SU(3)-breaking. This may prove too restrictive; we do not have good grounds for such simplification other than the good fit of (8.7), which had indeed been noticed by Glashow even before there was a theory to produce it.

For the baryons, such as assumption, leading for all hadrons to

$$M = M_0 + aY + b[I(I + 1) - \tfrac{1}{4}Y^2] + c\sigma(\sigma + 1) \qquad (8.8)$$

yields a value of $\sim$130 MeV (taken by solving (8.8) for "a" in the octet) for the spacing in the decimet (experimentally about 145 MeV). More sophisticated mass formulae have been tried in SU(6), based upon the arbitrary omission of some higher tensors contained in the most general mass operator [just as the SU(3) mass breaking is assumed to contain little **27**]. However, this approach does not seem to be as successful here for the eight-component contributions themselves; whatever breaks SU(3) and SU(6) is some combination of the allowed tensors, rather than one of them only. There is even some evidence that the symmetry breaking is a function of baryon numbers.[12] Note that in a Lagrangian model, SU(6) is broken by the kinetic energy term which is an SU(3) scalar; in fact it behaves in a quark model like an ω^0 meson in a **35**. This breaking can contribute to the mass in second order, i.e., it should contain all representations in the product (8.4). Some of these representations do not appear in **56** × **56*** and will thus not contribute to the baryon masses.

We now turn to the **56*** × **56** coupling to **35**, i.e., to the baryon-meson basic coupling; considering that the atonous (weak) and electromagnetic vector charges (i.e., the 4th components) form a 0^+ octet in a nonrelativistic approximation, and that the axial-vector transitions are spin-couplings when one neglects baryon recoil and therefore fit a 1^+ octet, we may regard this set of currents as a 35^+ and use the same coupling as in the baryon-meson problem. Note that this is also consistent with the Goldberger-Treiman relation; indeed, considering that the SU(3) generators (integrated) are a 0^+ octet, we have to couple the ρ, ϕ^0, K^* to the 0^+ part of the **35** in **56*** × **56** to get the universal **F**-type coupling. At the same time, the 0^- mesons will couple[1] via $\sigma \cdot \nabla\phi$, i.e., to the (**8**, **3**) part of the SU(6) generators; the (**1**, **3**) part would couple to a 0^- singlet in SU(3) which has thus replaced the ω^0 which has coupled universally to (**1**, **1**), the baryon charge. In this approach we have then replaced the $\mathbf{35}^-$ by a $\mathbf{35}^+$ which results from P-state coupling. This pattern is found whenever we use a no-recoil approximation.[13]

We shall now derive the three key parameters resulting from this coupling: μ_p/μ_n, G_A/G_V, D/F. These are easily worked out by the usual methods of tensor reduction; however, we shall use the quark picture and get at the key parameters without going through the entire reduction process.

It is easiest[14] to start with μ_p/μ_n. Operating on quarks only, we can take $\langle N_+ | Q\sigma_z | N_+ \rangle$ of constituent quarks in p_+ and n_+, or $p_{1/2}$ and $n_{1/2}$ where we use σ_z as a sub-index. Both states are in **56**(3, 0, 0, 0, 0), the totally symmetric product of 3 quarks; we can then use the wave functions assuming them to be properly symmetrized throughout. The highest state is $\Delta^{++}_{3/2}$, which has to be $(u_+u_+u_+)$; for $\Delta^+_{3/2}$, turn one "u" into "d" $(u_+u_+d_+)$. For $\Delta^+_{1/2}$, we lower one spin z-component, getting $\sim 2(u_-u_+d_+)$ and $(u_+u_+d_-)$ since it can be done twice in u and once in d. The $p_{1/2}$ is the orthogonal complement and should thus be given by $(u_- u_+ d_+)$ and $2(u_+ u_+ d_-)$ (phases and overall normalization are unimportant in this counting; this is not the explicit weighted wave function). For $\Delta^0_{3/2}$ we get $(u_+ d_+ d_+)$; $\Delta^0_{1/2}$ is then $(u_- d_+ d_+)$ and $2(u_+ d_- d_+)$, and the $n_{1/2}$ has then the orthogonal content $2(u_- d_+ d_+)$ and $(u_+ d_- d_+)$. This yields,

$$\langle p_{1/2} | Q\sigma_z | p_{1/2} \rangle \sim (-\tfrac{2}{3} + \tfrac{2}{3} - \tfrac{1}{3}) + 2(\tfrac{2}{3} + \tfrac{2}{3} + \tfrac{1}{3}) = 3$$

$$\langle n_{1/2} | Q\sigma_z | n_{1/2} \rangle \sim 2(-\tfrac{2}{3} - \tfrac{1}{3} - \tfrac{1}{3}) + (\tfrac{2}{3} + \tfrac{1}{3} - \tfrac{1}{3}) = -2$$

so that[15,16]

$$\mu_p / \mu_n = -\tfrac{3}{2} \tag{8.9}$$

This is to be compared with the experimental value −1.46; the nice fit was mainly responsible for drawing the attention of workers in the field to the promise held by the SU(6) algebra. Note that this is the same result that we got in Chapter VII from $U(3) \times U(3)_\chi$ when we put the nucleon in **(3, 6)** + **(6, 3)**. Indeed, the algebra is isomorphic: we have really used here only λ^a and $\sigma_z \lambda^a$, i.e., the subalgebra $SU(3) \times SU(3)$ of $(1 \pm \sigma_z)\lambda^a$; under this subgroup, the **56** decomposes into

(10, 1) and **(1, 10)**	for the $\sigma_z = \pm\frac{3}{2}$ states
(3, 6) and **(6, 3)**	for the $\sigma_z = \pm\frac{1}{2}$ states

mixing in the **8** and **10**. Moreover, there is even a physical connection[17]; if A and B are two particles of equal mass, we find that

$$\langle B(\mathbf{p}) | g(\gamma_5 \lambda^a;\ 0) | A(\mathbf{p}) \rangle = \frac{1}{E} \langle B(0) | \mathbf{p} \cdot g(\boldsymbol{\sigma}\lambda^a;\ 0) | A(0) \rangle \tag{8.10}$$

where the right-hand side contains a space-component of the axial-vector current, and the equation represents a Lorentz-transformation leading from a time to a space component. However, we note that the $\bar{\psi}\gamma^z\gamma_5\lambda^a\psi$ is indeed simply $\psi^\dagger\sigma_z\lambda\psi$, and we have now encountered a piece of SU(6) in the context of a current. Note however that in our $U(3)\times U(3)_\chi$ representation, we required a **10** with $j = \frac{1}{2}^-$, whereas the same role is fulfilled here by the $j = \frac{3}{2}^+$, **10**.

We now compute the D/F ratio of this magnetic coupling. As we saw in Chapter 2, these correspond to the commutator and anticommutator, when representing the baryons by 3×3 matrices (p and n correspond to ω_{V^-} and ω_{U^+} respectively, or E_3^1 and E_3^2). We find (μ_F is just proportional to Q) using Appendix II

$$\begin{aligned} \mu(p) &= \mu_F + \tfrac{1}{3}\mu_D \\ \mu(n) &= -\tfrac{2}{3}\mu_D \end{aligned} \tag{8.11}$$

which, when combined with (9) yields

$$\mu_D/\mu_F = \tfrac{3}{2} \tag{8.12}$$

This is then the ratio between the two types of coupling of $\mathbf{56}^*_{(8)} \times \mathbf{56}_{(8)}$ to $\mathbf{35}_{(8)}$ in the $\sigma_z\lambda^a$ part of the latter, which also represents the components we have chosen for the $\boldsymbol{\sigma}\cdot\nabla\phi$ coupling to the 0^- mesons. We thus have in SU(6), or in its $U(3)\times U(3)$ subgroup a ratio

$$D/F = \tfrac{3}{2} \tag{8.12'}$$

for the pseudoscalar coupling. The 1^- of course couple through F only. As we noted in Chapter 7 (7.18), the $(-G_A/G_V)$ ratio is $\frac{5}{3}$.

The μ_p/μ_n and G_A/G_V ratio result from our identification of the nucleon as a 3-quark product. At the quark level this corresponds to a minimal electromagnetic interaction (we took $Q\sigma_z$, i.e., we did not consider a quark anomalous magnetic moment in computing (8.9)) and $G_A = G_V$. It has generally been customary to think of the anomalous magnetic moments as results of the strong interaction coupling to the meson cloud; one therefore expected to get a dependence upon the strength of this coupling, going from $\mu(p) = 1$ (in units of $e/2m_N$), $\mu(n) = 0$ all the way to some limiting ratio when $g_{\overline{N}N\pi} \to \infty$. The ratio (8.9) does indeed correspond to that limit, since this is the value of $g_{\overline{N}N\pi}$ which allows U(6) to become an exact symmetry. In a Lagrangian model we could write a phenomenological term describing the $\overline{B}B\phi$ interaction (it would contain terms like $f_{ijk}\overline{B}_8^i\gamma_\mu\phi^{\mu j}B_8^k$, $(d_{ijk} - \frac{2}{3}if_{ijk})\overline{B}_8^i\gamma_5\phi^j B_8^k$, $t_{ijk}\overline{B}_{10}^{\mu i}\gamma_\nu\phi^{\nu j}B_{10\mu}^k$, etc.) which would be invariant under U(6) as far as its nonrelativistic components go. The kinetic energy terms of the baryons would violate this symmetry; but taking $g_{\overline{N}N\pi} \to \infty$ we would keep the symmetric situation, and it is in this limit (or in the limit of a static baryon) that we are considering all the above results. Recently,[12,13] that static model was revived in the form of bootstrap calculations based on the N/D method; neglecting baryon recoil makes these calculations U(6) invariant—they simply couple symmetrically $\mathbf{56}^* \times \mathbf{56}$ to $\mathbf{35}^+$ (the $\mathbf{35}^- \times L = 1$ produces such a $\mathbf{35}^+$). We shall see more of this picture in the next chapter.

Note that U(6) in the above form is closely related to the Wigner[18] supermultiplet theory.

THE SEARCH FOR A "RELATIVISTIC" U(6) THEORY; NONCOMPACT MERGER GROUPS

Within a short time after the introduction of U(6), a number of good predictions were derived: the D/F ratio, μ_p/μ_n, $\phi \not\to \rho + \pi$, the structure of **56** and **35** in themselves, the near equality in mass spacing in **56**, and several predictions for amplitudes which we shall review in the context of current-algebras or other U(6) groups. However, the situation was highly paradoxical since it was also clear that a process like $\rho \to 2\pi$ was also forbidden, as it does not conserve $\boldsymbol{\sigma}$; similarly, $\Delta \to N + \pi$ and all other decimet decays are forbidden for the same reason. Clearly, one could not work seriously with a theory of spin-independence because particle physics is a relativistic domain in which only total angular momentum is conserved, rather than spin and orbital motion separately.

We shall review very briefly the search for a "relativistic SU(6)." The proposed solutions turned out to involve difficulties of principle which invalidated them; more and more sophisticated schemes were developed, each hitting some new snag.

At first it seemed[1,19,20] that what was needed was a symmetry group containing both SU(3) and the Poincaré group ISL(2, C) or the Lorentz group at least [SL(2, C)]. This group should have as a little-group (or stability group—the subgroup commuting with the translations) SU(6) instead of SU(2); hopefully, it would then also lead to conservation of some structure containing total angular momentum $\times$SU(3), when orbital motion is involved. The smallest such group would be SL(6, C), the tensor envelope of SL(2, C) $\times$ SU(3), or perhaps the larger group GL(6); the generators of SL(2, C) transform like $\boldsymbol{\sigma}$ and $i\sigma$, and the new algebra would transform like $\vec{\sigma}\lambda^a$ and $i\vec{\sigma}\lambda^a$, with 72 generators ($\vec{\sigma}$ represents a Euclidean 4-vector, with $\sigma^0 = 1$). On the other hand, a relativistic quark Lagrangian is based upon a 4-spinor quark ($\times$3 unitary components, i.e., 12-components altogether); and to keep within the systematics of unitary groups, it was thought that one might well enlarge the space-time kernel of the group by using U(2, 2), the largest group leaving $\bar{\psi}\psi$ invariant; in the spinor space, $\bar{\psi}\psi = \psi^+\beta\,\psi$ has β as an invariant metric, induced by $g^{\mu\nu}$ of space-time. Requiring from the group that it leave β invariant (i.e., a diagonal matrix with eigenvalues 1, 1, -1, -1) imposes on the algebra the condition,

$$-G^+\beta + \beta G = 0 \tag{8.13}$$

We see that Hermitian γ_r matrices commuting with β (i.e., the even-parity current densities in a system of quark currents) fulfill the requirement; and so do anti-Hermitian γ_r matrices which anticommute with β (i.e., those which go into odd-parity currents). By going over to a 12×12 metric with six (+1) and six (−1) eigenvalues, i.e., $\beta\lambda^0$, we define U(6, 6), with 144 generators. The Hermitian set has 72 generators and forms a $U(6) \times U(6)_\beta$ compact subgroup [it is $U(2) \times U(2)$ for U(2, 2)]. Other such candidate merger groups could be $GL(6) \times GL(6)_{\gamma_5}$, where in a chiral-symmetric system one has separated left- and right-handed quarks, and it is possible to construct on each a group isomorphic to the Lorentz group, $\boldsymbol{\sigma}$ and $i\boldsymbol{\sigma}$.

LURE OF A GENERALIZED POINCARÉ GROUP; EXPERIMENTAL VERIFICATION OF THE COMPACTNESS OF THE CURRENT ALGEBRA

The Gursey-Radicati algebra happens to coincide with quark-spin when we reduce it to the U(3) scalar part. This seems to suggest the existence of a larger symmetry built upon the tensor-envelope of the Poincaré group and U(3).

Let us first note that this would really be impossible if the generator densities were to be represented by quark bilinears. The main error in this situation comes from the impression that systems like $\gamma^\mu\gamma^\nu$ or $\boldsymbol{\sigma}$ and $i\boldsymbol{\sigma}$ represent Lorentz-group generators. They do in the abstract, reproducing the correct commutation relations

$$[J_i, J_j] = i\epsilon_{ijk} J_k \qquad [J_i, \Lambda_j] = i\epsilon_{ijk}\Lambda_k$$

$$[\Lambda_i, \Lambda_j] = -i\epsilon_{ijk} J_k \tag{8.14}$$

including the minus sign in the commutator of two noncompact generators, as compared to a plus sign for 4-dimensional rotations in Euclidean space, for instance. However, a Lagrangian has to be Hermitian

$$\bar{\psi}(i\gamma^{\mu}\partial_{\mu} - m)\psi + \text{h.c.} \tag{8.15}$$

and when evaluating the 6 Lorentz generators

$$\begin{aligned} M^{\mu\nu} &= \int [\pi^{0r} \sum_{r}^{s\mu\nu} \phi_s - (t^{0\mu}x^{\nu} - t^{0\nu}x^{\mu})]\, d^3x \\ t^{\rho\sigma} &= \pi^{\rho r}\partial^{\sigma}\phi_r - g^{\rho\sigma}\mathcal{L} \end{aligned} \tag{8.16}$$

we find that M^{23}, M^{31}, M^{12} represent indeed J^1, J^2, J^3 with both spin and orbital parts; but M^{01}, M^{02} and M^{03}, representing Λ^1, Λ^2, Λ^3 have *only orbital parts*. The antihermicity of $\pi^{0r}\Sigma_r^{s\mu\nu}\phi_s$ for μ or $\nu = 0$ makes the spin contribution vanish. The Dirac bilinear of quark fields with nonhermitian $\psi^{+}(\gamma^0\gamma^{\mu})\psi$ is *not* a generator of U(2, 2) or U(6, 6); such a generator could be provided by orbital terms, similar to the $\int t^{00}x^{\nu}\, d^3x = -\int \mathcal{H} x^{\nu}\, d^3x$ of Lorentz-transformations. We then require 143 translations, with unresolved physics. Alternatively, we could replace the quarks with infinite-dimensional representations of the discrete type, reducing to a direct sum of triality-one representations under the compact subgroup $U(6) \times U(6)_{\beta}$.

As far as the quark-bilinear densities are connected with physical matrix-elements (and they would have to be, in a Lagrangian theory), the question of compactness was answered experimentally[22], by the success[21] of the Adler-Weisberger and related sum rules, which were based upon the use of a plus sign in the study of matrix-elements of the commutator [$G(\gamma_5\gamma_i)$ has odd parity and would be in the noncompact piece in $U(6, 6)_{\beta}$]

$$[\int a_i^0\, d^3x, \int a_j^0\, d^3x] = i f_{ijk} \int v_k^0\, d^3x \tag{8.17}$$

taking complete sets of intermediate states (a^0 is the axial vector charge density, v^0 the vector one; i, j, k are U(3) indices), or also as we shall see in commutators such as

$$[\int v_i^z \, d^3x, \int v_j^z \, d^3x] = if_{ijk} \int v_k^0 \, d^3x$$

Thus, we claim there is no connection between the current algebra—or even between a system of quark bilinear densities—and the Poincaré group. However, one might still possibly find a Lorentz-like U(6, 6) super symmetry, with discrete (or perhaps even continuous) infinite representations while we could have the currents forming a compact set of U(12) densities at the same time.

THE UNITARITY ISSUE AND UNITARY INFINITE-DIMENSIONAL REPRESENTATIONS

The least-effort solution seems to be the one in which unitarity is supplied by an extension of the translational part of the Poincaré algebra. Such extensions have been studied[23] in the abstract; the main point is to pick the dimensionality of the translation space so that it will transform like a nonunitary finite representation under the homogeneous part. This representation should reduce under the compact subgroup into a sum of unitary representations of that subgroup, including one one-dimensional scalar; this will allow the existence of representations in which the translation vector points in this singlet direction, i.e., it will commute with the compact subgroup which thus plays the part of a little-group.

For IU(6, 6), the **143** reduces under $U(6) \times U(6)_\beta$ into (**35**, **1**), (**1**, **35**), (**6**, **6***), (**6***, **6**), (**1**, **1**), so that the (**1**.**1**) here fulfills just that role. The difficulty consists in providing the new momenta with a physical interpretation; clearly, m^2 ceases to be a Casimir operator characterizing a particle. Instead, one has a continuous spectrum of masses for each representation of $U(6) \times U(6)_\beta$. It is conceivable that an appropriate reformulation could be worked out, restricting physical states to vanishing values of all new momenta; however, no useful theory has as yet been constructed in that way.

Alternatively, one can use a method defined by Michel[24] in which there is a complete doubling of the Lorentz group, appearing once as an "external" Poincaré group P' and once as an "internal" symmetry, an $SL(2, C)$ extension of the internal degrees of freedom of spin—which can be extended into $SL(6, C)$ or $U(6, 6)$. We now have a direct product[20] $U = U(6, 6) \times P'$ with elements (g, Λ, a) where $g \in U(6, 6)$, Λ is a homogeneous orbital Lorentz transformation and a is a translation. The complete physical Poincaré group consists of all elements (Λ, Λ, a) where the first Λ will act on the internal space, both for rotations and for velocity transformations.

Using U as a symmetry then produces a new difficulty: one degenerate mass for an infinite number of particles. This is because the mass is $(P')^2$, and we have one single value for a complete representation of $U(6, 6)$. Such a representation looks for instance like the spectrum of the hydrogen atom which we studied in Chapter 3; indeed this spectrum is a representation of $U(2, 2)$. For a symmetry group, the mass degeneracy theorem has been proved by O. Raifeartaigh.[25] Any loophole if it exists could exploit a possibility whereby only SU(3) and the Poincaré group in U are symmetries, and the other generators do not commute with the Hamiltonian. This would produce a SGA, i.e., a classification scheme with perhaps also a symmetric coupling. We shall return to this possibility in the next chapter.

Fronsdal and collaborators[26] have used $SL(6, C)$, assuming that the mass degeneracy might correspond to some idealized limit; they have constructed couplings and derived physical consequences which are assumed to subsist even after removal of the degeneracy. These include a correction to the electromagnetic form factors due to the fact that vector mesons are also part of an infinite-dimensional representation and cannot dominate the form factors in any single way. Other results can be derived from SL(6, C), such as

$$D/F = \tfrac{9}{5} \text{ for } \overline{B}{}^i_8 B^j_8 \phi^k_8 \qquad (8.18)$$

However, the entire system suffers from one important conceptual difficulty. The infinite-dimensional representation of U(6, 6) has no coupling with P′, and a term such such as $\gamma_\mu \partial^\mu$ cannot be included in the Lagrangian. Also, the "field" has Bose statistics. To correct this effect, one can have as the basic field a spinor under P′, with a Dirac equation; however, its spin is then the U(6, 6) spin plus $j' = \frac{1}{2}$, and we lose the good results of **56** in U(6) where no such additional angular momentum had been considered. The Fronsdal program thus depends critically upon the resolution of this paradox.

Returning to the case of finite representations, e.g., perhaps with the inhomogeneous system as a justification, one should mention the attempt to work[27-29] with "redundant components." In this method, the IU(6, 6) is used as a symmetry for couplings; one then projects out only one sub-multiplet of the compact $U(6) \times U(6)_\beta$ subgroup per IU(6, 6) representation, and regards the rest as "redundant" components. The choice of the "nonredundant" ones corresponds to some physical "boost," etc. We shall not go into the details; let us just point out the unitarity difficulty, using the concise method of Coleman.[20]

Let H be a larger Hilbert space, including all redundant ones; H_p is the physical Hilbert subspace, projected out by the operator P_0,

$$H_p = P_0 H \qquad (8.19')$$

We assume that the S-matrix is invariant under the full group; this S acts in H space. We can project out the physical S-matrix $S_p = P_0 S$. This is assumed not to be symmetric, but imposing the symmetry on S may have reduced for instance the number of allowed couplings in S_p.

In particular, U(6, 6) "symmetrizes" positive and negative energy components, and we may want to exclude the negative energy ones since their only other interpretation would lead to negative probabilities.

If we now define the T-matrix by $S = 1 + iT$, unitarity requires,

$$T_p - T_p^\dagger = iT_p T_p^\dagger \tag{8.19''}$$

with $T_p = P_0 T P_0$, so that

$$P_0(T - T^\dagger)P_0 = iP_0 T P_0 T^\dagger P_0 \tag{8.19}$$

This expression is paradoxical. Comparing the terms enclosed between two P_0 operators, we have on the left-hand side, T and $T^\dagger$ which are invariant under the large group; on the right-hand side, $TP_0T^\dagger$ is *not* invariant, since P_0 does not commute with that group. The only solution is $T = 0$, so that $S = 1$. The paradox has been presented in various ways[30] but they all stem from this fundamental difficulty.

Summing up, we see that even if we are prepared to have infinite multiplets—either all masses for one spin, or all spins for one mass—we still face serious further conceptual difficulties.

There is one more solution which has been attempted and which could lead to finite unitary representations: an infinite parameter group. Such a structure may turn out to be useful as a TOA, without bothering about closure; but requiring it to be a symmetry imposes an infinite number of conservation laws leading again to $S = 1$ as the only allowed solution.[20]

THE $[U(6) \times U(6)]_{\gamma_5}$ AND U(12) CURRENT-GENERATED ALGEBRAS

In the preceding chapter we have seen how the chiral system of $U(3) \times U(3)_\chi$ had provided an extremely useful TOA once we had identified its densities with time-components of physical vector and axial vector currents. Feynman and collaborators[31] suggested a similar identification for the Gürsey-Radicati U(6); we noticed that

$$\psi^\dagger \sigma\lambda^a \psi = \bar{\psi}\gamma_5 \boldsymbol{\gamma}\lambda^a \psi \tag{8.20}$$

so that for a quark at rest, the spin coincides with the Gamow-Teller density matrix. By generalizing to the space-integrals of all components of the vector and axial vector current densities, and assuming the integrals to have the commutation relations given by the quark field representation, we close on the algebra of $U(6) \times U(6)_{\gamma_5}$; moreover, if we generalize to all possible densities of a spinor quark-bilinear, $16 \times 9 = 144$ in all, we generate U(12). The justification is to be found in the fact that the quark field did reproduce faithfully the $U(3) \times U(3)_{\gamma_5}$ algebra which we derived from atonous (weak) universality and the octet behavior of observed transitions (see Chapter 7). To realize what the commutation relations are, it is best to rewrite all currents (having picked a metric and Dirac matrices set) in terms of σ, λ^a, β, and γ_5, just as we did for the axial vector current in (8.20).

Using our former notation, we are adjoining the space integrals of the space-components

$$G(\sigma^k \lambda^a;\ t) = \int d^3x\ g(\sigma^k \lambda^a;\ \mathbf{x}, t) = \int d^3x\ a^{ka}(\mathbf{x}, t) \tag{8.21}$$

and

$$G(\gamma_5 \sigma^k \lambda^a;\ t) = \int d^3x\ g(\gamma_5 \sigma^k \lambda^a;\ \mathbf{x}, t) = \int d^3x\ v^{ka}(\mathbf{x}, t) \tag{8.22}$$

We note that the axial current densities form Euclidean four-vectors $\vec{\sigma}\lambda^a$ when adjoined to the vector charge λ^a ($\vec{\sigma}$ has components $\sigma^0 = 1$, σ^k) and the vector current densities similarly "complete" the axial charges as Euclidean four-vectors $\gamma_5\vec{\sigma}\lambda^a$; these four-vectors have a unique 3-space parity for all 4-components, whereas the Poincaré group representations v^μ and a^μ have opposite parities for their time and space parts.

The 72 generators

$$G\left(\tfrac{1}{2}(1 \pm \gamma_5)\sigma^i\lambda^a;\ t\right) \tag{8.23}$$

close in the triplet model upon the algebra of $[U(6) \times U(6)]_{\gamma_5}$. We continue using the notation in which the physical algebra is characterized by the abstract group generated by exponentiation with a real parameter, and by an invariant characterizing it in the Dirac spinor space, here γ_5.

Before going any further in our physical analysis, we extend our mathematical framework of available generators to include space-integrals of all possible densities in the triplet model. We thus add 72 new generators

$$G\left(\tfrac{1}{2}(1 \pm \gamma_5)\cdot\tfrac{1}{2}(1 \pm \beta)\vec{\sigma}\lambda^a;\ t\right) \tag{8.24}$$

with (we use a metric 1, −1, −1, −1 and $\beta = \rho_3 \times 1$, $\boldsymbol{\gamma} = i\rho_2 \times \sigma$, $\gamma_5 = i\gamma_0\gamma_1\gamma_2\gamma_3 = \rho_1 \times 1$)

$$\begin{aligned} g(\beta\sigma^0\lambda^a;\ \mathbf{x}, t) &\sim \bar{\psi}\lambda^a\psi = s^a(\mathbf{x}, t) \\ g(i\beta\gamma_5\sigma^0\lambda^a;\ \mathbf{x}, t) &\sim i\bar{\psi}\gamma_5\lambda^a\psi = p^a(\mathbf{x}, t) \\ g(\beta\sigma^i\lambda^a;\ \mathbf{x}, t) &\sim \tfrac{1}{2}i\epsilon^i{}_{jk}\bar{\psi}\gamma^j\gamma^k\lambda^a\psi = t^{ia}(\mathbf{x}, t) \\ g(i\beta\gamma_5\sigma^i\lambda^a;\ \mathbf{x}, t) &\sim i\bar{\psi}\gamma^k\gamma^0\lambda^a\psi = q^{ia}(\mathbf{x}, t) \end{aligned} \tag{8.25}$$

where t^{ia} and q^{ia} represent the tensor current densities with two and one space indices respectively; we notice that they form Euclidean four-vectors with the scalar and pseudo-scalar densities, $\beta\vec{\sigma}\lambda^a$ for (s, t) and $i\beta\gamma_5\vec{\sigma}\lambda^a$ for (p, q). Note also that the entire systematics can be written in a "manifestly covariant" way.[22] For each g(x) we construct the operator

$$\int d^4x \;\; \delta(\hat{P}\cdot x - s)g(x) = \int d^4x \, g(x) \;\; \delta(\hat{P}\cdot x - s)$$

with $\hat{P}$ a unit 4-vector, $\hat{P} \equiv P^\mu/(P^\nu P_\nu)^{1/2}$, well defined for all states except for the vacuum. For any fixed x, these operators acting on states at rest in some frame carry them into states at rest in the same frame. The commutation relations can then be put in covariant form for equal values of x.

SUM RULES ASSUMING THE CONVERGENCE OF $[U(6) \times U(6)]_{\gamma_5}$ COMMUTATORS

In Chapter 7 we mentioned the emergence of singular Schwinger terms[32] in the equal-time commutator between current densities, when one of these densities is a space-component. Schwinger had originally showed that for the electromagnetic current (and thus for all our $v^{\mu a}$),

$$[v^0(\mathbf{x}, 0), \; v^k(\mathbf{x}', 0)] = C\partial^k \; \delta(\mathbf{x} - \mathbf{x}') \tag{8.26}$$

C is a seemingly infinite constant arising from the closed loop diagrams in field theory. As long as there are no Schwinger terms multiplied by operators, this seems tame enough.

Björken[33] has shown that the Schwinger term may be regarded as the difference between the time-ordered product $t^{\mu\nu}$ we used in (7.35) and throughout Chapter 7 to get sum rules.

$$t^{\mu\nu} = i \int d^4x \; e^{iqx} \langle A \,|\, T(g^{\mu a}(x)g^{\nu b}(0)) \,|\, B\rangle \tag{8.27}$$

which is in fact not an exact covariant tensor, and the truly covariant amplitude $A^{\mu\nu}$ for photon or lepton pair emission, which also involves the commutator $[g^{\mu a}(\mathbf{x}, 0), g^{\nu b}(0)]$, $g^{\nu b}(0)]$,

$$A^{\mu\nu} = t^{\mu\nu} + \text{Schwinger terms symmetric in } (a, b) \tag{8.27'}$$

Using this fact, Björken showed that in many cases one might be able to use commutators between $[U(6) \times U(6)]_{\gamma_5}$ *densities* to get sum rules. Such sum rules have indeed been derived by Adler[34] and Okubo[35] involving high-energy neutrino reactions, and by Okubo[35] and Björken[33] for high-energy Compton scattering of the nucleon.

Adler's calculation is in a way an extension of the sum rule (7.52) which he derived[36] from an integrated commutator; in that commutator, high-energy inelastic neutrino reactions were used to evaluate the axial charges' commutator matrix-elements directly, without using pole dominance. These were reactions in which the momentum-transfer (squared) between neutrino and out-going lepton (with $m_\ell \to 0$) is $q^2 = 0$. These results were first generalized to test the local commutators (7.34) of $U(3) \times U(3)_{\gamma_5}$; it turns out that this involves $q^2 > 0$. Assuming now local commutators corresponding to a quark field model (Adler's results check a somewhat more general system) he picks out the parts that are antisymmetric in the unitary spin indices, such as the v^{oc} in the commutator

$$[v^{na}(x), v^{mb}(y)]_{x_0 = y_0}$$

$$= i\,\delta^{nm} f^{ab}{}_c\, v^{oc}(x)\, \delta^3(\mathbf{x} - \mathbf{y}) + i\epsilon^{nm}{}_r\, d^{ab}{}_c\, a^{rc}(x)$$

$$\times\, \delta^3(\mathbf{x} - \mathbf{y}) + \text{more singular terms} \tag{8.28}$$

(we are using a normalization in which the σ and λ have the structure constants of **J** and **F**) and similar commutators between $v^{na}(x)$ and $a^{ma}(x)$ and between $a^{na}(x)$ and $v^{ma}(x)$. In each case, the sum rule derivation requires an assumption that some scattering amplitude obeys an unsubtracted dispersion relation in the energy variable, for fixed q^2. In reactions

$$\nu + N \rightarrow \ell + N'$$

(N' some hadron system with invariant mass W), taken in the laboratory frame,

$$q^2 = (k_\nu - k_\ell)^2 = 4E_\nu E_\ell \sin^2(\phi/2)$$
$$W = [2m_N(E_\nu - E_\ell) + m_N^2 - q^2]^{1/2} \qquad (8.29')$$

(ϕ is the $\nu - \ell$ scattering angle), the sum rules are for the $|\Delta S| = 0$ case,

$$2 = (f_A^+(q^2))^2 + (F_1^+(q^2))^2 + q^2(F_2^+(q^2))^2 + \int_{m_N+m_\pi}^{\infty} \frac{W}{m_N}\, dW \{\beta^{(-)}(q^2, W) - \beta^{(+)}(q^2, W)\} \qquad (8.29)$$

where $F_{1,2}^+$ are the Dirac electric and magnetic isovector factors' τ^+ components, f_A^+ is the $\gamma^\mu\gamma^5$ form factor, $f_V^+(q^2) = F_1^+(q^2) + 2m_N F_2^+(q^2)$

$$2 = 1 + (q^2/4m_N^2)(f_A^+(q^2))^2 + (q^2/4m_N^2)(f_V^+(q^2))^2 + \int_{m_N+m_\pi}^{\infty} \frac{W}{m_N}\, dW[\alpha^{(-)}(q^2, w) - \alpha^{(+)}(q^2, w)] \qquad (8.30)$$

and

$$\frac{f_V^+(q^2)f_A^+(q^2)}{m_N} = \int_{m_N+m_\pi}^{\infty} \frac{W}{m_N}\, dW\,[\gamma^{(-)}(q^2, W) - \gamma^{(+)}(q^2, W)] \qquad (8.31)$$

with similar results for $|\Delta S| = 1$. Rule (8.29) is derived from the $U(3) \times U(3)_{\gamma_5}$ local commutators of (7, 34); rule (8.30) from the unitary antisymmetric piece of (28) and the $[a^{na}(x), a^{mb}(y)]$ commutator; and rule (8.31) involves the $[v^{na}(x), a^{mb}(y)]$ commutator in a similar way, $\alpha^{\pm}$, $\beta^{\pm}$ and $\gamma^{\pm}$ are obtainable experimentally from (for $\Delta S = 0$; r_ℓ is the lepton solid angle; the ($\pm$) for ν, ℓ correspond to the ν, ℓ and $\bar{\nu}\bar{\ell}$ respectively)

$$\frac{d^2\sigma}{dr_\ell\, dE_\ell}(\nu(\pm) + p \to \ell(\pm) + N')$$

$$= \frac{G^2 \cos^2\theta}{(2\pi)^2}\frac{E_\ell}{E_\nu}\left[q^2\alpha^{\pm}(q^2, W) + 2E_\nu E_\ell \cos^2\left(\frac{\phi}{2}\right) \times \beta^{\pm}(q^2, W) \mp (E_\nu + E_\ell)\, q^2\gamma^{\pm}(q^2, W)\right] \qquad (8.32)$$

The method of derivation is again based upon a variant of (7.36); the analytical assumption is that an amplitude like

$$\mathfrak{J}(q^0, q^2) = \epsilon_{ab}{}^3 \int d^4x\, e^{-iqx}\theta(x^0) \times \sum_S \langle p|[\partial^0 a^{na}(x), \partial_t v^{mb}(0)] + [\partial^0 v^{na}(x), \partial_t a^{mb}(0)]|p\rangle \qquad (8.33)$$

with

$$0 = \frac{\partial}{\partial q_0}\mathfrak{J}(q^0, q^2)\Big|_{q_0=0}$$

satisfies an unsubtracted dispersion relation in q^0 [in this case we get the sum rule (8.31)] for $(\partial/\partial q_0)\mathfrak{J}$.

The analog for photon (Compton) scattering[37] involves the assumption that [all $\sigma_N^{\pm}$ are functions $\sigma_N^{\pm}(E, \cos\theta)$],

$$I(E, \cos\theta) = \sigma_p^{(+)} - \sigma_p^{(-)} - \sigma_n^{(+)} + \sigma_n^{(-)} \tag{8.34'}$$

decreases for large E at least faster than $1/(E \log E)^2$, an assumption whose validity may be questionable[35]; E is the photon energy in the laboratory frame, $\sigma_p^{(\pm)}$ and $\sigma_n^{(\pm)}$ are total corrections in the laboratory frame for the scattering of circularly polarized photons with ±1 helicities by the polarized proton (or neutron) at rest, and θ is the angle between the incident photon and the nucleon polarization vector. The sum rule is

$$-(G_A/G_V) = \frac{3}{2\pi e^2}\int_{m_\pi(1+m_\pi/2m_N)}^{\infty} dE\, \frac{E}{\cos\theta} \times I(E, \cos\theta) \tag{8.34}$$

Note that this sum rule can determine the sign of G_A. Okubo's derivation uses only integrated $U(6) \times U(6)_{\gamma_5}$ commutators, Björken's uses local commutators.

A sum rule[38, 39] involving $[v^{ka}(x), v^{jb}(y)]$ was in fact one of the first to be derived from the $U(6) \times U(6)_{\gamma_5}$ algebra. These involve moments, and can be derived using the method of Fourier transforms which we described in (7.78) etc.; they resemble the Cabibbo-Radicati sum rule (7.72) and connect the total proton magnetic moment with the electric radius. From the commutator,

$$\langle p|[\mu^{Z_1}, \mu^{Z_2}]|p\rangle = if^{12}{}_3\left\langle p\left|\frac{r^3}{6}\right|p\right\rangle$$

$$= i\left[\frac{d}{dq^2}\left(G_E^p(q^2) - G_E^n(q^2)\right) + \frac{1}{8m_N^2}\right] \tag{8.35'}$$

where μ^{ia} is the magnetic dipole operator,

$$\mu^{ia} = \frac{1}{2} \int d^3x \, \epsilon^{i}{}_{jk} x^j v^{ka}(x) \qquad r^a = \int d^3x \, x^2 v^{0a}(x)$$

Dashen and Gell-Mann and B. Lee got

$$\frac{\mu_p}{2m_N} = \left| \left\langle p \left| \frac{r^3}{6} \right| p \right\rangle \right|^{1/2} \tag{8.35}$$

where the experimental values are $0.82\,f^{-1}$ and $0.73\,f^{-1}$ respectively. However, this sum rule did not use dispersion methods for the evaluation of the commutator; it simply assumed saturation of the intermediate states by the $\Delta(1236)$ and used a U(6) coefficient to connect it with the nucleon, assuming the Δ to belong to **56**. This kind of derivation is thus very different from the former; it has to regard $U(6) \times U(6)_{\gamma_5}$ here as an ASA. Indeed, a similar treatment could yield the same radius for the axial vector divergence; Bietti has shown that we do get a good result there if we include higher states. He also derived[40] sum rules for magnetic quadrupole and electric dipole moments, using moment commutators

$$
\begin{aligned}
[E^{ia}, E^{jb}] &= i f^{ab}{}_c \int x^i x^j v^{4c} \, d^3x \\
[M^{ij,a}, M^{i'j',b}] &= i f^{ab}{}_c \int x^i x^{i'} (\delta^{jj'} x^2 - x^j x^{j'}) \, v^{4c} \, d^3x \\
&\quad + \text{symmetric terms in } (a, b) \\
[E^{ia}, M^{jk,b}] &= i f^{ab}{}_c \int x^i x^j \epsilon_{nmk} x^n v^{mc} \, d^3x \\
&\quad + \text{symmetric terms in } (a, b)
\end{aligned}
\tag{8.36}
$$

where

$$E^{ia} = \int x^i v^{4a} \, d^3x \qquad M^{ij,a} = \int x^i \epsilon_{nmj} x^n v^{ma} \, d^3x$$

and saturating them by using contributions from the lowest lying known resonance with the appropriate quantum numbers. Because of the odd parity of both E^{ia} and $M^{ij,a}$, this can only be a $j = \frac{1}{2}^-$ or $\frac{3}{2}^-$ state, and we reinsert $N^{**}(1518; \frac{3}{2}^-)$. The sum rules are then

$$
\begin{aligned}
|\langle N^{**} | E^{Z3} | p\rangle|^2 &= \tfrac{1}{12}\langle r^2\rangle^V \\
&= -\tfrac{1}{2}(dG_E^V(k^2)/dk^2)_{k=0} \\
|\langle N^{**} | M^{ZZ,3} | p\rangle|^2 &= 2[d^2 G_E^V(k^2)/(dk^2)^2]_{k=0} \\
\langle N^{**} | E^{Z3} | p\rangle\langle P | \overline{M}^{ZZ,3} | N^{**}\rangle &= \frac{i}{2m_N}(dG_M^V(k^2)/dk^2)_{k=0}
\end{aligned}
\tag{8.37}
$$

from which one gets

$$
\left\langle \frac{r^2}{6}\right\rangle^V \left[\frac{d^2 G_E^V(k^2)}{(dk^2)^2}\right]_{k=0} = \frac{1}{4m_N^2}\left(\frac{dG_M^V(k^2)}{dk^2}\right)^2_{k=0} \tag{8.37'}
$$

which is somewhat analogous to (8.35). Experimentally we find $2.7 \times 10^{-3} f^6$ and $2.8 \times 10^{-3} f^6$ for both sides of (8.37′), which seems to indicate that these saturation ideas could be useful. We shall now study the corresponding possibility of using these algebraic extensions of U(3) as ASA, in line with such results.

THE REST ASA; SATURATION

If we are interested in rest-states, we have to enquire after the commutation properties with β. Indeed, β represents the Lorentz scalar in spinor space. In a Lagrangian model, this is the behavior of the mass term; it may also represent in part the behavior of the only other surviving term in the Hamiltonian density, the interaction term. In that case, our group would stand a chance of being an ASA in this rest frame. Picking out the generators of U(12) fitting this criterion[22] gives us

$$[U(6) \times U(6)]_\beta$$

which contains the sets

$$G(\tfrac{1}{2}(1 \pm \beta)\sigma^i \lambda^a; t) \qquad i = 0, 1, 2, 3 \tag{8.38}$$

We noted in our discussion of U(6, 6) that this subalgebra is generated by all even-parity densities, because β happens also to represent parity in spinor space; this is the maximal compact group leaving $\bar{\psi}\psi$ invariant. Moreover, if we should consider these generators to satisfy a conservation law, we could anyhow represent the odd-parity generators of U(12) as some time-derivatives of moments of the even-parity algebra. This comes about through the continuity equations satisfied by the densities, which relate currents of both parities to each other. However, it was shown[41,42] that imposing such exact symmetry requirements would bring back the unitarity difficulties and S = 1. The most familiar situation—and only exact one—occurs when we study the vector currents. Writing[22]

$$\frac{d}{dt} \int d^3x \; v^0(x, t) = 0 \tag{8.39}$$

and using

$$\partial_\mu v^\mu = 0 \qquad \text{or} \qquad \partial^0 v^0 - \partial^i v^i = 0 \tag{8.40}$$

we find

$$G(\gamma_5 \sigma^k \lambda^a; t) = G(v^{ka}) = \frac{d}{dt} \int d^3x \; x^k v^{0a} \tag{8.41}$$

which can be checked by explicit calculation of the right-hand side.

Going over to the axial vector currents, we realize that the covariant completion of $\partial^0 a^k$, needed in

$$\frac{d}{dt}\int d^3x\ a^k(x, t) = 0 \tag{8.42}$$

would be

$$\partial^\mu a^\nu - \partial^\nu a^\mu \equiv r^{[\mu,\nu]} \tag{8.43}$$

However, the expression for $G(\gamma_5 \lambda^a; t)$ then involves $r^{[\mu,\nu]}$. Note that (8.43) is consistent with the pole dominance postulate of (7.21), as we can see by differentiating (8.43) first with ∂_ν,

$$C\partial^\mu \phi = \partial_\nu \partial^\nu a^\mu + \partial_\nu r^{[\mu,\nu]} \tag{8.44}$$

with differentiation by ∂_μ reducing (8.44) to an identity. On the other hand, if $r^{[\mu,\nu]} = 0$, Okubo[42] has noted that by multiplying (8.43) by x^λ and integrating by parts for λ, μ, $\nu \neq 0$, we find

$$\delta^{\lambda\mu} \int d^3x\ a^\nu(x) = \delta^{\lambda\nu}\int d^3x\ a^\mu(x)$$

and taking $\lambda = \mu \neq \nu$, $\nu = k$

$$G(\gamma_5 \sigma^k) = \int d^3x\ a^k(x) = 0 \tag{8.45}$$

Now Coleman[41] had proved that $r^{[\mu,\nu]} = 0$ was implied by $[U(6) \times U(6)]_\beta$ of the currents if this is a rest symmetry (even if it is a slightly broken one). We refer the reader to Coleman's paper or to Obubo's simplified proof[42]; the starting point is that

$$\int_{x_0=0} d^3x\ j^0(x)\,|\,0\rangle = 0 \rightarrow \partial_\mu j^\mu(x) = 0 \tag{8.46}$$

and

$$\int_{x_0 = 0} d^3x \ j^k(x) \,|\, 0\rangle = 0 \rightarrow \partial_\mu j^\nu(x) = 0 \qquad k = 1, 2, 3 \qquad (8.47)$$

i.e., if an integrated current generator destroys the vacuum (as it should if we deal with a symmetry, since the vacuum should then be represented by a singlet because it carries none of the integrated charges), the continuity equations are either 4-divergenceless or 4-curlless. Okubo further proved that

$$\int_{x_0 = 0} d^3x \ j^\mu(x) \,|\, 0\rangle = 0 \rightarrow j^\mu(x) = 0 \qquad (8.48)$$

which would make a $[U(6) \times U(6)]_{\gamma_5}$ chiral symmetry of all vector and axial vector components' space integrals absurd.

To avoid equation (8.45), we have to refine our definition of the role of the G^{ia} generators; the identification of the current-generated algebra as an ASA has to be somewhat modified, as suggested by Coleman.[41,20] Let us write the commutation relations of $U(6) \times U(6)_\beta$ between states at rest (the index i stands here for the 72 possibilities in (8.38))

$$\langle A(\mathbf{p} = 0) \,|\, [G^i, G^j] \,|\, B(\mathbf{p} = 0)\rangle$$
$$= f^{ij}{}_k \langle A(\mathbf{p} = 0) \,|\, G^k \,|\, B(\mathbf{p} = 0)\rangle \qquad (8.49)$$

Suppose we now insert intermediate states. With our former definition, G^j operating on B would lead to another state C(0) at rest, within the same representation as B, just as it did not connect the vacuum with anything; however, this created the paradox of (8.45). Now suppose instead that G^j takes B to one particle states C in the representation, but it also just as strongly leads out of the representation to some many particle states. In fact, using a free quark field theory, it is easy to see that G^j will indeed lead equally to $C + q + \bar{q}$ for instance, or C + some mesons. These are the well known disconnected loops of quantum field theory, and they may be located anywhere in x space. They do indeed lead from the vacuum to pairs etc.,

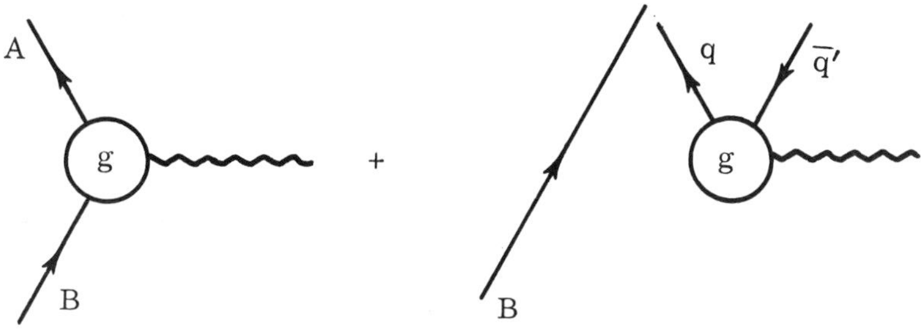

anything allowed by the various quantum numbers. If we now look at the commutator (8.49), we note that these contributions, consisting in $|\langle \pi | \zeta | 0 \rangle|^2$ for instance, just vanish. The commutation relations are *approximately saturated by one-particle states.* It is in this sense that a piece of a TOA—which could lead anywhere—can be assumed to form an ASA here. We are thus assuming that the *one particle states fit a classification as a representation of an abstract* $U(6) \times U(6)_\beta$; and that the *integrals of the current do not coincide with these abstract generators* as far as their action on one particle states goes, but that their *commutators taken between one-particle states are approximately saturated by these one-particle state representations.* The methods of Fubini etc., which we used for $U(3) \times U(3)_\chi$ then give us a way of estimating this saturation approximation itself.

This then is what we mean by an ASA when we go beyond the system of U(3) charges; we did not use it for $U(3) \times U(3)_\chi$ charges as these did not hold any promise as an ASA at rest anyhow, since they did not commute with β. However, we shall see further on that we can adopt the definition to that algebra too when working between states at

$\mathbf{p} \to \infty$, where the dominant part in a quark-field Hamiltonian density is the $\boldsymbol{\alpha} \cdot \mathbf{p}$ term rather than β.

There is one important loss when using the saturation definition: we can get predictions for 3-particle vertices (the $\langle A | [G^+, G^-] | A \rangle = 2 \langle A | G^3 | A \rangle$ gives these transitions, as we saw in Chapters V and VII), but not for an amplitude $A \times B \to C \times D$. This is because $A \times B$ is a piece of the continuum and there is not much chance hoping that the system will be saturated by just this type of continuum contributions; however, there may be room for some additional dynamical assumption which could pick out a certain piece in the continuum of two-particle states.

Note that with the saturation hypothesis, we can regard as an ASA in the usual sense (i.e., connecting mostly one-particle states nearby in the energies) the algebraic system which we can get by taking $P_1 G P_1 = G_1$, where P_1 is a projection operation which selects only matrix-elements between one-particle states. This G' algebra, which has the same commutation relations as G, can be used in a restricted sense as an ASA as defined by Dashen and Gell-Mann.[22]

APPLICATIONS OF $[U(6) \times U(6)]_\beta$ AND SUBGROUPS; THE QUARK-COUNTING GENERATOR

We now apply the $[U(6) \times U(6)]_\beta$ algebra as an ASA defined as above. We first notice that the Gursey-Radicati group which we denote $U(6)_\sigma$ is contained in our larger group; it is generated by the space-integrals of the densities $g(\vec{\sigma} \lambda^a; x)$. The two reduced pieces are $U(6)^+_\beta$ and $U(6)^-_\beta$ corresponding to $g((1 \pm \beta) \vec{\sigma} \lambda^a; x)$; we thus get the $U(6)_\sigma$ algebra in the sum of $U(6)^+$ and $U(6)^-$, and the representations d_σ of $U(6)_\sigma$ are to be found in the product $(d_+ \times d_-) = \epsilon_i d^i_\sigma$, where the $[U(6) \times U(6)]_\beta$ representation is given by $(d_+, d_-)^{\eta_P}$, η_P being the space parity.

To make a quark (i.e., $d_\sigma = \mathbf{6}$) we use $(\mathbf{6}, \mathbf{1})^+$; this is because we are only dealing with the positive-energy quark states with $\beta = +1$. The antiquark has opposite parity, i.e., its $\beta = -1$; it has $d_\sigma = \mathbf{6}^*$ and is thus represented by $(\mathbf{1}, \mathbf{6}^*)^-$. Note that if what we had in mind were creation operators, then the quark annihilation operator would be $(\mathbf{6}^*, \mathbf{1})^+$ and anti-quark annihilation would be performed by $(\mathbf{1}, \mathbf{6})^-$. Alternatively, if we so wish we could regard $(\mathbf{1}, \mathbf{6})^-$ as the basis for a hadron system of opposite intrinsic parity, a pseudo-quark. There is as yet no clear evidence that we need introduce representations involving pseudoquarks.

The 72 generators themselves transform like $(\mathbf{35}, \mathbf{1})^+$, $(\mathbf{1}, \mathbf{35})^+$, and $(\mathbf{1}, \mathbf{1})^+$ twice. One of these $(\mathbf{1}, \mathbf{1})^+$ generators is the banyon number operator $g(\sigma^0 \lambda^0)$, counting the number of quarks minus antiquarks; the other singlet is $g(\beta\sigma^0\lambda^0)$, and it counts the number of quarks *plus* antiquarks (it would subtract pseudoquarks, should they exist) because β inverts the sign of the λ^0 eigenvalue for the antiquark. We shall see in the next chapter that this generator, or in fact the entire $g(\beta\sigma^0\lambda^a)$ nonet seem to play an important role in the strong interactions.

We now turn to the baryons. The low lying ones with $j = \frac{1}{2}^+, \frac{3}{2}^+$ have $d_\sigma = \mathbf{56}$; they form a 3-quark product and lie in $(\mathbf{56}, \mathbf{1})^+$, with their antiparticles in $(\mathbf{1}, \mathbf{56})^-$. For the mesons, their qq^+ transformation properties correspond to $(\mathbf{6}, \mathbf{6}^*)^-$. They may dominate the $g(\gamma_5 \vec{\sigma}\lambda^a)$ densities as assumed in the meson pole-dominance picture, as the latter transform together with the $g(\beta\gamma_5\vec{\sigma}\lambda^a)$ as $(\mathbf{6}, \mathbf{6}^*)^-$ and $(\mathbf{6}^*, \mathbf{6})^-$ under our $W(6)_\beta$ algebra (we use Schwinger's rebus[11] notation).

For the odd-parity resonances, it is not yet clear whether we should be using $(\mathbf{1}, \mathbf{70})^-$ or $(\mathbf{126}, \mathbf{6}^*)^-$ i.e., a system of 4 quarks and an antiquark; or perhaps a quasi-*orbital* $\mathbf{L} = 1^-$ excitation of $(\mathbf{56}, 1)^+$ itself or of $(\mathbf{70}, 1)^+$, $(\mathbf{20}, 1)^+$ etc. Similarly, the question is as yet unsettled for the $j = 1^+, 2^+$ mesons, which could go into $(\mathbf{21}, \mathbf{21}^*)^+$ which contains $d_\sigma = 405^+, 35^+, 1^+$ or into $(\mathbf{15}, \mathbf{15})^+$ or $(6, 6^*)^-$ with an $\mathbf{L} = 1^-$. These quasi orbital $\mathbf{L}$ and their relativistic definition will be discussed under the next head.

The $(\mathbf{6}, \mathbf{6}^*)^-$ has $d_\sigma = \mathbf{35}^-, \mathbf{1}^-$. The singlet is assumed to be the $\eta(960, 0^-)$ which displays little mixing with $\eta(550, 0^-)$. We can thus assume that under $W(6)_\beta$ the Hamiltonian density must reduce to two main pieces—an invariant **(1, 1)** and a part which breaks $W(6)_\beta$ but is still invariant under $U(6)_\sigma$ and under the $G(\beta)$ operators. Such a term has to behave[43] like **(35, 35)**; the $W(6)_\beta$ properties of a quark kinetic energy term

$$\mathcal{H}_k(x) = -\frac{i}{2}(\bar{\psi}\gamma^i \partial_i \psi - \partial_i \bar{\psi}\gamma^i \psi)$$
$$= -\frac{i}{2}(\psi^+ (\boldsymbol{\alpha} \cdot \nabla)\psi - \nabla\psi^+ \cdot \boldsymbol{\alpha}\psi) \sim g(i\gamma_5 \sigma\lambda^0) \qquad (8.50)$$

would be **(6, 6*)** and **(6*, 6)** which could indeed contribute a **(35, 35)** piece in second order, containing both $d_\sigma = \mathbf{1}$ breaking $W(6)_\beta$ only and $d_\sigma = \mathbf{35}$ etc., breaking $U(6)_\sigma$. As for the **(1, 1)** $W(6)_\beta$-invariant part of the Hamiltonian, it seems phenomenologically that not only do they behave like $G(\beta)$ under $W(6)_\beta$, they even display an extremely rough universality property: the "central" masses in the $(\mathbf{6}, \mathbf{6}^*)^-$ and $(\mathbf{56}, \mathbf{1})^+$ multiplets are roughly 650 MeV and 1000 MeV, i.e., proportional to 2 and 3, the β-eigenvalues. It is this fact, coupled with the fractional charges of quarks (average e/3 in the proton) which gives the same e/2m at the quark field level and thus makes $\mu_p \sim 3$, from a minimal elec-magnetic interaction in terms of the fundamental fields. It is difficult to see how this picture of three 320 MeV "slices" glued together in the nucleon[44] can have anything to do with the hypothetical 10 BeV quarks. However, much of the work which has been done with a nonrelativistic quark model[45,46] is based upon the "effective" 320 MeV quarks. We shall return to this question in Chapter 9.

To understand the role of $U(6)_\sigma$ and $W(6)_\beta$ as ASA in strong interactions, we have to account for transfers of angular momentum from spin to orbital situations and vice versa, i.e., to exploit the fact that we do not deal with a "spin-independence" postulate.

When a hadron rest state $|\eta 0\rangle$ acquires a small velocity $\mathbf{k}/m \ll 1$ in the rest frame in which one integrates g(x), it is transformed by the Lorentz transformation $\mathbf{\Lambda}$,

$$|\eta\mathbf{k}\rangle = \left(1 + \frac{i}{m}\mathbf{k}\cdot\mathbf{\Lambda}\right)|\eta, 0\rangle \tag{8.51}$$

with

$$\mathbf{\Lambda} = \int d^3x\ \mathbf{x}\mathcal{H}(x) - t\mathbf{P} \tag{8.52}$$

The $\mathbf{P}$ part does not contribute when acting in (8.51). $\mathcal{H}(x)$ contains $\mathcal{H}_k(x)$ of (8.50), which is indeed the crucial element[22] through which the commutation relations (8.14) really operate: the commutator between two $\boldsymbol{\alpha}$ or $g(i\gamma_5\boldsymbol{\sigma})$ produces the $g(\boldsymbol{\sigma})$ "quark-spin" part in $\mathbf{J}$. It is this $\mathcal{H}_k$ term which now induces through (8.51) some representation mixing in $|\eta\mathbf{k}\rangle$, by multiplying $|\eta, 0\rangle$ by (**6**, **6***) and (**6***, **6**) or by **35** in $U(6)_\sigma$ (the ω^0-like component). This is how we can understand ("spurion" wise) a decay like

$$\rho \to 2\pi$$

which is forbidden in "static" $U(6)_\sigma$ since σ_z for instance is not conserved; the pions are in a P state, i.e., one of them is now multiplied by an ω^0 like operator which induces $\sigma_z = 1$. If we now check

$$\phi \not\to \rho + \pi$$

we see that this is still forbidden by $\mathbf{Y}_\sigma$ conservation, since $\boldsymbol{\alpha}$ (or ω^0) has $\mathbf{Y}_\sigma = 0$.

There are several selection rules from $W(6)_\beta$ with respect to interactions at rest, such as the fact that annihilation of baryons into two mesons at rest

$$B + \overline{B} \to 2\phi$$

is forbidden by β-conservation, whereas 3ϕ are allowed (6 quarks plus antiquarks); such an experimental situation seems indeed to occur, with suppressed 2-meson modes. However, this actually subsists beyond the rest picture, a fact which is difficult to understand since multiplication by $\mathcal{H}_k$ does indeed augment the β-eigenvalue by 2. Moreover, the whole status of such scattering amplitudes is doubtful as long as we have not supplied a more detailed dynamical assumption, as we saw in our discussion of saturation.

$U(6)_W$ AND W-SPIN

From the above analysis of $\mathbf{\Lambda}$, we can see that Λ_z or α_z commutes with $G(\sigma^0\lambda^a)$, $G(\sigma^z\lambda^a)$, $G(\beta\sigma^x\lambda^a)$ and $G(\beta\sigma^y\lambda^a)$, but not with the other nonets in $W(6)_\beta$; the latter are transformed away into ever larger (**6**, **6***) and (**6***, **6**) like operators. Checking in the approximation of degenerate masses within a $W(6)_\beta$ representation, we find that the matrix elements of the generators commuting with α_z do not vary; the other operators "leak" out, with the matrix elements between the given hadrons vanishing entirely at $k_z \to \infty$.

The mathematical picture of only Λ_z intervening corresponds to the physics of a collinear process. Suppose we had a rest state $|h\rangle$, with some $\sigma^z\lambda^8$ eigenvalue (Y_σ^3); if we now accelerate $|h\rangle$ in the z-direction, $Y_\sigma^3|h\rangle$ does not vary, as it is one of the operators which do commute with α_z. Lipkin and Meshkov[47] (and Barnes and collaborators[48] in a somewhat different context) noticed that the set of "well behaved" generators also closed on a U(6) group, which they named $U(6)_W$, with the term W-spin denoting the λ^0 part, a U(2) algebra generated by 1, σ_z, $\beta\sigma_x$, $\beta\sigma_y$. This is one of the "accidental" conservation laws allowed by kinematical considerations, which had been studied in field theory models by Stech, Calogero, etc.

The conceptual difficulty in applying $U(6)_W$ to collinear reactions is due to the fact that we have no guarantee that intermediate states will indeed be one-particle states. If they are, we operate within $U(6)_W$ eigenstates, but if the intermediate states contain several particles, collinearity is meaningless since the total collinear **k** can now arise from any vector-sum, and unitarity is not conserved. However, using the saturation definition, we can hope to get vertex functions and selection rules from saturated commutators, or from the G′ generators which may form an ASA and do project out only one-particle states.

First, let us study the representation structure.[49] For a quark, $d_W = \mathbf{6}$; for the antiquark, it is $\mathbf{6}^*$ as the W-spin still treats $\bar{q}$ as a spinor and the unitary spin is $\mathbf{3}^*$. However, the phases of the $G(\beta\sigma_x)$ and $G(\beta\sigma_y)$ are inverted, since $\beta = -1$ for $\bar{q}$. $\lambda^0|\bar{q}\rangle = -1$, but this introduces only an overall phase as far as the unitary singlet case only is considered. Therefore

$$G(\beta\sigma_x\lambda^0)|\bar{q}\rangle = -\sigma_x\lambda^0|\bar{q}\rangle, \quad G(\beta\sigma_y\lambda^0)|\bar{q}\rangle = -\sigma_y\lambda^0|\bar{q}\rangle \tag{8.53'}$$

while

$$G(\lambda^0)|\bar{q}\rangle = \lambda^0|\bar{q}\rangle, \quad G(\sigma_z\lambda^0)|\bar{q}\rangle = \sigma_z\lambda^0|\bar{q}\rangle \tag{8.53''}$$

When constructing higher representations from quarks only, W-spin is identical with "spin" and $U(6)_W$ has the same representations as $U(6)_\sigma$; the distinctions will come in when we deal with mesons or $qqqq\bar{q}$ baryons because these include $\bar{q}$ with its peculiarities.

Coupling together $q\bar{q}$ (we transform away the λ^0 phase) we see that $W_z^{tot} = \sigma_z^{tot}$, so that the $\sigma_z = \pm 1$ components $q_\pm\bar{q}_\pm$ have $\mathbf{W} = 1$. But $W_x^{tot} = \sigma_x(q) - \sigma_x(\bar{q})$ whereas $\sigma_x^{tot} = \sigma_x(q) + \sigma_x(\bar{q})$ and the same difference appears in $W_y^{tot} \neq \sigma_y^{tot}$. This causes the $\sigma_z = W_z = 0$ components $(q_+\bar{q}_- \pm q_-\bar{q}_+)$ with $S = 0, 1$ (S here is the Gamow-Teller spin-like SU(2) which coincides with true spin for a one quark state, or with the spin of serveral quarks in a non relativistic picture) to have $W = 1, 0$ respectively; this has been called the W-S flip. To see how it occurs, let us operate[49] with the S and W lowering operators on the $q_+ q_+$ state,

$$(\sigma_x - i\sigma_y)q_+\bar{q}_+ = [(\sigma_x - i\sigma_y)q_+]\bar{q}_+ + q_+[(\sigma_x - i\sigma_y)\bar{q}_+]$$

$$= q_-\bar{q}_+ + q_+\bar{q}_-$$

$$(W_x - iW_y)q_+\bar{q}_+ = [(\sigma_x - i\sigma_y)q_+]\bar{q}_+ - q_+[(\sigma_x - i\sigma_y)\bar{q}_+]$$

$$= q_-\bar{q}_+ - q_+\bar{q}_-$$

We see that W-spin leads to the orthogonal S = 0 state. The result for baryons and mesons is that they still belong to **56**$^+$ and **35**$^-$, **1**$^-$; however the **8**, 0^- now form $w_z = 0$ components of the **8**, 1^-, and the $\eta(960, 0^-)$ has moved into the **35** and makes up the $w_z = 0$ component of the ω^0 unitary singlet. The $j_z = 0$ components of **8**, 1^- and **1**, 1^- have replaced the 0^- states in the **35** and **1** respectively. Harari and collaborators[50] have worked out the formulae required for the $SU(6)_\sigma \longleftrightarrow SU(6)_W$ flip for any representation. In particular, since both groups are included in $W(6)_\beta$, this can take the form of a transformation leading from one subgroup to the other. It is performed by the matrix

$$C^{d(w)W\gamma}_{d(\sigma)S\alpha}(d_q, d_{\bar{q}}, \lambda, m)$$

$$= \sum_{R_q R_{\bar{q}}} (-1)^{S(\bar{q})-m(\bar{q})} \langle d(\sigma)\lambda S\alpha \mid d_q R_q; d_{\bar{q}} R_{\bar{q}}\rangle$$

$$\times \langle d_q R_q; d_{\bar{q}} R_{\bar{q}} \mid d(W)\lambda W\gamma\rangle \qquad (8.54)$$

where d_q and $d_{\bar{q}}$ are the (d_+, d_-) of $W(6)_\beta$, $d(\sigma)$ and $d(W)$

are the $U(6)_\sigma$ and $U(6)_W$ representations; λ (the U(3) representation) $m = \sigma_z = w_z$ do not vary in this transformation connecting a particular S (the $U(6)_\sigma$ spin) with a particular W (the $U(6)_W$ spin). R_q and $R_{\bar{q}}$ denote respectively the sets (λ, S, m, α) for d_q and $d_{\bar{q}}$ and α, γ are any additional quantum numbers necessary to the removal of degeneracy between several equivalent (λ, S) or (λ, W). within an SU(6) representation. The Clebsch-Gordan coefficients of SU(6) have been computed and tabulated by Carter Coyne and Meshkov[51] for the products **35** × **35**, **35** × **56**, **56** × **56***.

Considering that β is isomorphic to parity, many of the W-spin selection rules are identical with the requirements imposed by spin × parity. Lipkin and Meshkov[52] have clarified this geometrical connection; the reflection operators for the y-z and z-x planes are

$$R_x = Pe^{i\pi j_x} = \text{for one q } P^{\text{intrinsic}}\, e^{i\pi\sigma_x}$$

$$= 2i\, P^{\text{int}}\, \sigma_x = 2iW_x$$

$$R_y = 2iW_y$$

$$W_{x,y} = P^{\text{int}}\, \sigma_{x,y}$$

Horn[53] has used R_x for a system of $qq\ldots\bar{q}\bar{q}\ldots$

$$R_{x,y} = \exp(i\pi W_{x,y}) \qquad (8.55)$$

which shows that $R_{x,y}$ is less restrictive, since it allows

$$\Delta W_{x,y} \cong 0(\text{mod } 2) \qquad (8.56)$$

He has thus separated selection rules which really derive only from W-spin from those which are imposed anyhow by Lorentz invariance and parity.

The trivial selection rules for 3 particle vertices forbid PPP (three W = 1 objects) and V^0V^0P ($1 \nrightarrow 0 + 0$ in W), where P is a 0^- meson and V^0 is the $j_z = 0$ component of a 1^- meson; note that W-S flip then implies that $U(6)_\sigma$ forbids $V^0V^0V^0$ and PPV^0 respectively (this is the $\rho \nrightarrow 2\pi$). We thus see that $\rho \rightarrow 2\pi$ is now allowed etc.

The real restriction of W-spin occurs in the $\overline{B}{}^*BV^0$ vertex which is forbidden (B is a $j = \frac{1}{2}^+$ baryon, B^* has $j = \frac{3}{2}^+$). This is the flip-transform of $\Delta \nrightarrow N + \pi$ in $U(6)_\sigma$. Using W-spin for $\Delta(1238)$ photoproduction, Harari and Lipkin thus predict pure M1 transitions[54] which is confirmed by experiment. On the other hand, it is this W-spin restriction which is apparently responsible for the complete disagreement encountered in scattering predictions of $U(6)_W$ of the type

$$\sigma(K^+p \rightarrow K^*p) = \tfrac{2}{3}\sigma(K^+p \rightarrow K^{*0}\Delta^{++})$$

$$\sigma(K^-p \rightarrow \overline{K^0}n) = \tfrac{3}{16}\sigma(K^-p \rightarrow K^{*-}p) \text{ etc.}$$

$$\sigma(K^-p \rightarrow \pi^+Y_1^{*-}) = 4\sigma(K^-p \rightarrow \pi^-Y_1^{*+}) \text{ etc.}$$

or that $K^+p \rightarrow K^*p$ and $K^+p \rightarrow K^*\Delta$ should produce unpolarized resonances.

We know from our discussion of saturation[20] that we should not expect scattering amplitudes to display $U(6)_W$ symmetry, as had been first suggested.[22,47,49] However, Jackson's[55] comparison with experiment throws much light on the mechanism involved. Take the Y^* production equality; it is well established that such resonance production occurs peripherally, via the exchange of a 1^- meson, in a low energy analysis. However, this can only be true of the right hand side, where a $\overline{K}{}^*$ is exchanged, whereas only baryon exchange or some more complicated process can yield the left hand side where $|\Delta Q| = 2$ for the baryon. $U(6)_W$ invariant vertices do not allow the $\overline{K}{}^*$ exchange on the right hand side and then predict this suppression by a factor 4 relatively to the left hand side; now a peripheral process is indeed a beautiful example of the intermediate states not being collinear: the two incoming one-particle states have yielded a 3-particle intermediate state which obviously cannot be collinear. We thus see that we cannot use $U(6)_W$ for the off-mass shell vertices making up our amplitude; but $U(6)_W$, together with pole-dominance of the vector currents by vector mesons will still ensure that an on-mass shell collinear $B^* \to B + V$ won't occur.

An example where the dynamics seem to favor collinearity in the intermediate states is the $\pi + N \to \pi + \Delta$ near threshold, studied by Olsson.[56] This is a predominantly S-state production, with no important peripheral contributions; indeed the $(A_{1/2}/A_{3/2})$ ratio of the two I-spin amplitudes in $\pi + N \to \pi + \Delta$ is predicted by $U(6)_W$ to be $\sqrt{10}$, and the observed value is 3.4 ± 0.3. Note that N and Δ exchange give $\sqrt{\frac{8}{5}}$, ρ-exchange $-\sqrt{\frac{2}{3}}$.

Another situation where $U(6)_W$ should be expected to hold is the two-particle on-mass shell decay of higher resonances. Horn and collaborators[57] have noticed that resonances belonging to higher U(3) representations have both production and decay blocks. An $I = j = 2$ boson belonging to **27**$^+$ in d_σ = **405**$^+$ cannot be produced peripherally by 0^- or 1^- exchange, from Lorentz invariance; at the same time it could not decay into PP or VP because of $U(6)_W$. It would have to be produced in more complicated reactions such as $p\bar{p}$ annihilation and would decay into VV, PPP etc. To show this, they use Z-spin, a subgroup of $U(6)_W$ with the generators

$$Z_Z = W_Z = G(\sigma_Z \lambda_0)$$

$$Z_{x,y} = G(\beta\sigma_{x,y}(\lambda^0\sqrt{6} + 2\lambda^8/\sqrt{3})) = (\tfrac{1}{3} + 2Y)W_{x,y} \tag{8.57}$$

which invert the $W_{x,y}$ phases for the third quarks s. Thus for any system containing u, d, and s^+ only, **Z**-spin is just σ; the $Y = 2$ states in **405, 700, 1134** are bound to have this decomposition, and are therefore forced to conserve σ in two body decays, i.e., they have only s-wave decays. This then has to hold by U(3) invariance for the entire U(3) multiplet. Similarly, $j = \frac{5}{2}^-$ baryon resonances in **10***, **27**, **35** of U(3), in $U_\sigma(6)$ **700**$^-$ or 1134$^-$ are not allowed to decay into B(**8**, $\frac{1}{2}^+$) + P(**8**, 0^-) or B + V(**8**, 1^-) or B* (**10**, $\frac{3}{2}^+$) + P(**8**, 0^-). Again, $j = \frac{3}{2}^-$ resonances in **10***, **27**, **35** of **700** and **1134** are not allowed to decay into B(**8**, $\frac{1}{2}^+$) + P(**8**, 0^-).

These results make the experimental proof of the existence of the larger SU(3) and SU(6) multiplets very hard to come by. We shall have to remember this point in our discussion of spectrum generating algebras SGA. There is one more important case in which $U(6)_W$ predictions for scattering amplitudes seem to hold—these are the Johnson-Treiman relations[58] for forward scattering and total cross sections, derived first in $U(6)_\sigma$ but then shown to hold for $U(6)_W$. However their validation seems to be connected with a definite dynamical situation which we shall discuss in the next chapter.

Before the clarification of the conceptual problem relating to the intermediate states in $U(6)_W$, it was thought that one could further use the generators contained in the intersection of two orthogonal $U(6)_W$ systems—say those relating to motion in the z and x directions—and impose[22] a U(3) × U(3) hybrid ASA on coplanar processes; the generators in this case would be $G(\lambda^a)$ and $G(\beta\sigma_y\lambda^a)$. However, such processes are scattering amplitudes which are not expected to saturate with one particle states (or with two one-particle states here) and are thus not guaranteed to have purely coplanar intermediate states. Indeed the evidence of nucleon-nucleon scattering[59] seems to invalidate any hopes of such a symmetry holding true. It had also been noted[43, 60] that $U(6)_W$ and $U(6)_\sigma$ share a common subgroup U(3) × U(3) with generators $G(\lambda^a)$ and $G(\sigma_z\lambda^a)$. This is then a smaller and less restrictive collinear group which at the same time also commutes with the (**35**, **35**) piece of the Hamiltonian which separates $\eta(960, 0^-)$ from the meson **35**⁻. It turns out that this subgroup contains most of the restrictions imposed by U(6); indeed we have seen in equation (8.10) that $G((1 \pm \sigma_z)\lambda^a) \sim G((1 \pm \gamma_5)\lambda^a)$, and that the (**3**, **6**) and (**6**, **3**) behavior of the $(\mathbf{8}, \frac{1}{2}^+)$ states fixes the D/F ratios, μ_p/μ_n and G_A/G_V. The conclusion is that one can really use the $G((1 \pm \sigma_z)\lambda^a)$ for most $U(6)_W$ results; but this has no influence whatsoever on the failure of scattering predictions, which are generally implied by the smaller group too (except indeed for the coplanar group, which now reduces to U(3) itself).

It is clearly the intermediate states' noncollinearity which is involved.

The most useful results of $U(6)_W$ consist in fixing the electromagnetic form factors. It is clear from our calculation (8.9) of the $(\mu_p/\mu_n) = -\frac{3}{2}$ ratio that we used only $G(\sigma_z\lambda^a)$, i.e., it will hold in the $U(6)_W$ vertex; moreover[48] this is a prediction for the form-factor at any q^2, so that

$$\frac{G_M^p(q^2)}{G_M^n(q^2)} = -\frac{3}{2} \tag{8.58}$$

Similarly, we get for the electric $G_E(q^2)$ form factors the pure F universal charge-coupling implied by **35** (which appears only once in $\mathbf{56} \times \mathbf{56}^*$), and thereby get the prediction

$$G_E^n(q^2) = 0 \tag{8.59}$$

which is also extremely well verified experimentally. If we now use pole-dominance, we also note that although the $g(\gamma_5\sigma\lambda^a)$ and $g(i\gamma_5\lambda^a)$ behave like $(\mathbf{6}, \mathbf{6}^*) + (\mathbf{6}^*, \mathbf{6})$ only their $(\mathbf{6}, \mathbf{6}^*)$ pieces are effective. This is sufficient in itself to impose a relation between G_M and G_E, reducing at $q^2 = 0$ to

$$\mu_p = \frac{2m_N}{m_V} \sim \frac{2 \times 940}{750} = 2.57 \tag{8.60}$$

where the matrix elements are evaluated through the Gell-Mann, Sharp and Wagner method[61] which we reviewed in Chapter V. On the other hand, $G_E(4m_N^2)$ and $G_M(4m_N^2)$ can be considered as a $\gamma p\bar{p}$ coupling at rest, thus involving $W(6)_\beta$; β-conservation then requires both form factors to vanish at that time-like value of the momentum-transfer squared. The experimental situation in that region is not conclusive, although it seems one indeed does not encounter $p + \bar{p} \to e^- + e^+$ for instance.

Khanna and Okubo[62] have shown that (8.9), (8.58), (8.59) can be derived as sum rules from commutators of various components of the $SU(6)_W$ algebra; this seems not to require the ASA assumption directly, but since only states within the **56** are used to saturate the commutators, it is in fact equivalent to it. From the commutator between nucleons with $\mathbf{p}(0, 0, p)$

$$\langle N | [G(\beta\sigma_i \lambda^a; t), g(\beta\sigma_j \lambda^b; x)]_{t=x^0} | N \rangle$$

which involves $g(\sigma_z \lambda^c)$ via $d^{ab}{}_c$ when $i = x$, $j = y$ or $g(\lambda^c)$ through $f^{ab}{}_c$ if $i = j = x$ or y, and inserting only states in $\mathbf{8}_{\frac{1}{2}}^+$ and $\mathbf{10}_{\frac{3}{2}}^+$, i.e., $\mathbf{56}^+$, one finds (8.59) or

$$G_E^{(d)}(q^2) = 0 \tag{8.59'}$$

and (G_P is the induced pseudoscalar term in the weak axial vector transition)

$$\frac{G^{(d)}(q^2)}{G^{(f)}(q^2)} = \frac{3}{2} \qquad G = G_A(q^2) - \frac{q^2}{2m_N} G_P(q^2) \tag{8.61}$$

and the (7.18) result

$$\frac{G_A(0)}{G_V(0)} = -\frac{5}{3}$$

When now taking in addition

$$[G(\sigma_z \lambda^a;\ t),\ g(\gamma_5(\sigma_x + i\sigma_y)\lambda^b;\ x)]$$

leading to $g(\gamma_5(\sigma_x + i\sigma_y)\lambda^c;\ x)$ via $d^{ab}{}_c$, one gets

$$\frac{G_M^{(d)}(q^2)}{G_M^{(f)}(q^2)} = -\frac{3}{2} \qquad (8.62)$$

which yields (8.58).

We do not discuss here the weak interactions, as $U(6)_W$ is in fact more restrictive then the current-commutator calculations of Chapter VII, and yields similar results with less insight.

INTERNAL L

Gell-Mann[63] has shown that using $G(\sigma\lambda^0)$ as an ASA automatically involves one further notion, a quasi-orbital internal angular momentum **L**. This is because conservation of angular momentum **J** and quasi-conservation of **S**, the $G(\sigma\lambda^0)$ algebra, fixes

$$\mathbf{L} = \mathbf{J} - \mathbf{S} \qquad (8.63)$$

since

$$[J_i,\ J_j] = i\epsilon_{ijk} J_k,\ [S_i,\ S_j] = i\epsilon_{ijk} S_k$$
$$[J_i,\ S_j] = i\epsilon_{ijk} S_k \qquad (8.64)$$

In a quark model, this L is indeed the orbital angular momentum of the quarks in a given hadron, but the above definition is more general. Of course, in collinear motion, only L_z is conserved.

The lowest lying baryons and mesons have L = 0 (we would otherwise loose the $\frac{3}{2}$ ratio etc). However, higher spins may involve **56, 70, 20, 700,** or **1134** for baryons, and **1, 35, 189, 405** for mesons with L = 0, 1, 2 etc. Gell-mann also conjectured that the supposed Regge-recurrences may represent sequences with $(\Delta L) = 2$. We shall review these aspects in our discussion of SGA.

Our former discussion with respect to spurions (or $\mathcal{H}_k$) in $U(6)_\sigma$ now has to include the L quantum number. We note that contributions to the mass can only come from 2nd order terms in $\mathcal{H}_k$, since $L(\mathcal{H}_k) = 1$ as can be noticed from the explicit expression in (8.50); indeed they will transform like **189** and **405** which are the only representations in **35** × **35** containing a unitary singlet with S = 0. One notes[64] indeed that the **189** and **405** tensors do account for the unitary singlet contribution to the breaking of $U(6)_\sigma$ representations into $SU(2)_\sigma \times U(3)$ submultiplets.

SATURATION AT INFINITE MOMENTUM

We have seen in (7.17), (7.18), (7.51) and (7.51′) how on the one hand the (**6**, **3**) and (**3**, **6**) assignment (or **56** in $U(6)_\sigma$, as shown in (8.9), (8.12) and (8.12′) predict

$$\frac{G_A}{G_V} = -\frac{5}{3} \qquad \left(\frac{D}{F}\right)_{\overline{B}B\phi} = \frac{3}{2} \text{ etc.}$$

and on the other hand, the experimental values are reproduced exactly by such sum rules as the Adler-Weisberger (7.51′) or the Cabibbo-Radicati one (7.72) which contain contributions from states beyond the (**8**, $\frac{1}{2}^+$) and (**10**, $\frac{3}{2}^+$). Indeed, had there been only (**10**, $\frac{3}{2}^+$) contributions in the integral over cross sections in the Adler-Weisberger sum rule (7.40), we would have

$$\left(\frac{G_A}{G_V}\right)^2 = 2$$

as the integral is then ~1; the higher states diminish $(G_A/G_V)^2$ by about 0.5. In the Cabibbo-Radicati (7.72) sum rule, the $(\mathbf{10}, \frac{3}{2}^+)$ contributes with a wrong sign altogether, but this is again corrected by the higher states.

Gell-Mann[65, 66] suggested a study of the representation structure at $\mathbf{p} \to \infty$, since all these sum rules were calculated by sandwiching the commutators between hadrons with infinite momentum. If the $G(\gamma_5\lambda^i)$ lead from the proton positive helicity state to some higher resonances, then this state at $\mathbf{p} \to \infty$ must already be a mixture of $(\mathbf{6}, \bar{\mathbf{3}})$ and some other representation whose other components consist in these higher resonances. Saturation by a few such states then means representing the low lying baryons by a reducible representation space of $U(3) \times U(3)_{\gamma_5}$ or of a larger $[W(3) \times W(3)]_{\gamma_5 \alpha_z}$. The latter is a subgroup of the chiral $[U(6) \times U(6)]_{\gamma_5}$ which commutes with α_z just as $U(6)_W$ is the corresponding subgroup in $[U(6) \times U(6)]_\beta$. This is then again an appropriate algebra for collinear motion (we take $p_z \to \infty$) in the z-direction; its generators are

$$G(\lambda^a),\ G(\gamma_5\lambda^a),\ G(\sigma^z\lambda^a),\ G(\gamma_5\sigma^z\lambda^a)$$

We can even discuss a larger algebra by dropping the requirement of commutation with γ_5, which was only introduced in order to reproduce the physical fact that only chiral currents have been observed to date. Taking the subalgebra of U(12) which commutes with α_z only, we find a $[U(6) \times U(6)]_{\alpha_z}$ consisting of the above and

$$G(\beta\sigma^x\lambda^a),\ G(\beta\sigma^y\lambda^a),\ G(i\beta\gamma_5\sigma^x\lambda^a),\ G(i\beta\gamma_5\sigma^y\lambda^a)$$

We now have to account for one more fact. We saw in

(8.10) that $G(\sigma^z \lambda^a)$ and $G(\gamma_5 \lambda^a)$ have their matrix elements connected with each other by a Lorentz transformation; the same is true for all pairs which differ by a factor α_z, the algebraic representative here of that Lorentz transformation. Indeed the above $[U(6) \times U(6)]_{\alpha_z}$ thus has to be dedoubled. This can be achieved in several ways, e.g., by imposing commutation with β, which yields $U(6)_W$; or if we have to identify our matrix elements with $G(\gamma_5 \lambda^a)$ rather than $G(\sigma^z \lambda^a)$, we can impose commutation with α_x (or α_y of course). Note that reaching from the chiral direction β has no particular importance since we either have a model with no mass term for fundamental fermion fields (chiral symmetry) or have the kinetic energy become very large ($p_z \to \infty$) which reduces again to the possibility of neglecting the mass term.

The chiral transform of $U(6)_W$ is thus $U(6)_{\alpha_z \alpha_x}$ which consists in,

$$G(\lambda^a),\ G(\gamma_5 \lambda^a),\ G(\beta\sigma^y \lambda^a),\ G(i\beta\gamma_5 \sigma^y \lambda^a)$$

and its essential subalgebra is $W(3)_{\gamma_5, \alpha_z, \alpha_x}$ which is our old $U(3) \times U(3)_\chi$.

A number of authors[67-70] have dealt with the problem of pinpointing the $W(3)_{\gamma_5 \alpha_z \alpha_x}$ and $U(6)_{\alpha_z \alpha_x}$ exact assignments for the low lying baryons. It should be noted that working at $\mathbf{p} \to \infty$ also implies that without mixing we would have vanishing anomalous magnetic moments.[66] The anomalous moment in the x-y plane connects two states with opposite momenta in that plane; to achieve this inversion it must have $\Delta L_z = 1$ and therefore has no matrix elements between two states of the 56 with $L_z = 0$ for instance.

By mixing $[(\mathbf{6}, \mathbf{3})\ L_z = 0]$ with $[(\mathbf{3}^*, \mathbf{3})\ L_z = 0]$ and $[(\mathbf{3}, \mathbf{3}^*)\ L_z = 1]$ to describe the positive helicity $j_z = \frac{1}{2}$ state of the nucleon, i.e., an admixture with **8** and **1** resonances, probably with odd parity and $j = \frac{1}{2}^-, \frac{3}{2}^-$, Harari was able to fit the entire data (5 numbers) with 2 parameters; in fact, with just one parameter, an angle $\eta \sim 37^0$ in

$$|N, j_z = \tfrac{1}{2}\rangle = \cos\eta\,|(\mathbf{6}, \mathbf{3}), L_z = 0\rangle$$
$$+ \sin\theta\{(\tfrac{1}{3})^{1/2}|(\mathbf{3}^*, \mathbf{3})\, L_z = 0\rangle$$
$$- (\tfrac{2}{3})^{1/2}|(\mathbf{3}, \mathbf{3}^*)\, L_z = 1\rangle\} \tag{8.65}$$

((3, 3*) has $w^z = \sigma^z = -\frac{1}{2}$) he gets $G_A = 1.18$, G* (the axial vector N-Δ transition, experimentally ~1) 1.05, $\alpha = 0.65$ (experimentally ~0.67; this is a "D/F" parameter defined so that $D/F = \alpha/1 - \alpha$), and $\mu(N\text{-}\Delta)/\mu_A(n) = -\sqrt{2}/\cos\theta$, $\mu(N - \Delta) \sim 3.4$ nucleon magnetons (the experimental estimate is 3.36 ± 0.05). For the magnetic moments ratio he then has, with k undetermined

$$\mu_A(p)/\mu_A(n) = -1 + k\tan\theta \tag{8.66}$$

so that picking $k = -1$ he gets $\mu_A(p) = -\mu_A(n)$.

In $U(6)_{\alpha_z\alpha_x}$ the mixture (8.65) can best be fitted in **70**, $L_z = 1$; if fitted into two representations instead, with the choice such that they cannot be connected by **35**, $k = 0$ automatically.

LOCAL CURRENT ALGEBRA AT INFINITE MOMENTUM

We saw in (7.78) and (7.79) the practical advantages of working with the algebra of Fourier-transforms of the current densities. At $\mathbf{p} \to \infty$, the matrix elements of $v^{0a}(x)$ or $a^{0a}(x)$ between a state with $p_z = \infty$ and transverse momentum $\mathbf{p}_T$ and another state with $p_z = \infty$, $\mathbf{p}'_T$ have no $(\mathbf{p}_T + \mathbf{p}'_T)$ dependence.[71,72] This means that these Fourier transforms behave somewhat like generators, and one can construct a matrix representation in which all states are labelled by I (the internal quantum number) and h (the helicity), with $v^{0a}(\mathbf{k})$ and $a^{0a}(\mathbf{k})$ absorbing the momentum transfer. Considering that working at $\mathbf{p} \to \infty$ also rids us from the isolated pairs we discussed in the beginning of this chapter, the algebraic structure holds much promise. One also has the advantage of having $q^2 = 0$ for the G^{ia} (or fixed $t = -q^2$ in (7.78)) instead of $q^2 = m_A^2 - m_j^2$, where A is the initial or final state and j is the intermediate state. This allows PCAC and improves convergence properties[73]; otherwise, whenever we hit a point in the continuum of intermediate states where $m_j^2 = m_A^2 + m_R^2$, R – some resonance of the form factors, we get a strong enhancement of the transition. Also, (7.37) requires fixed t.

Dashen and Gell-Mann[66,71] have initiated a program for the construction of the infinite momentum algebra representations. The problem consists in the definition of operators that will fulfill in that particular situation the roles of $U(6)_W$ or $U(6)_\sigma$ and L. They use the transformed angular-momentum operators

$$I_z = J_z, \; I_x = J_x\gamma + \Lambda_y\beta\gamma, \; I_y = J_y\gamma - \Lambda_x\beta\gamma \quad (8.67)$$

with

$$\beta = \frac{v}{c}, \; \gamma = \left(1 - \left(\frac{v}{c}\right)^2\right)^{-1/2}$$

which are considered as the operators connecting different helicity states of a single particle, up to $\beta \to 1$. The G^{ia} of $U(6)_{\alpha_z,\alpha_x}$ (or $U(6)_W$) and $W(3)_{\gamma_5\alpha_z\alpha_x}$ (or $W(3)_{\gamma_5\alpha_z\beta}$, our $G(1 \pm \sigma^z\lambda^a)$ collinear subgroup) can be checked for their $|\Delta \mathbf{I}|$ properties; the $|\Delta I_z|$ is simply $|\Delta\sigma_z|$ or $|\Delta W_z|$. For the states in a representation,

$$I_z = \tfrac{1}{2}G(\sigma_z) + L_z \quad (8.68)$$

which is now generalized so that for a quark one would have,

$$\mathbf{I} = \frac{\Sigma}{2} + \mathbf{R} \quad (8.69)$$

where $R_z = L_z$ and Σ is a transform of the $U(6)_\sigma$ spin,

$$\sigma = U\Sigma U^{-1} \tag{8.70}$$

and similarly for the entire $U(6)_\sigma$. U is a unitary transformation of Foldy-Wouthuysen type, performed on the internal variables. For example, one could have in a nonrelativistic naive model.

$$v^{oa}(\mathbf{k}_T) \sim U^{-1}\left\{\sum_n \tfrac{1}{2}\lambda^{(n)} \exp(i\mathbf{k}_T\cdot\mathbf{x}^{(n)},\right\}U \tag{8.71}$$

for n quarks, thus fulfilling the commutation relations (7.78), with

$$a^{oa}(\mathbf{k}_T) \sim U^{-1}\left\{\sum_n \tfrac{1}{2}\lambda^{(n)}\sigma_z^{(n)} \exp(i\mathbf{k}_T\cdot\mathbf{x}^{(n)}\right\}U \tag{8.71'}$$

Antiquarks have U', somewhat different from U, and U can then be chosen such that

$$x \to (1/M)(Q_x + L_y) \qquad y \to (1/M)(Q_y - L_x)$$
$$\mathbf{Q} = M\mathbf{x} - \{(\mathbf{p}\cdot\mathbf{x}), (\mathbf{p}/2M)\}, \quad \mathbf{L} = \mathbf{x}\wedge\mathbf{p} \tag{8.72}$$

$\mathbf{Q}$ and $\mathbf{L}$ then generate SL(2, C), so that we then have infinite-dimensional representations resembling the systematics of Regge recurrences which we discuss in the last chapters. A physical calculation of the exact $v^{oa}(\mathbf{k}_\perp)$, $a^{oa}(\mathbf{k}_\perp)$ angular momentum properties,[71] using (k_T is taken in the x-direction here)

$$\langle I', h' \,|\, v^{oa}(\mathbf{k}_\perp) \,|\, I, h\rangle$$
$$= \left\langle I', h', \mathbf{p}\left(\frac{k}{2}, 0, \infty\right) \,|\, v^{oa}(0) \,|\, I, h, \mathbf{p}\left(-\frac{k}{2}, 0, \infty\right)\right\rangle \tag{8.73}$$

and transforming into the Breit frame, yields matrix

elements which can be expressed in terms of multipole form factors. The result is that the coefficient of $(k)^\ell$ contains $1 \leq |\Delta I| \leq \ell + 1$ for odd ℓ, and only even $|\Delta I| \leq \ell$ for even ℓ. For a conserved current, $I = I'$, $h = h'$ and $|\Delta I| \leq \ell$. For $a^{0a}(\mathbf{k}_T)$, the matrix element is odd under $P \exp(i\pi I_y)$, and the coefficient of k^ℓ has $1 \leq |\Delta I| \leq \ell + 1$ with $|\Delta I|$ odd for odd ℓ.

This program seems to be crystallizing these days, and may play an important part in the further application of the current algebras. It is interesting that it may yield a spectrum with a strong resemblance to a non-relativistic quark model[45]; in fact (8.72) would yield it, "apart from the interpretation, the irrelevance of the existence of real quarks, and the crucial operator U."[71]

REFERENCES

1. F. Gürsey and L. A. Radicati, *Phys. Rev. Letters* **13**, 173 (1964).
2. B. Sakita, *Phys. Rev.* **136**, B1756 (1964).
3. G. Zweig, *Proc. of the 1964 Intern. School of Physics "Ettore Majorana,"* Academic Press, New York, 1965.
4. O. W. Greenberg, *Phys. Letters* **13**, 598 (1964).
5. A. Pais, *Phys. Rev. Letters* **13**, 175 (1964).
6. J. C. Carter, J. J. Coyne, and S. Meshkov, *Phys. Rev. Letters* **14**, 523 and 850 (E) (1965).
7. Y. Dothan, M. Gell-Mann, and Y. Ne'eman, *Phys. Letters* **17**, 148 (1965).
8. J. J. Coyne, S. Meshkov, and G. B. Yodh, to be published.
9. R. W. Griffith, *Phys. Rev.* **139**, B667 (1965).
10. S. Meshkov, *Third Coral Gables Conf. (1966) on Symmetry at High Energy*, p. 150.
11. J. Schwinger, *Phys. Rev.* **135**, B816 (1964).
12. H. Harari and H. J. Lipkin, *Phys. Rev. Letters* 14, 570 and 850 (E) (1965).
13. R. H. Capps, *Phys. Rev. Letters* **14**, 31 (1965); J. G. Belinfante and R. E. Cutkosky, *Phys. Rev. Letters* **14**, 33 (1965).

14. Y. Ne'eman, in *High Energy Physics* (Tokyo Seminar 1965), Syokabo and Benjamin, Inc., pub., 1966, p. 68.
15. M. A. Beg, B. W. Lee, and A. Pais, *Phys. Rev. Letters* **13**, 514 (1964).
16. B. Sakita, *Phys. Rev. Letters* **13**, 643 (1964).
17. N. Cabibbo and L. A. Radicati, *Phys. Letters* **19**, 697 (1966).
18. E. P. Wigner, *Phys. Rev.* **51**, 106 (1937).
19. For survey of various attempts at "relativistic SU(6)" see the summary lectures of the 1965 and 1966 Coral Gables Conferences; see also Y. Ne'eman, "Algebraic Methods and their Observational Implications," in "Strong Interactions," M. Moravcsik, ed., Gordon and Breach, New York, 1966.
20. S. Coleman, "Comptes Rendus du Colloque du CNRS sur l'Extension du Groupe de Poincaré aux Symmetries Internes des Particules Elementaires," Paris, to be published.
21. S. L. Adler, *Phys. Rev. Letters* **14**, 1051 (1965); W. I. Weisberger, *Phys. Rev. Letters* **14**, 1047 (1965).
22. R. F. Dashen and M. Gell-Mann, *Phys. Letters* **17**, 142 (1965).
23. Y. Ne'eman, *Commun. Math. Phys.* **3**, 181 (1966).
24. L. Michel, *Second Coral Gables Conf. (1965) on Symmetry at High Energy*, W. H. Freeman, pub., San Francisco, 1966, p. 331.
25. L. O'Raifeartaigh, *Phys. Rev.* **139**, B1052 (1965) and *Phys. Rev. Letters* **14**, 575 (1965). See also the stronger proof by R. Jost to be published in *Helv. Phys. Acton.*
26. C. Fronsdal, presented at the *Thirteenth Intern. Conf. on High Energy Physics*, Berkeley, 1966.
27. A. Salam, R. Delburgo, and J. Strathdee, *Proc. Roy. Soc. (London)* A284, 146 (1965).
28. M. A. B. Beg and A. Pais, *Phys. Rev. Letters* **14**, 267 (1965).
29. B. Sakita and K. C. Wali, *Phys. Rev.* **139** B1355 (1965).
30. M. A. B. Beg and A. Pais, *Phys. Rev. Letters* **14**, 509 and 577 (1965).

31. R. P. Feynman, M. Gell-Mann, and G. Zweig, *Phys. Rev. Letters* **13**, 678 (1964).
32. J. Schwinger, *Phys. Rev. Letters* 3, 296 (1959) and *Phys. Rev.* **130**, 406 (1963).
33. J. D. Björken, *Phys. Rev.* **148**, 1467 (1966).
34. S. Adler, *Phys. Rev.* **143**, 1144 (1966).
35. S. Okubo, *Nuovo Cimento* **44**, 276 (1966).
36. S. Adler, *Phys. Rev.* **140**, B736 (1965).
37. S. Okubo, *Ann. Phys.* **38**, 377 (1966) and *Phys. Letters* **20**, 195 (1966).
38. R. F. Dashen and M. Gell-Mann, *Phys. Letters* **17**, 145 (1965).
39. B. W. Lee, *Phys. Rev. Letters* **14**, 676 (1965).
40. A. Bietti, *Phys. Rev.* **142**, 1258 (1966).
41. S. Coleman, *Phys. Letters* **19**, 144 (1965).
42. S. Okubo, *Nuovo Cimento* **42** A, 1029 (1966).
43. Y. Ne'eman, in Ref. 19, Lecture III.
44. M. Gell-Mann, private communication.
45. For reviews of "naive" quark-model treatments, see the rapporteur reviews of R. Dalitz and L. Van Hove, *Thirteenth Intern. Conf. on High Energy Physics*, Berkeley (1966). Also, R. H. Dalitz, in *High Energy Physics* (Gordon and Breach, N.Y., 1966), p. 253
46. J. J. J. Kokkedee and L. Van Hove, *Nuovo Cimento* **42**, 711 (1966).
47. H. J. Lipkin and S. Meshkov, *Phys. Rev. Letters* **14**, 670 (1965).
48. K. J. Barnes, P. Carruthers, and F. von Hippel, *Phys. Rev. Letters* **14**, 82 (1965); K. J. Barnes, *Phys. Rev. Letters* **14**, 798 (1965).
49. H. J. Lipkin in *High Energy Physics and Elementary Particles (1965 Trieste Seminar)*, IAEA Vienna (1966) p. 549, is a good review of the various aspects of $U(6)_W$.
50. H. Harari, D. Horn, M. Kugler, H. J. Lipkin, and S. M Meshkov, *Phys. Rev.* **146**, 1052 (1966).
51. J. Carter, J. Coyne, and S. Meshkov, *Phys. Rev. Letters* **14**, 523 (1965).
52. H. J. Lipkin and S. Meshkov, *Phys. Rev.* **143**, 1269 (1966).
53. D. Horn, *Phys. Rev.*, **150**, 1218 (1966).

54. H. Harari and H. J. Lipkin, *Physics* **140**, B1617 (1965).
55. J. D. Jackson, *Phys. Rev. Letters* **15**, 990 (1965).
56. M. G. Olsson, *Phys. Rev. Letters* **15**, 710 (1965).
57. D. Horn, H. J. Lipkin, and S. Meshkov, *Phys. Rev. Letters* **17**, 1200 (1966).
58. K. Johnson and S. B. Treiman, *Phys. Rev. Letters* **14**, 189 (1966).
59. P. B. Kantor, T. K. Kuo, R. F. Peierls, and T. L. Trueman, *Phys. Rev.* **140**, B1008 (1965). The situation has been recently reviewed by M. Moravcsik (preprint).
60. F. Buccella and R. Gatto, *Nuovo Cimento* **40**, 684 (1965).
61. M. Gell-Mann, D. H. Sharp and W. Wagner, *Phys. Rev. Letters* **8**, 261 (1962).
62. M. P. Khanna and S. Okubo, *Nuovo Cimento* **44**, 229 (1966).
63. M. Gell-Mann, *Phys. Rev. Letters* **14**, 77 (1965).
64. M. A. B. Beg and V. Singh, *Phys. Rev. Letters* **13**, 418 (1964).
65. M. Gell-Mann, *Proc. of the Oxford (1965) Conf. on High Energy Physics*.
66. R. F. Dashen and M. Gell-Mann, *Third Coral Gables Conf. (1966) on Symmetry at High Energy*, p. 168.
67. H. Harari, *Phys. Rev. Letters* 16, 964 (1966) and **17**, 56 (1966).
68. R. Gatto, L. Maiani and G. Preparata, *Phys. Rev. Letters* **16**, 377 (1966); *Phys. Letters* **21**, 459 (1966); same authors and G. Altarelli, *Phys. Rev. Letters* **16**, 918 (1966).
69. I. S. Gerstein and B. W. Lee, *Phys. Rev. Letters* **16**, 1060 (1966).
70. D. Horn, *Phys. Rev. Letters* **17**, 778 (1966).
71. R. E. Dashen and M. Gell-Mann, *Phys. Rev. Letters* **17**, 340 (1966).
72. K. J. Barnes and E. Kazes, *Phys. Rev. Letters* **17**, 978 (1966).
73. R. F. Dashen and S. C. Frautschi, *Phys. Rev.* **145**, 1287 (1966).

9

AN ALGEBRA OF FACTORIZED REGGE RESIDUES

THE ALGEBRAIC POSTULATE

In this chapter we present a recent approach[1,2] based upon the identification of an algebra of scalar and vector currents in the structure of the residue functions associated with Regge trajectories, somewhat in analogy to the way in which the weak and electromagnetic transitions of the hadrons define the system of vector and axial-vector currents. Applying the theory directly to high-energy scattering, we find we can predict some hitherto unexplained features. In so doing, we also produce a theoretical interpretation of a number of good results[3-7] whose derivation has generally been considered to imply a composite-particle structure for the hadrons.

Physical intuition based upon somewhat unrealistic models has twice before within recent years opened up new extensions of unitary symmetry; in both cases[8,9]—nonrelativistic SU(6) and too-relativistic SU(6, 6)—excellent results have been obscured at times by difficulties and dilemmas in the theoretical foundations.[10] Much clarification, a new understanding and a series of new results were each time provided by the definition of an algebraic methodology[11,12] which was gradually improved and made consistent with relativistic quantum theory.[12] Cabibbo et al.[1] ("HCN") contend that the use of a "naive" quark model—leading to a new subparticle physics with methods emulating those used in nuclear structure and the many-body problem—should be regarded in the same light as the previous suggestive break-ins.[13]

It is with this motivation in mind—an algebraic foundation for the high-energy results—that HCN make their suggestions. They deal with the simple case of forward scattering, though it is probable that the treatment can be extended to other situations. This formulation should be regarded as a first rough definition, to be further refined extensively.

The description of high-energy baryon-baryon and baryon-meson phenomena in terms of Regge trajectories has been highly[14] successful, and supplies the most appropriate framework for such a treatment. In a series of recent studies,[15] one finds a useful and consistent parametrization of the data, based upon the residue functions $\beta(t)$ and the pole trajectories $\alpha(t)$, where t is the square of the momentum transfer, and the energy dependence is explicit. The real part of the trajectory is effectively described by its intercept $\alpha(O)$ and its slope at that point.

The factorization theorem[16] allows us to replace $\beta(t)$ by a product of two vertex strength functions $\gamma_C^{AB}(t)$, which are analogous to form factors in quantum electrodynamics; γ_C^{AB} stands for example for an upper vertex where the trajectory C occurs as an intermediate state in the t channel scattering of incoming particles A and $\overline{B}$, and as an exchanged system (Regge pole) in the s channel scattering of A into B.

Actual high-energy phenomenology has achieved a general fit of known processes in terms of vertex strength functions coupled to two even intrinsic-parity trajectories with opposite signature, dominated by two meson unitary nonets with $j = 1^-$ and 2^+. Some differences exist between the workers in the field, mainly with respect to the number of 2^+ unitary singlet-dominated trajectories. We shall here adopt the view that one is faced with an octet-singlet set for each signature, including the Pomeranchuk trajectory.

Observations indicate that apart from the latter (whose intercept $\alpha_{s0}(0) \lesssim 1$, where s^i denotes an even-signature trajectory corresponding to the ith unitary index, counting from 0 to 8), all trajectories s^i and v^i (v denotes odd signature) have $\alpha(0) \sim 0.5$. Deviations from the Pomeranchuk limit $\sigma^{AB} = \sigma^{\bar{A}B}$ should thus tend to disappear with increasing energy at some general common rate for any A, B. The entire variegation in the "law of force" for different A, B seems to result from differences between residues.

We assume that the vertex strengths $\gamma_C^{AB}(0)$ in the limit of forward scattering are given by matrix elements of algebraic operators belonging to a U(12) algebra. We introduce a system of nine *strengths* S^i with scalar densities; when adjoined to a second nonet of strengths V^i with the same algebraic properties as the unitary spin generators, they close on a $U(3) \times U(3)$ sub-algebra completely isomorphic to the $[U(3) \times U(3)]_\beta$ contained in the $[U(6) \times U(6)]_\beta$ defined by Dashen and Gell-Mann.

The matrix elements of the system of S^i and V^i strengths are to be identified with the $\gamma_{s^i}^{AB}(0)$ and $\gamma_{v^i}^{AB}(0)$ respectively through the relation

$$\delta^3(\mathbf{p}_A - \mathbf{p}_B)\gamma_{s^i}^{AB}(0) = \langle A | \int \mathfrak{D}(\beta\sigma^0\lambda^i;\ \mathbf{x}, 0)\ d^3x | B \rangle \tag{9.1}$$

$$\delta^3(\mathbf{p}_A - \mathbf{p}_B)\gamma_{v^i}^{AB}(0) = \langle A | \int \mathfrak{D}(\sigma^0\lambda^i;\ \mathbf{x}, 0)\ d^3x | B \rangle \tag{9.2}$$

where the integrals are carried out in the rest frame of the incident particle. Note that it is not clear that our strengths are really to be identified with the space integrals of the currents associated directly with *weak* transitions. For instance, we may be dealing with a class of source currents of strong transitions, consistently definable in terms of the Regge formalism. The complete U(12) algebra of strengths would contain pseudoscalar and axial-vector operators (corresponding to trajectories with 0^- and 1^+ exchange). To account for spin flip we may have to use an "L" like algebra or an entire set of U(6) × U(6) generators. In the following we shall deal with elastic scattering only, thus using in fact σ^0 with i = 0, 3, 8 only. The S^i and V^i would be written in a quark representation as

$$S^i = \frac{1}{2} \int d^3x \; q\dagger \beta \lambda^i q \tag{9.3}$$

$$V^i = \frac{1}{2} \int d^3x \; q\dagger \lambda^i q \tag{9.4}$$

We note that

$$[S^i \; S^j] = if^{ij}_{\;\;k} V^k \tag{9.5}$$

$$[V^i, S^j] = if^{ij}_{\;\;k} S^k \tag{9.6}$$

The effect of β in the U(12) algebra can be thought of in terms of constituent (1, 0, 0) representations—mathematical quarks[17]—as an "additive" operation on quark and antiquark unitary charges. S^0, for example, has eigenvalues proportional to the number of "quark charges" plus "antiquark charges" (in opposition to V^0 which is proportional to baryon charge, i.e., to the number of "quark charges" minus "antiquark charges"). S^i adds up λ^i contributions of quarks plus $\lambda^{i\sim}$ contributions of antiquarks (V^i picks out the differences, since $-\lambda^{i\sim}$ is the unitary spin representation of the antiquarks). It is for the above reason that using S^i densities reproduces the results of "quark-additivity" and "quark counting" applied in composite models. As a simplest example, consider this crude derivation of the $\sigma_{\pi^+ P}/\sigma_{PP}$ ratio. Figure 9-1 shows the t channel exchange of a Pomeranchuk trajectory. Assuming this to be dominant at the highest energies, we derive for the total cross-sections the Levin-Frankfurt ratio[3]

$$\frac{\sigma_{\pi P}}{\sigma_{PP}} = \frac{\gamma^{\pi\pi}_{S^0}(0)\,\gamma^{PP}_{S^0}(0)}{\gamma^{PP}_{S^0}(0)\,\gamma^{PP}_{S^0}(0)} \cong \frac{2}{3} \tag{9.7}$$

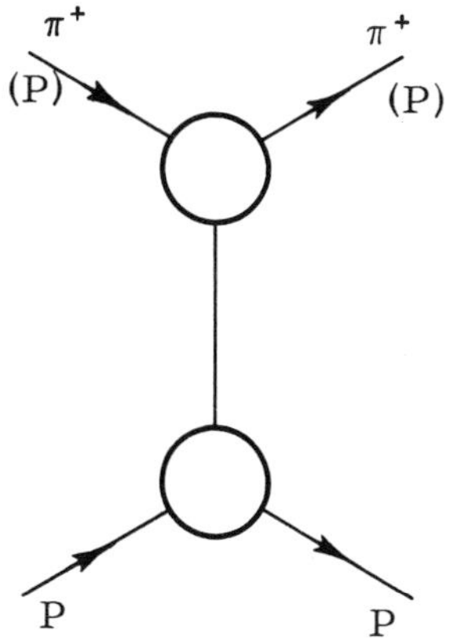

Fig. 9-1

since $\gamma_{s^0}(0)$ is, according to its definition, just the eigenvalue n_{s^0} of the generator S^0. We have used, of course, the $[U(6) \times U(6)]_\beta$ assignments of $(56, 1)^+$ and $(6, 6^*)^-$ for baryons and mesons respectively.

Similar considerations with both s^0 and s^8 contributing predict $\sigma_{\pi P} > \sigma_{KP}$ as can be seen from the table below.

Note however that we do not have to bring in the entire algebraic machinery of $[U(6) \times U(6)]_\beta$ representations, as long as we deal with non spin flip scattering. We could use a $[U(3) \times U(3)]_\beta$ notation based on the system introduced in Ref. 17 and which we used for U(3). A baryon octet is then $[(2, 1, 0), (0, 0, 0)]$, the meson octet is $[(1, 0, 0), (0, 0, -1)]$ and the antibaryons are $[(0, 0, 0), (0, -1, -2)]$ in a $[(h_1, h_2, h_3)(k_1, k_2, k_3)]$ notation, with

$$\begin{aligned} 3B = n(\lambda_0) &= \left(\sum_1^3 h_i + \sum_1^3 k_i\right) \\ n(\beta\lambda_0) &= \left(\sum_1^3 h_i - \sum_1^3 k_i\right) \end{aligned} \tag{9.8}$$

In this connection we wish to emphasize an approximation, implicit up to this point: we have hitherto defined the vertex strengths at each vertex independently taking the representations at rest. It may be that a complete theory would require treating both vertices simultaneously, and that the same classification of states in upper and lower vertices cannot be maintained as far as the S^i part of $[U(3) \times U(3)]_\beta$ goes. The possibility of an alteration in F/D ratio at one vertex should therefore be taken into account for the S^i matrix elements (this is the only allowed alteration since the V^i are conserved); we discuss this later in connection with the comparison of these ideas with experiment.

Note that the commutation relations being nonlinear fix the relative scales of γ_{si} and γ_{vi}.

We assume that the elastic scattering amplitude is given by (γ^A now stands for γ^{AA}, and the representations are taken at rest)

$$T_{AB}(\nu, t) = -\sum_{i=0,3,8} \Bigg\{ \gamma^A_{si}(t)\, \gamma^B_{si}(t)\, g(\alpha^s_i) \times \frac{1 + e^{-i\pi\alpha^s_i}}{\sin \pi\alpha^s_i} \, \frac{\tau(\alpha^s_i + \frac{3}{2})}{\tau(\alpha^s_i + 1)} \left(\frac{\nu}{\nu_{si}}\right)^{\alpha^s_i(t)} + \gamma^A_{vi}(t)\, \gamma^B_{vi}(t)\, \frac{1 - e^{-i\pi\alpha^v_i}}{\sin \pi\alpha^v_i} \times \frac{\tau(\alpha^v_i + \frac{3}{2})}{\tau(\alpha^v_i + 1)} \left(\frac{\nu}{\nu_{vi}}\right)^{\alpha^v_i(t)} \Bigg\} \tag{9.9}$$

where

$$\nu = (\text{total energy in c.m.}) + \frac{t}{2} - m^2_A - m^2_B$$

$g(\alpha^s_i)$ is a ghost-killing factor which we have to separate explicitly in order to cancel out the pole at $\alpha^s_i = 0$ if the trajectory does pass through this point. We shall assume that in the neighborhood of t = 0, $g(\alpha_i^S) \sim 1$. Since these trajectories describe the exchange of 2^+ or 1^- particles respectively, the absolute signs of their contributions are determined by the requirement that they give rise to forces between like particles which are respectively attractive and repulsive. We assume no ambiguity is introduced by the t dependence. We neglect at this stage $\omega - \phi$ mixing since we consider the case in which their trajectories are essentially degenerate. Our identification of s^0 with the Pomeranchuk trajectory requires no $s^0 - s^8$ mixing at $\alpha = 0$.

The $j = 1^-$ trajectory may couple to the 1^- particles in the usual way. As for the $j = 2^+$ mesons, they cannot couple directly to scalar quantities, but our prescription is appropriate for the coupling of their trajectory at $\alpha = 0$. The problem of coupling to Regge recurrences is not special to the scalar, but occurs also for the other trajectories.

The contribution of each trajectory to the total cross-section is equal to the product of vertex strengths defined according to Eqs. (9.1) and (9.2), a factor t_i^V or t_i^S depending upon $\alpha_i^V(0)$ or $\alpha_i^S(0)$ and the energy scales ν_V^i or ν_S^i, and a sign determined by the signature in Eq. (9.9) (negative for the vector $\alpha_V = 1^-$ pole). The basic result is given in Table 9-1, where a normalization corresponding to tr $\lambda_i^2 = 2$ is used to avoid fractional coefficients.

The coefficients of the t_i actually correspond to over-all F coupling for the vector trajectories, and for the mesons and baryons D and F coupling, respectively, to the scalar trajectories. SU(3) symmetry would imply the equality $t_3^S = t_8^S$ and $t_3^V = t_8^V$; U(3) among the vector contributions would imply $t_0^V = t_8^V$, and $[SU(3) \times SU(3)]_\beta$ excluding t_0^S, would finally imply that all but the Pomeranchuk coeffients are equal. A rest symmetry in the t channel implies degeneracy of the trajectories at $t = M^2$ which could be assumed to hold roughly at t = 0. We note that $t_3^S = t_3^V$ alone immediately implies that[7]

$$K^+ P = K^+ N \tag{9.10}$$

Table 9-1. Total Cross-Sections

$\bar{P}N =$	$6t_0^S$	$+ 3t_8^S$	$- t_3^S$	$+ 6t_0^V$	$+ 3t_8^V$	$- t_3^V$
$PN =$	$6t_0^S$	$+ 3t_8^S$	$- t_3^S$	$- 6t_0^V$	$- 3t_8^V$	$+ t_3^V$
$PP =$	$6t_0^S$	$+ 3t_8^S$	$+ t_3^S$	$- 6t_0^V$	$- 3t_8^V$	$- t_3^V$
$\bar{P}P =$	$6t_0^S$	$+ 3t_8^S$	$+ t_3^S$	$+ 6t_0^V$	$+ 3t_8^V$	$+ t_3^V$
$\pi^+ P =$	$4t_0^S$	$+ 2t_8^S$				$- 2t_3^V$
$\pi^- P =$	$4t_0^S$	$+ 2t_8^S$				$+ 2t_3^V$
$K^+ P =$	$4t_0^S$	$- t_8^S$	$+ t_3^S$		$- 3t_8^V$	$- t_3^V$
$K^- P =$	$4t_0^S$	$- t_8^S$	$+ t_3^S$		$+ 3t_8^V$	$+ t_3^V$
$K^+ N =$	$4t_0^S$	$- t_8^S$	$- t_3^S$		$- 3t_8^V$	$+ t_3^V$
$K^- N =$	$4t_0^S$	$- t_8^S$	$- t_3^S$		$+ 3t_8^V$	$- t_3^V$

This relation is well satisfied between 6 and 20 GeV/c, and may be interpreted in this theory as a close degeneracy between the s_3 and v_3 intercepts (both contributions become small, however at higher energies).

The parameter t_0^S is positive; it follows from our basic picture that all t_i^S and t_i^V are positive numbers, and we derive the following inequalities, valid without any other restriction:

$$\begin{aligned} K^- P &> K^- N \\ \pi^- P &> \pi^+ P \\ K^- P &> K^+ P \\ K^- P &> K^+ N \\ K^- P - K^- N &> |K^+ P - K^+ N| \\ K^+ P + K^- P &> K^+ N + K^- N \end{aligned} \tag{9.11}$$

The relations (9.11) are strikingly verified (see Fig. 9.12) For baryon-baryon scattering we obtain

$$\begin{aligned} \bar{P}P &> PP \\ \bar{P}P &> PN \\ \bar{P}P &> \bar{P}N \\ \bar{P}P - PP &> \bar{P}N - PN \\ \bar{P}P + PP &> \bar{P}N + PN \end{aligned} \qquad (9.12)$$

Four identities also follow since there are 10 relations and only 6 parameters:

$$\begin{aligned} K^+P - K^+N &= PP - NP && \text{(Ref. 7)} \\ K^-P - K^-N &= \bar{P}P - \bar{P}N && \text{(Ref. 7)} \\ 3(\pi^+P + \pi^-P) &= \bar{P}N + PN + PP + \bar{P}P && \text{(Ref. 4, 6)} \\ K^+P + \pi^-P + K^-N &= K^-P + \pi^+P + K^+N && \text{(Ref. 4)} \end{aligned} \qquad (9.13)$$

Following the procedure used for Table 9-1 we obtain

$$\Lambda P = 6t_0^S + 6t_0^V \qquad (9.14)$$

and therefore

$$\Lambda P - PP = K^-N - \pi^+P \quad \text{(Ref. 4)} \qquad (9.15)$$

Antisymmetric, t_i^S cancelling, relations follow from SU(3)

$$\begin{aligned} K^-P + 2\pi^+P &= K^+P + 2\pi^-P \\ K^-P + 2K^+N &= K^+P + 2K^-N \end{aligned} \qquad (9.16)$$

These are the Johnson-Treiman relations.[18] Assuming U(3) invariance, we get the Freund[5] relation,

$$\bar{P}P - PP = \tfrac{5}{4}(\bar{P}N - PN) = 5(\pi^-P - \pi^+P) \qquad (9.17)$$

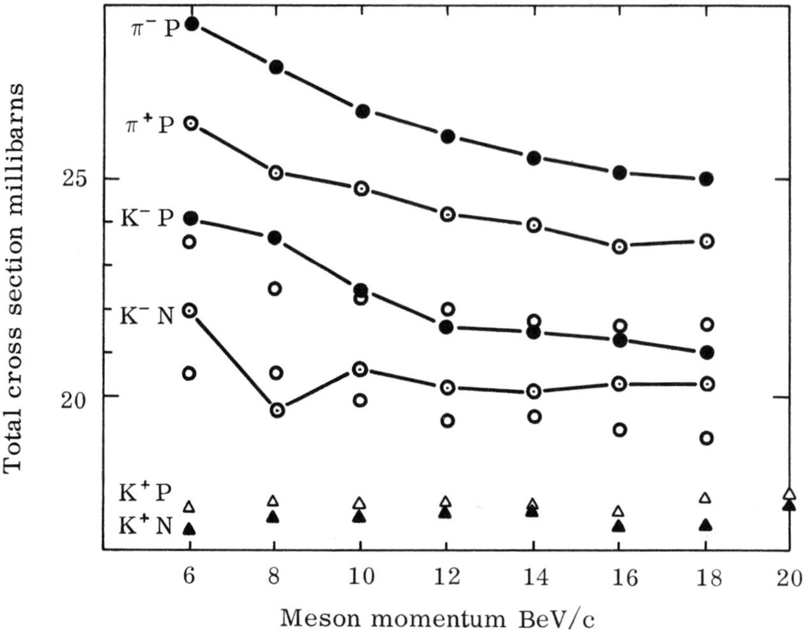

Fig. 9-2. Meson-baryon cross sections and relations (9.18), and (9.20). ○ left- and right-hand sides (halved) of Eq. (9.18) ● left- and right-hand sides of Eq. (9.20a), ⊙ left- and right-hand sides of Eq. (9.20b).

As to other "symmetric" (t_i^V cancelling) relations of Lipkin and Scheck (see Fig. 9-2)

$$PP + \overline{P}P = 2[\pi^+ P + \pi^- P] - \tfrac{1}{2}[K^+ P + K^- P]$$

$$K^+ P + K^- P = \tfrac{1}{2}[\pi^+ P + \pi^- P + K^+ N + K^- N] \qquad (9.18)$$

they require SU(3) among the scalar trajectories, which is a stronger condition and seems to be much less well satisfied.

Imposing the $[SU(2) \times SU(2)]_\beta$ relation $t_3^S = t_3^V$ [known as "exchange degeneracy"[26] and leading immediately to (9.10)] as well as SU(3) among the vector trajectories ($t_3^V = t_8^V$) we obtain

$$K^- N = \tfrac{1}{2}(K^- P + K^+ P)\ ,^7 \tag{9.19}$$

which is well satisfied. However, setting also $t_3^S = t_8^S$ [imposing SU(3) among the scalar trajectories] one obtains[7]

$$\pi^- P = K^- P \tag{9.20a}$$

$$\pi^+ P = K^- N \tag{9.20b}$$

which are again not as good. As mentioned above we should expect some mixing of the (56, 1) with other $[U(6) \times U(6)]_\beta$ states, which would generate some D coupling at the scalar trajectory nucleon vertex, affecting mainly t_8^S. Adjoining a small negative admixture of D coupling to this vertex, the experimental meson-nucleon data can be fit to within a millibarn, taking common t_i^V and t_j^S $(j \neq 0)$. Alternatively, solving for the coefficients from experiment, one notices that t_8^S is rather large as implied by D.

POSSIBLE VANISHING OF STRONG INTERACTIONS CROSS SECTION

It has thus been proposed[1] that high-energy scattering could be described in terms of two nonets of algebraic operators coupled to Regge trajectories. In this way, HCN obtained very satisfactory relations among total cross-sections, some of which had been previously obtained in the composite model, in particular the asymptotic relation (9.7). A careful investigation, however, of the energy dependence of cross-sections within this model then showed[2] that a good fit to the *entire* experimental data could not be obtained—without altering the algebraic structure—with the assumption that all total cross-sections approach non-zero asymptotic limits. Moreover, an excellent fit was then obtained (KHCN[2]) by taking the value of 0.925 ± 0.008 for the intercept of the Pomeranchuk trajectory. This implies the vanishing of all total cross-sections as

$$\sigma \sim s^{-(0.075 \pm 0.008)} \tag{9.21}$$

where s is the square of the center of mass energy.

Although this conclusion runs counter to widely held theoretical beliefs, the existing data, including cosmic ray results are not sufficient to distinguish between a constant cross-section and one which vanishes as slowly as suggested by (9.21). Cosmic ray data on proton-nucleus total cross-sections exist up to very high energy[19] indicating constant "geometric" cross-sections. G. Cocconi has pointed out that this result does not imply a constancy of the P-nucleon cross-section, which can well decrease by a factor ~ 2 at 10^6 GeV, as suggested by Eq. (9.21). The reason is that the nucleus would still behave as an essentially opaque sphere and the cross-section would remain $\approx \pi R^2$. In fact a slowly decreasing P-nucleon cross-section could even correspond, in a large energy range, to increasing P-nucleus cross-sections due to the shrinking of the diffraction peak.

This vanishing of the cross-sections has of course far reaching implications of a general nature, in particular, as far as dispersion relations and sum rules are concerned.

Furthermore, the fact that the Pomeranchuk trajectory has an intercept different from unity also implies that for all elastic amplitudes T,

$$\left(\frac{\mathrm{Re}\,T}{\mathrm{Im}\,T}\right)_{t=0} \xrightarrow[s\to\infty]{} -\tan\left[\frac{1-\alpha_0^S(0)}{2}\,\pi\right] \tag{9.22}$$

where $\alpha_0^S(0)$ is the intercept of the Pomeranchuk trajectory. For $\alpha_0^S(0) = 0.925$, this ratio becomes -0.118.

Let us rewrite the results of the preceding discussion, this time for the "averaged" total cross-sections. From Table 9.1 we have

$$S_N = 6t_0^S + 3t_8^S \tag{9.23a}$$

$$S_\pi = 4t_0^S + 2t_8^S \tag{9.23b}$$

$$S_K = 4t_0^S - t_8^S \tag{9.23c}$$

where

$$S_N = \tfrac{1}{4}(PP + PN + \overline{P}P + \overline{P}N) \qquad (9.24a)$$

$$S_\pi = \tfrac{1}{2}(\pi^+ P + \pi^- P) \qquad (9.24b)$$

$$S_K = \tfrac{1}{4}(K^+ P + K^- P + K^+ N + K^- N) \qquad (9.24c)$$

and t_0^S and t_8^S are the reduced absorptive parts for the unitary singlet and octet eighth-component even-signature trajectories. AB represents the total cross-section for scattering of hadrons A and B. If we assume t_0^S to be a constant [which corresponds to $\alpha_0^S(0) = 1$], Eqs. (9.23) would imply that S_K approaches its asymptotic limit from below, while S_N and S_π approach their limits from above. Experimentally, all cross-sections are known to be decreasing functions of the energy, so that Eqs. (9.23) would not fit the data.

In order to obtain a better result, one may introduce the following modifications:

a. As was pointed out above, an admixture of D type octet coupling in the baryon vertex strengths should be expected to occur, and is in fact necessary to achieve a fit to the data at any given energy. This in itself, however, does not supply a good fit at *all* energies if we assume constant t_0^S, since it multiplies t_8^S in both S_π and S_K by the same factor. We cannot therefore get both S_π and S_K decreasing properly with a D/F correction alone.

b. A mixing between t_0^S and t_8^S analogous to ϕ-ω mixing. This represents SU(3) breaking and introduces differences between the asymptotic σ_{KP} and $\sigma_{\pi P}$.

Using both a and b, formulae (9.23) become:

$$S_N = (\alpha\sqrt{6} + \beta\lambda\sqrt{3})^2 t_0^{S'} + (\beta\sqrt{6} - \alpha\lambda\sqrt{3})^2 t_8^{S'} \qquad (9.25a)$$

$$S_\pi = 2(\alpha\sqrt{2} + \beta)(\alpha\sqrt{2} + \beta\lambda)\, t_0^{S'} + 2(\beta\sqrt{2} - \alpha) \times (\beta\sqrt{2} - \alpha\lambda)\, t_8^{S'} \qquad (9.25b)$$

$$S_K = (2\alpha\sqrt{2} - \beta)(\alpha\sqrt{2} + \beta\lambda)\, t_0^{S'} + (2\beta\sqrt{2} + \alpha) \times (\beta\sqrt{2} + \alpha\lambda)\, t_8^{S'} \qquad (9.25c)$$

where $t_0^{S'}$, $t_8^{S'}$ are used for the mixed intercepts and λ describes the F/D mixing,

$$\lambda = (F - \tfrac{1}{3} D) \qquad (9.26)$$

(the choice results from $f_{8\,NN}/d_{8\,NN} = 3$) and α and β represent the t_0^S, t_8^S mixture, with mixing angle ϕ:

$$\alpha = \cos\phi \qquad \beta = \sin\phi \qquad (9.27)$$

Cabibbo and collaborators[2] tried to fit Eqs. (9.25) to the experimental data of Galbraith et al.[20] No acceptable fit was achieved for constant t_0^S; trying to obtain the correct decreasing behaviour for S_N, S_π and S_K destroys the fit as far as the ratio of S_π/S_K at all energies is concerned.

The only available alternative appears to consist in abandoning the idea that t_0^S represents the contribution of a single pole with intercept $\alpha_0^S(0) = 1$. One such possibility would be to adjoin to the Pomeranchuk pole an additional SU(3) singlet scalar trajectory. This has been known to give a good fit to the data,[21] but it would then imply some extension of the algebraic approach. In fact, at least one of the two singlets, or a linear combination thereof would be outside the algebra of $[U(6) \times U(6)]_\beta$. Considering that there is no natural prescription for the matrix structure of the additional operator, one would lose the asymptotic prediction of Eq. (9.7) which appears experimentally validated. Indeed, if a second even signature singlet were necessary, it would seem more natural to propose a complete doubling of the whole family of trajectories, the new family being also coupled to members of a $U(6) \times U(6)$ algebra. In this way one could preserve the prejdiction of Eq. (9.7). However, it is simpler—and seems more natural at this stage to assume a single family of trajectories.

Wishing then to remain in the framework of the algebraic U(3) × U(3) one therefore has to consider the possibility that t_0^S corresponds to a single pole with intercept $\alpha_0^S(0) < 1$; for momentum transfer t = 0, we write

$$t_0^S(\nu) = t_0^S(1)\,\nu^{\alpha_0^S(0)-1}$$
$$t_8^S(\nu) = t_8^S(1)\,\nu^{\alpha_8^S(0)-1} \qquad (9.28)$$

Substituting Eqs. (9.28) into Eqs. (9.25) one gets an excellent fit to the Galbraith et al. data, with the following parameters

$$\begin{array}{ll} t_0^S(1) = 7.43 \pm 0.56 & t_8^S(1) = 2.08 \pm 0.26 \\ \alpha_0^S(0) = 0.925 \pm 0.008 & \alpha_8^S(0) = 0.76 \pm 0.04 \\ \tan\phi = -0.066 \pm 0.048 & \lambda = 2.44 \pm 0.09 \end{array} \qquad (9.29)$$

The χ^2 for the fit is 5.8, to be compared with an expected value of 14. Note that these results remain essentially unchanged when we take $\phi = 0$.

From Eqs. (9.25) and the above values of the parameters, one finds at this stage for $s \to \infty$

$$\frac{S_N}{S_\pi} = 1.39 \qquad \frac{S_\pi}{S_K} = 0.93$$

If there were no mixing, one would obtain for S_N/S_π the value given by Eq. (9.7), and S_π/S_K would reduce to unity. Note, however, that substituting (9.29) into Eqs. (9.25), one finds $S_\pi > S_K$ up to momenta of 10^5 GeV/c, after which they cross, and the above asymptotic limit is approached at

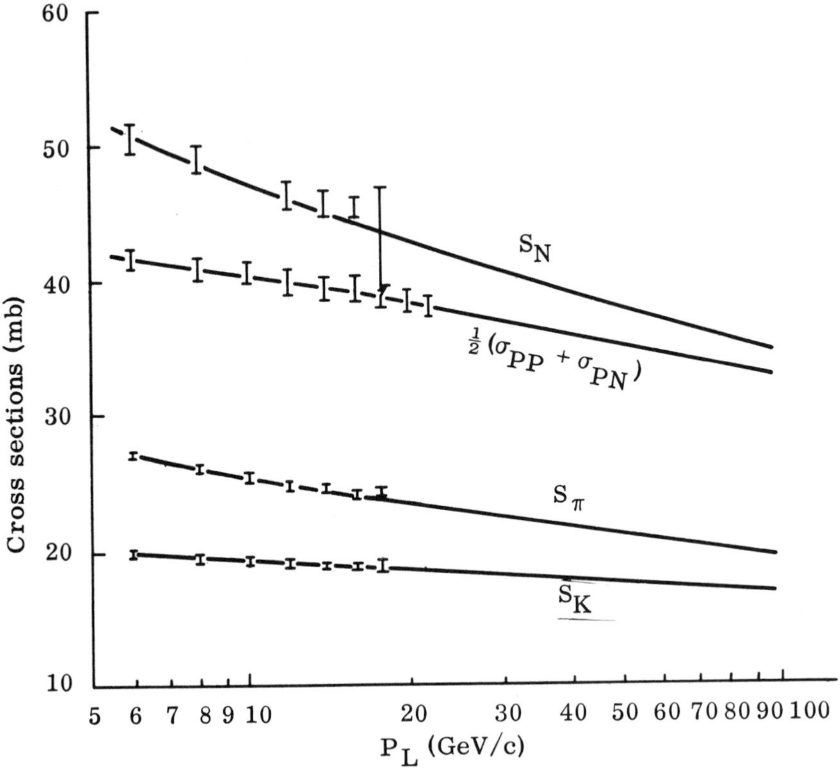

Fig. 9-3. Comparison between the data of Galbraith et al.[20] for S_N, S_π, S_K, and $\frac{1}{2}$[PP + PN] and the $KHCN^2$ fit.

extremely high energies. Note that the existence of D implies mixing with $qqqq\bar{q}$ configurations. Also, if the D contribution results from the relative motion of the two vertices, this could be ν-dependent and should be reformulated as a correction to the ν-dependent term in (9.9).

Figure 9-3 displays the comparison between the Galbraith et al.[20] data for S_N, S_π, S_K and the $KHCN^2$ fit.

We note that at high energy, the t_0^S contribution still dominates each cross-section, so that in a (log σ, log ν) plot, they approach a straight line asymptotically. A cross-section which approaches this asymptote from below may appear to be constant throughout a large energy region. This explains the behaviour of K^+–nucleon and P-nucleon cross-sections above 5 GeV/c. Moreover, all elastic amplitudes in the forward direction tend asymptotically to the form

$$T(\nu, 0) \propto -\frac{1 + e^{-i\pi\alpha_0^S(0)}}{\sin \pi\alpha_0^S(0)} \nu^{\alpha_0^S(0)} \tag{9.28}$$

so that the ratio[2] of real to imaginary part approaches the negative limit of Eq. (9.22).

The fit was extended to include individual cross-sections at all energies. This is done by using the total cross-sections of Table 9-1 with the above-mentioned modifications for the t_0^S and t_8^S. The four contributions t_3^S, t_3^V, t_0^V, t_8^V are proportional to differences of cross-sections, so that they cannot be determined accurately. For the I = 0 poles, we find

$$t_0^V(\nu) = 0.65\left(\frac{\nu}{24}\right)^{-0.65}$$

$$t_8^V(\nu) = 0.65\left(\frac{\nu}{24}\right)^{-0.56}$$

No ϕ-ω mixing was required by the data, and we also assume no D/F admixture in the vector contributions in accordance with the algebraic hypothesis. The combination $\frac{1}{2}$(PP + PN), e.g., is expressed as:

$$\tfrac{1}{2}(PP + PN) = S_N - 6\,t_0^V - 3\,t_8^V$$

This is also compared to experimental points in Figure 3, showing excellent agreement. In going to individual cross-sections, one needs also t_3^S and t_3^V. These can be determined again from meson-nucleon cross-sections. Their intercepts are found to be consistent with those determined from the analysis of $\pi^- P \to \eta N$[22] and $\pi^- P \to \pi^0 N$.[23] Using

Table 9-2
Ratio of Real to Imaginary Parts
of Elastic Amplitudes in the Forward Direction

p_L (GeV/c)	PP	$\overline{\text{P}}$P	π^+P	π^-P
8	−0.434	−0.119	−0.244	−0.125
12	−0.385	−0.133	−0.231	−0.129
14	−0.372	−0.135	−0.227	−0.129
16	−0.362	−0.140	−0.226	−0.132
18	−0.349	−0.140	−0.219	−0.130

the results to compute individual nucleon-nucleon cross-sections gives again a fair agreement—albeit a very unenlightening one, given the large experimental errors in the differences PP-PN and $\overline{\text{P}}$P-$\overline{\text{P}}$N.

Finally, using all of our numbers to compute Re T/Im T for π^+ P, π^- P, PP and $\overline{\text{P}}$P, we list a few values in Table 9-2.*

The vanishing of all total cross-sections as $\nu \to \infty$ is seen to be strongly suggested by this algebraic interpretation of the Regge pole model. The existing experimental data does not contradict the relinquishing of the constant asymptotic cross-section hypothesis; however, only accurate measurements of cross-sections at higher energies than now available could give a clear cut answer. Such measurements could be obtained by the use of an intersecting storage ring (ISR), or cosmic ray experiments on hydrogen. An accurate measurement of the PP cross-sections in the 30 to 70 GeV/c range—available at the new Serpukhov accelerator—would also be relevant since the fit predicts a drop of ≈ 3 mb in this range (see Fig. 9-3).

Note that $\alpha = 1$ is known to be an upper limit to acceptable intercepts, and therefore, in a certain sense, a point of

*It would seem that the reasoning which has led to allowing D-type coupling for the s^i should yield terms linear in λ for (9.25a). Moreover (9.7) is then unchanged.

high singularity, such that a pole with $\alpha(0) = 1$ would be entirely set apart from other poles with $\alpha(0) < 1$. Since the s_0 trajectory is assumed to be a member of a nonet, it is rather natural that its properties should be only quantitatively—not qualitatively—different from those of other poles of even signature.

SOME CLUES

The connection between this algebra of "strong currents" and the algebra of weak and electromagnetic currents has not been studied to date. There are various vague clues. The high energy behavior of the differential nucleon-nucleon cross-section has been fitted[6,24] by a curve following the 4th power of the electromagnetic form factors; this could follow naturally from (9.9), as

$$\frac{d\sigma}{dt} \propto \beta^2(t)\, s^{2[\alpha(t)-1]} \sim [\gamma(t)]^4$$

On the other hand, Equation (9.9) can then not be used just in the given form for time-like t, as we would get the pole in both the residue and signature terms at the same time. Moreover, possibly $\gamma(0) \sim f_{\rho NN}$ rather than $\gamma(0) \sim F_e(0)$.

When using dispersion relations, we get universal couplings for the vector-mesons at m_V^2; is this true for our case too, and do we have to correct for that—or on the contrary, is $t = 0$ the correct choice for a universal strong coupling?

For the s^i system, the situation is even more mysterious. The 2^+ mesons could be somehow coupled to s^i for instance. On the other hand, from taking a gravitational form factor and assuming that a gravitational matrix element is dominated by a 2^+ meson, we would get this meson coupled universally to $\theta^{\mu\nu} - \frac{1}{4}g^{\mu\nu}\theta^\sigma{}_\sigma$; is there any connection between the two expressions s^i and $\theta^{\mu\nu}$ or $\theta^{\mu\nu} - \frac{1}{4}g^{\mu\nu}\theta^\sigma{}_\sigma$? From the additional fact that the average meson mass is ~ 625 MeV and the average baryon is ~ 1000 MeV, we would tend to put $\theta^{00} \sim s^0$; however, this cannot be a straightforward connect as it would correspond to $\sigma PP/\sigma\pi P \sim m_P/m_\pi$, i.e., about 7 instead of 1.5. Indeed, only the $[U(6) \times U(6)]_\beta$ invariant part of θ^{00} can couple to the Pomeranchuk trajectory and forms a "high energy current".[25]

REFERENCES

1. N. Cabibbo, L. Horowitz and Y. Ne'eman, *Phys. Letters* **22**, 336 (1966). ["HCN"]
2. N. Cabibbo, L. Horowitz, J. J. J. Kokkedee and Y. Ne'eman, *Nuovo Cimento* **45**, 275 (1966). ["KHCN"]
3. E. M. Levin and L. L. Frankfurt, *Zhur. Eksp. i Teoret. Fiz. Pisma v. Redak.* **2**, 105 (1965) [English translation *JETP Letters* **2**, 65 (1965)].
4. H. J. Lipkin and F. Scheck, *Phys. Rev. Letters* **16**, 71 (1966).
5. P. G. O. Freund, *Phys. Rev. Letters* **15**, 929 (1965).
6. J. J. J. Kokkedee and L. Van Hove, *Nuovo Cimento* **42**, 711 (1966).
7. H. J. Lipkin, *Phys. Rev. Letters* **16**, 1015 (1966).
8. F. Gürsey and L. A. Radicati, *Phys. Rev. Letters* **13**, 173 (1964); G. Zweig, "Symmetries in elementary particle physics" (1964 International School of Physics, Ettore Majorana), A. Zichichi, Ed., Academy Press, N.Y. (1965).
9. A. Salam, R. Delbourgo and J. Strathdee, *Proc. Roy. Soc. (London)* **A284**, 146 (1965); M. A. B. Bég and A. Pais, *Phys. Rev. Letters* **14**, 267 (1965); B. Sakita and K. C. Wali, *Phys. Rev.* **139**, B1355 (1965).
10. S. Coleman, *Phys. Rev.* **138**, B1262 (1965); M. A. B. Bég and A. Pais, *Phys. Rev. Letters* **14**, 509, 577 (1965).
11. R. P. Feynman, M. Gell-Mann, and G. Zweig, *Phys. Rev. Letters* **13**, 678 (1964).
12. R. F. Dashen and M. Gell-Mann, *Phys. Rev. Letters* **17**,

142 (1965). We use the notation and definitions of this reference in the present work.
13. F. M. Montgomery of Alamein, *El Alamein to the River Sangro,* Hutchinson & Co., London, p. 13, 16 etc.
14. R. J. N. Phillips and W. Rarita, *Phys. Rev.* **139**, B1336 (1965).
15. V. Barger and M. Olsson, *Phys. Rev. Letters* **15**, 930 (1965), for example.
16. M. Gell-Mann, *Phys. Rev. Letters* **8**, 263 (1962); V. N. Gribov and I. Ya. Pomeranchuk, *Phys. Rev. Letters* **8**, 343 (1962).
17. H. Goldberg and Y. Ne'eman, *Nuovo Cimento* **27**, 1 (1963).
18. K. Johnson and S. B. Treiman, *Phys. Rev. Letters* **14**, 189 (1965).
19. D. Perkins, Berkeley High Energy Physics Study, UCRL 10022 (1962).
20. W. Galbraith et al., *Phys. Rev.* **138**, B913 (1965).
21. V. Barger and M. Olsson, University of Madison preprint.
22. R. J. N. Phillips and W. Rarita, *Phys. Rev. Letters* **15**, 807, 942 (1966).
23. G. Höhler et al., *Phys. Letters* **20**,79 (1966).
24. L. Van Hove, *Proceedings of the Stony Brook Conference on High Energy Two body reactions*
25. C. Frahm, Y. Ne'eman and J. Yellin, *Proceedings of the Fourth (1967) Coral Gables Conference on Symmetry at High Energy.*
26. R. C. Arnold, *Phys. Rev. Letters* **14**, 657 (1965).

10

SEARCH FOR THE HADRON SPECTRUM-GENERATING ALGEBRA

INTRODUCTION

In our algebraic treatment of the hydrogen atom in Chapter 3, we introduced the concept of a spectrum-generating algebra (SGA.). In Chapters 5, 7, and 8 we went beyond the symmetry concept, in applying transition-operator algebras (TOA) to the hadrons. We shall now present some highly hypothetical suggestions which have been put forward in an attempt to provide an algebraic description of the complete hadron spectrum. We are looking for systems that will supply predictions for both even and odd parity higher excited hadrons.

Historically, this search emerged out of a number of independent developments—probably introducing thereby some bias in the choice of candidate SGA:

1. After the failure of "naive" relativistic SU(6) schemes, with the $[U(6) \times U(6)]_\beta$ group surviving as a rest ASA, one wondered whether any of the merger groups $SL(6, C)_{\gamma_5}$ or $U(6, 6)_\beta$, used with correct unitary representations, could still be useful for classification purposes.[1-4]

2. Independent of these considerations, an attempt was

made to replace the analytical systematics of rotational excitations—Regge recurrences—by an algebraic picture.[5-7]

3. Similarly, one looked for an algebraic characterization of the only relatively well understood bootstrap structure, i.e., the making of baryons. The approximations implied by the modern N/D method reproduce in fact the systematics of the static model and strong-coupling theories of the early forties. It was now worth checking whether these results could be described algebraically.[1-3,5-6]

4. Naive quark-molecular pictures could be fitted to SU(6) and beyond, and used to predict hadron systematics. This approach thus also aims at the same goal[8]; and it can even be given in algebraic language, just as can be done for spinning tops, molecules and nuclei.[9,10]

SEQUENCES OF ROTATIONAL EXCITATIONS—ANALYTICAL DESCRIPTION

The notion of hadrons as Regge poles,[11] and the related idea of a system of recurrences, represented an attempt at basing a classification upon dynamical concepts. The scheme was first superimposed upon the "internal" order. With the inclusion of spin-like transformations in SU(6) and the higher rest-ASAs, some understanding of the connections between the two structures has now become essential to further progress.

The genesis of Regge poles was in potential theory and entirely inspired by the methods of analysis. To connect them with symmetries, we first have to bring out their algebraic structure. We therefore review the analytical Regge poles structure of the Coulomb potential, the 3-dimensional oscillator, and the signature[12] appearing in exchange potentials. We then find the SGA corresponding to these examples. We proceed to identify the various noncompact sub-algebras whose unitary representations provide the sequence of rotational recurrences. In our algebraic discussion, we do not comment upon the analytical continuation in J as an issue[13] in itself.

The Coulomb Potential[14, 15]

The Schrödinger equation for the ℓ-th partial wave leads to an S matrix where the bound states of the Coulomb potential are given by the singularities which correspond to the poles of

$$\Gamma\left(\ell + 1 - \frac{i\,e^2}{n}\sqrt{\frac{M}{2E}}\right)$$

The corresponding Regge trajectories are thus:

$$\alpha_n(E) = -n_s + \frac{i\,e^2}{n}\sqrt{\frac{M}{2E}} \qquad n_s = 1, 2, \ldots \qquad (10.1)$$

from which we see that the nth Regge pole crosses physical ℓ values at energies

$$E(n) = \frac{-Me^4}{2(n_s + \ell)^2\hbar^2} \qquad n_s = 1, 2, \ldots \qquad (10.2)$$

(n_s is connected with the number of nodes of the radial function).

Three Dimensional Harmonic Oscillator

The radial Schrödinger equation leads in this case to Regge trajectories given by:

$$\alpha_n(E) = \frac{E}{\hbar\omega} - 2n_s - \frac{3}{2} \qquad (n_s = 0, 1, \ldots) \qquad (10.3)$$

Consequently the nth Regge pole crosses physical ℓ values at

$$E(n) = \hbar\omega\,(2n_s + \ell + \tfrac{3}{2}) \qquad (n_s = 0, 1, 2, \ldots) \qquad (10.4)$$

Exchange Potentials

Corresponding to the Coulomb case we can consider a potential of the form

$$V = \frac{-2M}{\hbar^2 r} \left[e^2 + (-1)^{\ell} f^2 \right] \tag{10.5}$$

which has a behavior analogous to exchange forces in the relativistic domain.

Separating the Schrödinger equation into two independent parts, one for even ℓ and one for odd ℓ leads to two Regge trajectories:

$$\alpha_{\text{even}}(E) = -n_s + i \sqrt{\frac{M}{2E}} \frac{(e^2 + f^2)}{\hbar}$$

$$n_s = 1, 2, 3, 4, \ldots \tag{10.6}$$

$$\alpha_{\text{odd}}(E) = -n_s - 1 + i \sqrt{\frac{M}{2E}} \frac{(e^2 - f^2)}{\hbar}$$

Correspondingly the Regge poles on the even trajectory cross physical values at energies,

$$E^{(e)}_{(n)} = \frac{-M(e^2 + f^2)^2}{2(n_s + \ell_{\text{even}})^2 \hbar^2} \qquad \ell_{\text{even}} = 0, 2, 4, \ldots \tag{10.7}$$

and on the odd trajectory cross at energies

$$E^{(0)}_{(n)} = \frac{-M(e^2 + f^2)^2}{2(n_s + \ell_{\text{odd}} + 1)^2 \hbar^2} \qquad \ell_{\text{odd}} = 1, 3, \ldots \tag{10.7'}$$

THE SGA AND ALGEBRAS OF ROTATIONAL STATES (ARS)

The Coulomb Potential

Let us now view the complete set of energy levels of the Coulomb potential (i.e., the hydrogen spectrum we studied in Chapter 3).

E(n)	levels				(j_1, j_2)
E(4):	4s	4p	4d	4f	$(\frac{3}{2}, \frac{3}{2})$
E(3):	3s	3p	3d		(1, 1)
E(2):	2s	2p			$(\frac{1}{2}, \frac{1}{2})$
E(1):	1s				(0, 0)

In this tabulation we have also given the degenerate levels in terms of the SO(4) representations (j_1, j_2), with the Pauli SU(2) quasi-spins (3.3)

$$\mathbf{j}_1 = \mathbf{L} + \mathbf{M} \qquad \mathbf{j}_2 = \mathbf{L} - \mathbf{M}$$

where L is the orbital angular momentum and $\mathbf{M}$ the quantized Laplace-Lentz operator with the appropriate normalization (3.2). We note that $\mathbf{A} \cdot \mathbf{L} = 0$, which requires $j_1 = j_2$. The degeneracy ASA is in fact SO(4) $\times$ SO(2), where the SO(2) or U(1) stands for the generator $H^{-1/2}$ whose eigenvalues n label the levels.

The entire spectrum of the Coulomb potential forms, as we have seen, one infinite-dimensional representation of the SGA SO(1, 4) with its compact subalgebra SO(4) as an ASA. Alternatively, we can use SO(2, 4) with the above mentioned compact SO(4) $\times$ SO(2) ASA subsystem. If u^i denoted either the abstract coordinate unit-vector in a metric space supporting the Pauli SO(4) ASA or an L = 1 wave function ASA, we can construct the non-compact generators of SO(1, 4) by using Gell-Mann's formula.[16]

$$N^i = \frac{i}{2}[L^2 + M^2, u^i] \tag{10.8}$$

To get SO(2, 4), we adjoin

$$M^j = \frac{i}{2}[L^2 + M^2, v^j] \tag{10.9}$$

with the condition

$$\mathbf{u} \cdot \mathbf{v} = 0 \tag{10.10}$$

The Regge trajectories are characterized by their ground-state energies E_s, or by the n-value of the S-state n_s

$$n = n_s + \ell$$

We note that these sequences lie along the dotted lines in our tables and form infinite-dimensional representations $(n_s, 0)$ of the homogeneous Lorentz group[17]

$$\ell = 0, 1, 2, 3, \ldots$$

where we have characterized the representations by (n_s, ℓ_{min}). This abstract Lorentz group SL(2, C) is the SO(3, 1) subgroup of the SO(4, 1) SGA which we get when we reduce the SO(4) ASA to the SO(3) L subgroup. This is typical of the other cases we shall study: every representation of the compact subgroup occurs only once.[17,18]

We now go over to the signature-dependent situation. In this case we require an SGA which picks out either even or odd states. This is the SL(4, R) group whose noncompact generators behave like **(1, 1)** and are given by

$$N^{ia} = \frac{i}{2} [L^2 + M^2, r^{ia}] \tag{10.11}$$

where r^{ia} is a $j_1 = j_2 = 1$ unit tensor or wave function (i and a are the j_1 and j_2 indices respectively). These generators close with the Pauli SO(4) set J_1 and J_2 upon SL(4, R), provided $j_1 = j_2$ and (see further discussion of this group[2,3] under the next head)

$$\begin{aligned} r^{ia} r_{ja} &= \delta^i_j \\ r^{ia} r_{ib} &= \delta^a_b \end{aligned} \tag{10.12}$$

We can now trace the corresponding sub-algebra of the rotational states. Again, we take the L subgroup of $J_1 \times J_2$ only: our SL(4, R) is now reduced to SL(3, R), with the non-compact generators

$$R^m = \frac{i}{2} [L^2, r^{mn}] \tag{10.13}$$

where r^{mn} is the symmetric 2nd rank tensor **(1, 1)** in 3-space, normalized.

The Oscillator

The energy levels of the 3-dimensional oscillator are:

E(n)	levels				(n, r, s)
E(3)		3p		3d	(3, 0, 0)
E(2)	2s		2d		(2, 0, 0)
E(1)		1p			(1, 0, 0)
E(0)	0s				(0, 0, 0)

In this tabulation, (n, r, s) denote the representations of the U(3) degeneracy ASA, whose generators are[6]:

$$U^a = \lambda^a_{ij}\, a^{i\dagger}\, a^j \tag{10.14}$$

λ^a_{ij} is the $(i, j)^{th}$ matrix element of the λ^a matrices of U(3); $a^{i\dagger}$ and a^j are the usual creation and annihilation operators.

The SGA is U(1, 3), with the noncompact generators

$$\frac{1}{(2)^{1/2}} (H - \tfrac{1}{2})^{1/2}\, a^{i\dagger}$$

and

$$\frac{1}{(2)^{1/2}}\, a^i (H - \tfrac{1}{2})^{1/2}$$

The rotational sequences correspond to the reduction of the U(3) ASA to its SO(3) subgroup: the U(1, 3) SGA then yields an SO(1, 3) spectrum generating sub-algebra, with representations $(n_s, 0)$ lying along the dotted lines and characterized by even values of n_s.

Introducing a signature picks out odd or even levels as bound states in a trajectory. The complete SGA is now the [9,19] Lipkin-Goshen Sp(6, R) whose noncompact generators (behaving like L = 0 and 2)

$$N^A = s^A_{ij}\, (a^{i\dagger}\, a^{j\dagger} + a^i\, a^j)$$

and

$$\frac{1}{i}\, s^A_{ij}\, (a^{i\dagger}\, a^{j\dagger} - a^i\, a^j) \tag{10.15}$$

where s^A_{ij} are the $(i, j)^{th}$ symmetric reduction coefficients of 3×3 or $3^* \times 3^*$. The Regge sub-algebra is again reached by taking the L subgroup of the U(3) degeneracy ASA; we get an SL(3, R) subgroup of Sp(6, R), with the non-compact generators reducing to the L = 2 parts of the N^A.

Spinor Representations

What happens if the pre-signature situation corresponded to a half-integer j_0 in an SL(2, C) representation,

$$\tfrac{1}{2}, \tfrac{3}{2}, \tfrac{5}{2}, \tfrac{7}{2}, \ldots$$

of the Gelfand-Naimark type? On the one hand, we may describe the situation in perturbative language: the representation is still one supermultiplet, with the Hamiltonian splitting it into two multiplets with different energy-dependences [instead of different masses in an SU(3) supermultiplet, for instance]. However, we cannot regard each multiplet

$$\tfrac{1}{2}, \tfrac{5}{2}, \tfrac{9}{2}, \ldots$$

or

$$\tfrac{3}{2}, \tfrac{7}{2}, \tfrac{11}{2}, \ldots$$

as an irreducible representation of a simple group, whether or not it is a subgroup of SL(2, C). We can only speak of an infinite direct sum of irreducible $SU(2)_J$ representations. Alternatively, we could use integer L sequences merged into an SL(3, R) representation, and combine them with a "spin" with half integer value, say $\frac{1}{2}$; we would then get again both sequences from their sum.

Summary

We have the following picture: when dealing with the signature in the integer L cases, it is convenient to replace the SL(2, C) ≈ SO(1, 3) rotational spectrum-generating sub-algebra by SL(6, R), built as the envelope of

$$SL(3, R)_{\text{even } n_s} \times SL(3, R)_{\text{odd } n_s}$$

The exchange potential "breaks" the larger SL(6, R), i.e., it distorts the energy so as to make it depend upon the two independent n_s values in SL(3, R) × SL(3, R) instead of it being a function of one simple n_s characterizing the entire SL(6, R) representation. Each signature-characterized trajectory is now just a representation of one of the two SL(3, R) sets, or also of the "summed" SL(3, R). We could of course evoke this picture for the entire spectrum, replacing SO(2, 4) of hydrogen by SL(8, R) built upon $SL(4, R)_{\text{even}} \times SL(4, R)_{\text{odd}}$; for the oscillator this would correspond to using as the SGA Sp(12, R) built upon Sp(6, R) × Sp(6, R), instead of U(1, 3). The method is correct for integer angular momenta; we cannot repeat the trick for spinors, where we can only keep SL(2, C) as the rotational SGA and lack a simple break up other than straight to $SU(2)_j$.

STRONG COUPLING THEORIES

In the static approximation, the nucleon is replaced by a source term and the Hamiltonian (omitting I-spin at this stage) becomes[20,21]

$$H = \int d^3 r \left\{ \frac{1}{2} [\dot{\phi}^2 + (\nabla\phi)^2 + \mu\phi^2] + \frac{g}{\mu} \rho \boldsymbol{\sigma} \cdot \nabla\phi \right\} - \epsilon_0 \tag{10.16}$$

In a partial wave expansion, we find that only the $\ell = 1$ pions contribute. The reduced Hamiltonian

$$H = W \sum_j a_j^+ a_j + \bar{g} \sigma_j (a_j + a_j^+) - \epsilon_0$$

becomes

$$H_\sigma = \tfrac{1}{2}(\mathbf{p}^2 + W^2 \mathbf{q}^2) + g' \boldsymbol{\sigma} \cdot \mathbf{q} - \tfrac{3}{2} W - \epsilon_0 \tag{10.17}$$

where $\mathbf{q}$ is the radial meson field variable and $\mathbf{p}$ its conjugate momentum (at the position of the nucleon),

$$p_j = -i\,(a_j - a_j^+)\,\frac{W}{2}^{1/2}$$

$$q_j = (a_j + a_j^+)\left(\frac{1}{2W}\right)^{1/2}$$

$$[q_j, p_{j'}] = i\,\delta_{jj'}$$

$$\mathbf{q}^2 = \sum_{j=1}^{3} q_j^2$$

$$g' = \bar{g}\,(2W)^{1/2}$$

The form (10.17) emphasizes the analogy to a 3-dimensional oscillator coupled to a spin through $\boldsymbol{\sigma}\cdot\mathbf{q}$, in elementary wave mechanics. Similarly, the symmetric (i.e., with I-spin) case is described by

$$H_{\sigma\tau} = \sum_{j\alpha} \tfrac{1}{2}(p_{j\alpha}^{\tau} + W^2\, q_{j\alpha}^2) + f'\,\sigma_j\,\tau_\alpha\, q_{\alpha j} - \tfrac{9}{2}\,W - \epsilon_0 \tag{10.18}$$

An expression similar to Eq. (10.17) with $\boldsymbol{\sigma}$ replaced by $\vec{\tau}$ corresponds to the symmetric scalar case H_τ.

Let us now analyze the algebraic properties of these systems. The Hamiltonians all possess some good symmetry: H_σ commutes with angular momentum J, H with I-spin and $H_{\sigma\tau}$ with both J and I. Those operators are given by the orbital quantum numbers of the pions and the $\frac{1}{2}\sigma$, $\frac{1}{2}\tau$ spin and I-spin of the nucleons.

$$\mathbf{J} = \tfrac{1}{2}\boldsymbol{\sigma} + \mathbf{q} \times \mathbf{p} \tag{10.19}$$

$$\vec{\mathbf{I}} = \tfrac{1}{2}\vec{\tau} + \vec{q} \times \vec{p} \tag{10.20}$$

Thus, H_σ has an $SU(2)_J$ symmetry, H_τ an $SU(2)_I$, and $H_{\sigma\tau}$ obeys $SU(2)_J \times SU(2)_I$. On the other hand, these systems also contain a part (the interaction term) which commutes with the q_j, q_α, or $q_{j\alpha}$ respectively. The q operators thus enlarge the algebra; since they form an Abelian subalgebra, they generate a semidirect product of a simple (or semisimple) Lie subalgebra and an Abelian one. Replacing q by $i(\delta/\delta p)$ will make it clear that we are dealing with the groups $E_3(J)$ and $E_3(I)$ of Euclidean motions in the p three-space for H_σ and H_τ respectively, and a more complicated $G_9(I, J)$ for $H_{\sigma\tau}$.

These algebras are approximate symmetries only if we are prepared to omit the kinetic energy of the pions themselves. This was generally the view in strong coupling theory; we prefer to leave the system as it is and regard them here as SGA. It can be shown that the unitary representation corresponding to our problem in terms of the compact symmetry subgroup is just the sequence predicted by strong coupling theory. This becomes easier to handle if we replace the solvable algebras by semisimple ones active in the same problems and yielding identical results. We define[2] the noncompact generators,

$$N_j = \frac{i}{2}[J^2, \hat{q}_j] = \frac{1}{2}(\hat{\mathbf{q}} \times \mathbf{J})_j - \frac{1}{2}(\mathbf{J} \times \hat{\mathbf{q}})_j \qquad (10.21)$$

$$N_\alpha = \frac{i}{2}[I^2, \hat{\mathbf{q}}_\alpha] = \frac{1}{2}(\vec{\hat{q}} \times \vec{I})_\alpha - \frac{1}{2}(\vec{I} \times \vec{\hat{q}})_\alpha \qquad (10.22)$$

($\hat{q}$ is a unit vector). The N_J and J close upon an algebra generating SL(2, C),

$$\begin{aligned} [J_j, J_k] &= i\,\epsilon_{jk\ell}\,J_\ell \\ [J_j, N_k] &= i\,\epsilon_{jk\ell}\,N_\ell \\ [N_j, N_k] &= -i\,\epsilon_{jk\ell}\,J_\ell \end{aligned} \qquad (10.23)$$

this $SL(2, C)_J$ SGA is isomorphic to the homogeneous Lorentz group and has the same unitary representation[16] defined by a number c and j_0, the lowest j. The representation is then given by the direct sum of $SU(2)_J$ representations

$$j_0, j_0 + 1, j_0 + 2, \ldots$$

For the nucleon, this entails the sequence

$$\tfrac{1}{2}, \tfrac{3}{2}, \tfrac{5}{2}, \ldots$$

for spin or I-spin respectively. Note that the algebra closes only upon the respective conditions

$$\sum_j \hat{q}_j^2 = 1 \qquad \sum_\alpha \hat{q}_\alpha^2 = 1 \tag{10.24}$$

which limit the meson variable to a fixed "radius" (in the inhomogeneous E_3 case, it corresponds to fixing the Casimir operator of the "translations").

For the $H_{\sigma\tau}$ we define,

$$I_\alpha = \tfrac{1}{2}\tau_\alpha + \sum_{\beta\gamma j} \epsilon_{\alpha\beta\gamma}\, q_{j\beta}\, p_{j\gamma}$$

$$J_j = \tfrac{1}{2}\sigma_j + \sum_{k\ell\alpha} \epsilon_{jk\ell}\, q_{k\alpha}\, p_{\ell\alpha}$$

$$\begin{aligned} N_{j\alpha} &= -\frac{i}{2}[J^2 + I^2, e_{j\alpha}] \\ &= \tfrac{1}{2}(\epsilon_{jk\ell}\, e_{k\alpha}\, J_\ell + \epsilon_{\alpha\beta\gamma}\, e_{j\beta}\, I_\gamma) \\ &\quad - \tfrac{1}{2}(\epsilon_{jk\ell}\, J_k\, e_{\ell\alpha} + \epsilon_{\alpha\beta\gamma}\, I_\beta\, e_{j\gamma}) \end{aligned} \tag{10.25}$$

where we may temporarily regard the $e_{j\alpha} \sim \hat{q}_{j\alpha}$. The $N_{j\alpha}$, J_j, I_α close upon the algebra of SL(4, R) provided

$$\langle f | \epsilon_{jk\ell} e_{k\alpha} J_\ell | i \rangle = \langle f | \epsilon_{\alpha\beta\gamma} e_{j\beta} I_\gamma | i \rangle \tag{10.26}$$

$$e_{j\alpha} e_{k\alpha} = \delta_{jk} \qquad e_{j\alpha} e_{j\beta} = \delta_{\alpha\beta} \tag{10.27}$$

The first condition fixes $I^2 = J^2$ for the problem's representations; the second is exactly what one gets through[21] the conventional "oscillator" treatment where one diagonalizes the $\sigma_j \tau_\alpha q_{j\alpha}$ term. The correspondence is

$$q_{\alpha j} = \frac{f'}{W^2} e_{\alpha j} \tag{10.28}$$

with the triad $e_{\alpha j}$ serving to define projection operators into eigenstates of J_j, I_α, $q_{j\alpha}$ with lowest eigenvalue f'/W^2.

$$P = \tfrac{1}{4}(1 - \sigma_j \tau_\alpha e_{j\alpha})$$

The unitary representation of SL(4, R) which is the solution of our problem[1] is then [we give the method of construction further on in our discussion of U(6.6)]

$$(\tfrac{1}{2}, \tfrac{1}{2}), (\tfrac{3}{2}, \tfrac{3}{2}), (\tfrac{5}{2}, \tfrac{5}{2}), (\tfrac{7}{2}, \tfrac{7}{2}), \ldots$$

in terms of (J, I). We recognize the N and Δ as the two lowest states; the approximate mass formula is

$$m = A + BJ(J + 1) + CI(I + I) \tag{10.29}$$

and with $J^2 = I^2$ this contains only one parameter for Δm and predicts a $\psi(\tfrac{5}{2}, \tfrac{5}{2})^+$ at 1740 MeV and a $\Gamma(\tfrac{7}{2}, \tfrac{7}{2})^+$ at 2440 MeV. These would decay respectively[22] into $N + 2\pi$, 3π or more pions (see also p. 232).

This study of strong coupling theories in algebraic terms exhibits the role of the SGA, represented here as in the atomic case by noncompact groups. We observe again that the definition of the SGA is equivalent to a dynamical solution by analytical methods. The groups can only become approximate symmetries in the complete degeneracy case, which is altogether uninteresting. However, they fulfill an extremely important function in possessing as a representation the complete set of solutions with the necessary exact conditions imposed upon the variables of the system.

For SU(3), this treatment yields SL(3, C) as SGA. For $SU(2)_\sigma \times SU(3)$—and for $SU(6)_\sigma$ it generates $SL(6, C)_\sigma$. In the latter case, the noncompact generators $N_{j\lambda}$ possess even parity and the representation for baryons would be

$$56^+,\ 700^+,\ \ldots$$

This should not be confused with the $SL(6, C)_{\gamma_5}$ [or, when we include baryon number, $GL(6)_{\gamma_5}$] mentioned[4] in connection with either a merger[23] of SU(3) with the Lorentz group or with respect to a suspected[24] noncompactness of the algebra of current components; these have odd parity noncompact generators and lead to the representation

$$56^+,\ 700^-,\ \ldots$$

Similarly, if SU(12) represents a symmetry of the hadrons, we would generate SL(12, C).

SPIN AND ORBITAL EXCITATIONS FOR THE HADRONS

There are two ways of exciting hadron states. On the one hand, we may imbed the ASA (at rest, or perhaps at $\mathbf{p} \to \infty$) in a larger algebra, with the quark quasi-spin subalgebra $SU(2)_\sigma$ [the one-particle states projection of $G(\sigma\lambda^0)$] appearing inside an SL(2, C) algebra. These are then excitations of the SU(6) spin itself, leading at the same time to larger representations of $SU(6)_\sigma$ or $[U(6) \times U(6)]_\beta$. We are increasing the highest weights of unitary spin at the same time as we are doing it for spin.

Alternatively, we may assume that the excitations are of "orbital" nature. This amounts to assuming a sequence of L_q-states, with L_q defined as in (8.63)

$$J \text{ (angular momentum at rest)} = L_q + S_\sigma$$

For a nonrelativistic situation, this would coincide with the orbital motion of constituent quarks in a hadron. For this reason, we have here the excitation-mode corresponding to all "molecular" hadron views. The L_q itself is then embedded in an SO(3, 1) or in an SL(3, R) SGA which multiplies the hadron ASA.

In the first type of SGA (we confine our discussion to rest-states only) we can go[1,2]

from $SU(6)_\sigma$	to $SL(6, C)_{\gamma_5}$
from $[U(6) \times U(6)]_\beta$	to $U(6, 6)_\beta$
from U(12)	to SL(12, C)

Note that the meson $(6, 6^*)^-$ picture encourages us to use the $[U(6) \times U(6)]_\beta \rightarrow U(6, 6)_\beta$ view; on the other hand, with no known physical materialization of tensor, scalar and pseudoscalar currents, it seemed more profitable[4] to work with $SU(6)_\sigma$ and $SL(6, C)_{\gamma_5}$. As to the use of U(12), the main advantage seems to be a seemingly more economical structure of the lowest lying baryons with odd parity. With SU(12) as a compact SGA (or subalgebra) rather than as an ASA, we regard its basic **12** as made of a quark $\mathbf{6}^+$ and a pseudo-quark $\mathbf{6}^-$. This gives **143** lowest mesons consisting of

$$(\mathbf{6}, \mathbf{6}^*)^-, (\mathbf{35}, \mathbf{1})^+, (\mathbf{1}, \mathbf{35})^+, (\mathbf{1}, \mathbf{1})^+, (\mathbf{6}^*, \mathbf{6})^-$$

and 364 baryons,

$$(\mathbf{56}, \mathbf{1})^+, (\mathbf{21}, \mathbf{6})^-, (\mathbf{6}, \mathbf{21})^+, (\mathbf{1}, \mathbf{56})^-$$

In $SU(6)_\sigma$ terms, we have for mesons $\mathbf{35}^- + \mathbf{1}^-$, $\mathbf{35}^+$, $\mathbf{35}^+$, $\mathbf{1}^+$, $\mathbf{35}^- + \mathbf{1}^-$ (this is a charge-conjugation doublet structure). For baryons we have $\mathbf{56}^+$, $\mathbf{56}^-$, $\mathbf{70}^-$, $\mathbf{70}^+$, $\mathbf{56}^+$, $\mathbf{56}^-$. Assuming that a pseudo-quark is "heavier" than a quark, with a linearized mass formula, would give a pattern

$\mathbf{35}^-$	$\mathbf{56}^-$
$\mathbf{35}^+\ \mathbf{1}^+\ \mathbf{35}^+$	$\mathbf{56}^+\quad \mathbf{70}^+$
	$\mathbf{56}^-\quad \mathbf{70}^-$
$\mathbf{35}^-$	$\mathbf{56}^+$

We have already discussed the baryons in an $SL(6, C)_{\gamma_5}$ SGA,

$$\mathbf{56}^+,\ \mathbf{700}^-,\ \mathbf{4536}^+,\ \ldots$$

For mesons, we get

$$(\mathbf{1}^+),\ \mathbf{35}^-,\ \mathbf{405}^+,\ \mathbf{2695}^-,\ \ldots$$

The rotational SL(2, C) can be identified by taking the λ^0 subset of generators. We get sequences 0^-, 1^+, 2^-, 3^+, ... and 1^-, 2^+, 3^-, ... for mesons, $\frac{1}{2}^+$, $\frac{3}{2}^-$, $\frac{5}{2}^+$, ... and $\frac{3}{2}^+$, $\frac{5}{2}^-$, $\frac{7}{2}^+$, ... for baryons, Couplings and some physical results have been derived in the $SL(6, C)_{\gamma_5}$ case.[26] They lead to a D/F ratio of $\frac{9}{5}$.

For the orbital type of excitation, we may try to assume[1] inclusion of L_q as a subalgebra in a noncompact SL(3, R) SGA arising from commutation with the time-derivatives of the gravitational quadrupole moments. These behave like symmetric $x_i p_j$ combinations, as against the antisymmetric ones forming L (or L_q in our case). Relativistically, of course, this is (η_a is isomorphic to $i\lambda_a$ for a = 1, 3, 4, 6, 8)

$$U_a = \int d^3x\, x_i\, \eta_a^{ij}\, \theta^{4j} \tag{10.31}$$

The representations of this algebra are given in terms of L_q submultiplets:

0, 2, 4, ...

1, 3, 5, ...

which would enable us to treat higher hadron excitations as recurrences in L_q, every $L_q = 0$ state of SU(6), or $[U(6) \times U(6)]_\beta$ or U(12) reappearing with $L_q = 2$, $L_q = 4$, etc., in a sequence of the Regge type. We may in fact superimpose this scheme upon the spin-type excitation SGA itself, thus getting for instance an entire $U(6, 6)_\beta$ tower with some sequence of L_q.

Note that we now have available[27] a different representation structure, in terms of a quark ladder, for the observed spectrum of excited hadron states. This interpretation would replace the set of additional internal degrees of freedom implied by the spin-statistics correlation as we noted in Chapter 4, by "intrinsic" quasi-orbital angular-momentum multiplicities. The central notion is that the "effective" quark *states* then belong like all other hadrons to systems of angular momentum excitations—perhaps Regge-type recurrences. Quark-*fields* may represent a fundamental system in some sense, but these hypothetical quark states are as nonelementary as any hadron. The following discussion should be considered as highly speculative, and is given here only for the sake of completeness with respect to the statistics issue. The "effective" quarks we discuss may be construed in the sense of the systematics of $p \to \infty$ representations of the currents, for instance.[35]

We apply the notion of the "quasi-orbital" L_q angular momentum to single quarks, and use SL(3, R) superimposed upon $SU(6)_\sigma$ or $[U(6) \times U(6)]_\beta$, or even $U(6, 6)_\beta$.

As an example, suppose the nucleon and delta were to appear as the ground state in a $(J, I)^P$ sequence,

$$\begin{aligned}
&(\tfrac{1}{2}, \tfrac{1}{2})^+ \text{ and } (\tfrac{3}{2}, \tfrac{3}{2})^+ \text{ in } (\mathbf{56}, \mathbf{1}),\ L_q = 0 \\
&(\tfrac{5}{2}, \tfrac{1}{2})^+ \quad (\tfrac{7}{2}, \tfrac{3}{2})^+ \\
&\qquad \text{and } (\tfrac{5}{2}, \tfrac{3}{2})^+ \text{ in } (\mathbf{56}, \mathbf{1}),\ L_q = 2 \\
&(\tfrac{3}{2}, \tfrac{1}{2})^+ \quad (\tfrac{3}{2}, \tfrac{3}{2})^+
\end{aligned} \tag{10.32}$$

etc.

Actually, in the model we mention here, this sequence does not describe the sequence of N-Δ resonances. However, let us note at this stage that a state with $j = L_q \pm \frac{1}{2}$ may be tentatively identified with a N-π resonance with

$$L(\pi) = L_q \pm 1 \tag{10.33}$$

For instance, the $N(\frac{5}{2}^+, 1688)$ is produced as an F-state pionic resonance; in terms of L_q it could be assigned to (**56**, **1**) $L_q = 2$ as in (10.32).

We now assign the quark to a similar sequence, i.e., it is the $L_q = 0$ level of a system of rotational excitations of the same nature. The correlation (10.33) enables us to interpret the quark excitations in the same way, even though they may in fact be connected with further structure at the quark level, such as a suitable combination of a quark and a quark-antiquark pair. The $L_q = 2$ quark, for instance, can thus be regarded as either a P-state or an F-state π-quark resonance or bound state, with $J = \frac{3}{2}^+$ or $\frac{5}{2}^+$ accordingly.

To simplify algebraic considerations, let us replace the infinite sequences

$$L_q = 0, 2, 4, 6, \ldots \tag{10.34}$$

$$L_q = 1, 3, 5, 7, \ldots \tag{10.35}$$

by finite ones, e.g.,

$$L_q = 0, 2 \qquad (10.34')$$

$$L_q = 1 \quad \text{or} \quad L_q = 1, 3 \qquad (10.35')$$

The latter can be considered respectively as a 6-component representation (2, 0) of a harmonic-oscillator $SU(3)_L$ or as the 3-component (1, 0) or the 10-component (3, 0) of an oscillator spectrum.

We are in fact replacing as a simplification the ∞-dimensional unitary representation of the noncompact $SL(3, R)_L$ by a finite unitary representation of an $SU(3)_L$ of the oscillator or of the nuclear-physics Elliott type,[28] in which the angular momentum subgroup is L_q. Our quark band is then some (n, 0) representation of $SU(3)_L$ with dimensionality $\frac{1}{2}(n + 1)(n + 2)$, direct-multipled by the representation **6** of $SU(6)_\sigma$, or by (**6**, **1**) of $U(6) \times U(6)_\beta$.

To achieve a totally antisymmetric state in $SU(3)_L$, we have to multiply 3 quark-based supermultiplets; and the $SU(6)_\sigma$ or $[U(6) \times U(6)]_\beta$ will take totally symmetric index-structure. We thus get the **56** or (**56**, **1**) with $L_q = 0$ as the saturated most deeply bound $SU(3)_L$ scalar. We could have done the same for any of the $SU(3)_L$ representations (n, 0) with larger n describing the sequences (10.34) and (10.35) with arbitrary higher cut-off; and the result may be carried over to the original $SL(3, R)_L$ representations realized by the arrays (10.34) and (10.35) themselves.

Note that the simplest example for such a structure would consist in assuming that the basic constituents of the nucleon are quarks with the excitations of (35'); reducing the sequence to its lowest state with intrinsic $L_q = 1$, we make the nucleon and delta out of three $j = \frac{1}{2}^+$ and three $j = \frac{3}{2}^+$ "excited" quarks (the unexcited state and the quark field would then have odd intrinsic parity relatively to the nucleon); the L_q-vector parts of the wave functions [multiplying the $SU(6)_\sigma$ parts] are coupled to $L_q = 0$ via the determinant pattern $\epsilon^{\alpha\beta\gamma} x^\alpha y^\beta z^\gamma$.

It is clear that Fermi-Dirac statistics would still be obeyed if we were to pick any three-particle amplitude out of the set of 816 states,[29]

$$\begin{array}{lll} (\mathbf{56}, \mathbf{1}; 0)^+ & & \\ (\mathbf{70}, \mathbf{1}; 1)^+ & \text{and} & (\mathbf{70}, \mathbf{1}; 2)^+ \\ (\mathbf{20}, \mathbf{1}; 1)^+ & \text{and} & (\mathbf{20}, \mathbf{1}; 3)^+ \end{array} \tag{10.36}$$

and the total L_q content in (10.36) corresponds to $SU(3)_L$ representations **1** (for 56), **8** (for 70) and **10** (for 20).

However, we may try to classify states while keeping to the belief that none but the lowest scalar $SU(3)_L$ representation really exists. It can be produced from either (10.34) or (10.35); in (10.34), and using for example (10.34′) the $SU(3)_L$ intrinsic scalar contains $L_q = 2$ quarks (with even relative parity for the quark field). Alternatively, the entire U(6, 6) ladders could be replaced by the set of states reached from these Fermi-statistics products of three quarks with all excitations of SL(3, R).

Note that the (**56**, **1**) is a scalar in both L_q and $SL(3, R)_L$. The system of baryon rotational excitations would thus not be reached from (**56**, **1**) via an L_q sequence. The (**56**, **1**) may still be regarded as the lowest rung of a U(6, 6) or SL(6, C) ladder.

$U(6, 6)_\beta$ AS THE SGA

If we adjoin to $[U(6) \times U(6)]_\beta$ 72 negative noncompact odd parity operators behaving like $(\mathbf{6}, \mathbf{6}^*)^-$ and $(\mathbf{6}^*, \mathbf{6})^-$, we close upon $U(6, 6)_\beta$. The noncompact generators could just create and annihilate the mesons, or describe some strong coupling with 36 odd-parity mesons in an S-state and 36 even-parity mesons (with opposite charge parity) in a P-state; they could even[30] be connected with commutators involving the current divergences for $g(\vec{\sigma}\lambda)$. Note that this $U(6, 6)_\beta$ is really what it is called, to be distinguished from the U(12) schemes which used either U(12) or $IU(6, 6)_\beta$. Our compact generators have Dirac bilinear quark densities, but the noncompact ones are *not* the Dirac bilinears at all: they have only infinite-dimensional nontrivial unitary representations. Thus this SGA will not violate unitarity as far as $\mathbf{p} = 0$ situations are considered. In fact, it could therefore even be tried[31] as a rest ASA.

We present a simple construction[1] of the ladder representations, that has been cast into an elegant mathematical form by Feynman, whose notation we employ. We use creation and destruction operators a^+_α and a_α with $\alpha = 1 \ldots 6$ for fictitious bosonic quarks at rest and another set of creation and destruction operators b^+_α and b_α for equally fictitious bosonic antiquarks. (These quarks and antiquarks are not to be thought of as particles; they merely supply tensor indices.) The 6×6 matrices $\lambda_i \sigma_j$, with $i = 0, 1, \ldots 8$ and $j = 0, 1, 2, 3$, act on the indices α. We then construct the twelve-component column vector $\phi = (a, ib^+)$ and the Hermitian conjugate row vector $\phi^+ = (a^+, -ib)$. Using $\gamma_5 \equiv \begin{pmatrix} 0 & 1 \\ 1 & 0 \end{pmatrix}$ and $\beta \equiv \begin{pmatrix} 1 & 0 \\ 0 & -1 \end{pmatrix}$, we form the even parity 12×12 matrices $\frac{1}{2}(1 + \beta)\lambda_i \sigma_j$ and $\frac{1}{2}(1 - \beta)\lambda_i \sigma_j$ (any of these will be denoted by X) and the odd parity 12×12 matrices $\gamma_5 \lambda_i \sigma_j$ and $i\beta\gamma_5 \lambda_i \sigma_j$ (denoted by Y). The Hermitian matrices X and Y would generate the algebra of the compact U(12). However, we define $\bar{\phi} \equiv \phi^+ \beta$ and construct the Hermitian operators

$$E(X) \equiv \bar{\phi} X \phi$$

$$F(Y) \equiv i\bar{\phi} Y \phi$$

and observe that these operators obey the rules of the noncompact algebra U(6, 6), by virtue of the relation $[\phi_\alpha, \phi_\beta] = \delta_{\alpha\beta}$. (Note that $\bar{\phi}$ is used where in a quark field theory we would use q^+ and not $\bar{q}$.)

We now consider all the states generated from the "vacuum" by creating arbitrary numbers n_u (upper indices) of "quarks" and n_ℓ of "antiquarks" (lower indices). For each value of the baryon number $\frac{1}{3}(n_u - n_\ell) = \frac{1}{3}E(1) + \text{const.}$, we have a single irreducible representation of the group U(6, 6). Each such representation is exhibited as a direct sum of irreducible representations of the maximal compact subgroup by considering the various values of $n_u + n_\ell = E(\beta) + \text{const}$. The meson representation is then the sum of **(1, 1)** with $n_u + n_\ell = 0$, **(6, 6*)** with $n_u + n_\ell = 2$, **(21, 21*)** with $n_u + n_\ell = 4$, etc. Similarly, the baryon representation is the sum of **(56, 1)** with $n_u + n_\ell = 3$, **(126, 6*)** with $n_u + n_\ell = 5$, etc. The compact operators E(X) generate the compact subgroup U(6) × U(6), while the noncompact operators F(Y) raise and lower $n_u + n_\ell$ by two units. Finally, we construct an isomorphism in which the "states" of our mathematical representation go over into idealized states of hadrons at rest, the operators E(X) go over into the space integrals of positive parity current components, and the operators F(Y) into other, so far unspecified operators capable of creating and destroying **(6, 6*)**$^-$ mesons in S-states. If this scheme has any utility, then the algebra of the positive parity $[U(6) \times U(6)]_\beta$ is a subalgebra simultaneously of the noncompact algebra of U(6, 6), used for classifying the states, and of the compact algebra of U(12) generated by the space integrals of the current components.

Using the ladder representations of U(6, 6), we can put the mesons in the band **(1, 1)**$^+$ containing the submultiplets,

$$(1, 1)^+, (6, 6^*)^-, (21, 21^*)^+, (56, 56^*)^-, \ldots$$

and the baryons in $(\mathbf{56}, \mathbf{1})^+$ with the content

$$(\mathbf{56}, \mathbf{1})^+, (\mathbf{126}, \mathbf{6}^*)^-, (\mathbf{252}, \mathbf{21}^*)^+, \ldots$$

We label the band by its lowest $[U(6) \times U(6)]_\beta$ multiplet. In terms of upper U(6) **6** indices and lower **6*** indices, we get only totally symmetric tensors in the upper and in the lower indices. Adjacent $[U(6) \times U(6)]_\beta$ submultiplets alternate parities and are connected by the noncompact generators.

In terms of $SU(6)_\sigma$, the even-parity mesons $(\mathbf{21}, \mathbf{21}^*)^+$ consist of $\mathbf{405}^+$, $\mathbf{35}^+$, $\mathbf{1}^+$. There is indeed some evidence[32] that the 2^+ meson $\mathbf{8} + \mathbf{1}$ fits into $\mathbf{405}^+$ (i.e., $q \times q \times q^+ \times q^+$, two "aligned quarks" and two "aligned antiquarks" in an S-state, in a nonrelativistic picture) rather than into **35** with $L_q = 1$ (i.e., a quark-antiquark pair in a P-state). The energy levels within a $[U(6) \times U(6)]_\beta$ representation are found to be higher, the smaller the SU(6) dimensionality in these multiplets. Thus $\mathbf{405}^+$ would be lighter than $\mathbf{35}^+$, and $\mathbf{1}^+$ would be heaviest. This should be compared with a (**35**, **35**) mass formula.

For the baryons with odd parity, we have $\mathbf{700}^-$ and $\mathbf{56}^-$. These assignments are not excluded,[33] but we shall have to wait until experiments do indeed prove the existence of a representation like $\mathbf{700}^-$ before accepting such high dimensionalities.

If we regard U(6, 6) as an SGA, we can expect the energy to behave like the Casimir operator of the compact $[U(6) \times U(6)]_\beta$ subgroup; or, alternatively, it could act like the singlet compact generator $E(\beta)$ transforming like $\beta\lambda^0$, i.e., $\frac{1}{3}(n_u + n_\ell)$ where n_u and n_ℓ represent as above stated the number of upper 6 indices (quarks) and the number of lower **6*** indices (antiquarks) [note that the other compact singlet $\frac{1}{3}(n_u - n_\ell)$ is baryon number $E(1)$]. In the latter case, we would get a rough equal spacing along the band, as the $[U(6) \times U(6)]_\beta$ submultiplets have $E(\beta)$ rising by $\frac{2}{3}$ between any two adjacent steps of the ladder. Note that if we take only the λ^0 subset (i.e., if we use baryon number only, and leave out unitary spin), we get SU(2, 2), the hydrogen spectrum SGA; E(β) is then the principal quantum number n.

The main value of this postulated U(6, 6) at this stage is in the determination of the spectrum of stable and resonant states. In addition, if U(6, 6) were still a rest ASA in some sense, the collinear $U(6)_W$ and U(3) itself would become parts of noncompact kinetic ASA's, $GL(6, C)_W$, and GL(3, C). These symmetry assumptions could readily be checked.

U(6, 6) contains an $SL(2, C)_\sigma$ rotational subalgebra. Its compact generators are the integrated space-components of the axial-vector λ^0 density; its noncompact part behaves in the abstract like $\sqrt{-1}$ times the corresponding vector density space-component spatial integrals. We can trace its patterns

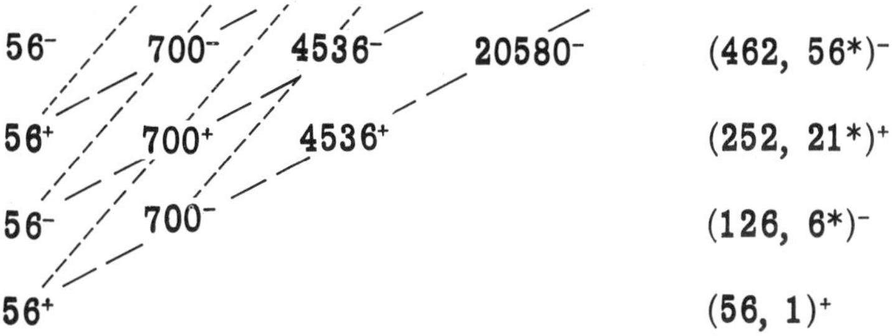

for baryons, and

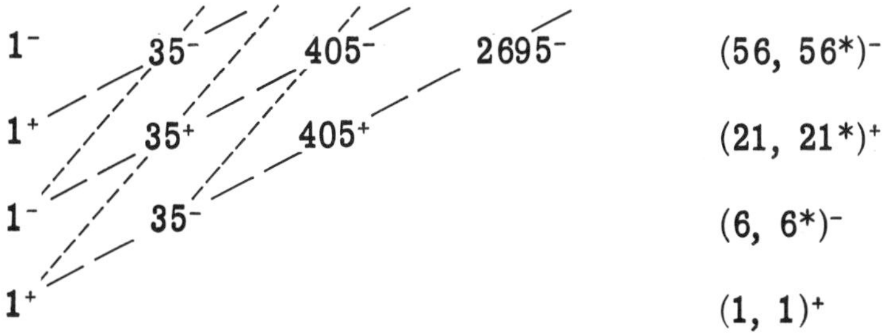

for mesons.

The dashed lines follow infinite-dimensional alternating-parity representations of the $SL(6, C)_{\gamma_5}$ subgroup containing $SL(2, C)_\sigma$ whose compact piece is plain $SU(6)_\sigma$ and whose noncompact generators behave like s-wave mesons in a $\mathbf{35}^-$.

We note that U(6, 6) also contains the other SL(6, C) we encountered when dealing with strong coupling ideas, with even parity noncompact generators behaving like p-wave mesons in a $\mathbf{35}^-$, i.e., they form a $\mathbf{35}^+$ as in the original strong-coupling static model. These leave every other row out and mark the sequences $\mathbf{56}^\pm$, $\mathbf{700}^\pm$, $\mathbf{4536}^\pm$, ... starting at various values of the $n(\beta)_{min}$ eigenvalues. Similarly, we get for the mesons such sequences $\mathbf{1}^+$, $\mathbf{35}^+$, $\mathbf{405}^+$, ... We have marked these representations with dots.

The SL(6, C) rotational sequences of course include two coupled trajectories of different parities. To separate out the subgroup corresponding to $\Delta j = 2$ fixed-parity trajectories, we could have tried to use the SL(3, R) subgroup of the SL(4, R) contained in the double-step SGA when taking the λ^0 U(3) content. [Remember that upon reduction to the scalar U(3) content, U(6, 6) reduces to U(2, 2) and we are back at the mathematics of the Coulomb case.] However, baryons come under the spinor case, and we cannot then get representations with $\Delta j = 2$ only.

The above ladder representations do not possess an invariant S-state coupling. This is already true for $[U(6) \times U(6)]_\beta$, where $(\mathbf{56}, \mathbf{1}) \times (\mathbf{1}, \mathbf{56^*})$ does not contain $(\mathbf{6}, \mathbf{6^*})^-$. However, this does not have to weaken the model, as physical coupling of hadrons may yet be of the derivative types. In motion, only the kinetic subgroups hold and couplings become plentiful.

In Chapter 8, we discussed the recent idea of a local algebra at $\mathbf{p} \to \infty$. Recent studies[34,35] of current-commutators have indicated that at $\mathbf{p} \to \infty$, the $(\mathbf{56}, \mathbf{1})$ baryons become highly mixed with some $L_q^z \neq 0$ states, $L_q^z = \pm 1$ mostly; otherwise, there would be no anomalous magnetic moment, and $-G_A/G_V = \frac{5}{3}$. A detailed analysis[36,37] has shown that the mixing is probably with a U(6) representation **70** with $L_q^z = 1$.

On the other hand, if a Lorentz transformation behaves like **35** with $L_q = 1$, it connects **56** $L_q = 0$ with **70** $L_q = 1$ indeed and does not yield a **20**. The same argument in favor of **70** $L_q = 1$ can be deduced from the properties of the nucleon anomalous magnetic moment.[37] Note however that the Lorentz transformation would lead to **700** $L_q = 1$ and **56** $L_q = 1$ if we use $[U(6) \times U(6)]_\beta$; these possibilities have not yet been checked.

The suggested picture should then be one in which we have several different $[U(6) \times U(6)]_\beta \times SL(3, R)_L$ representations, with Lorentz transformations varying the admixtures—or perhaps even similar $[U(6, 6)]_\beta \times SL(3, R)_L$ towers with representation-admixture. The (**56**, **1**) based tower has $L_q = 0$, and gets mixed with a tower based upon (**70**, **1**) with $L_q = 1$ (for the entire tower).

These assignments are just a first guess. A real check of the usefulness of the SGA could come via some sum-rule which would contain the matrix elements of a noncompact commutation relation; this has not been done to date.

REFERENCES

1. Y. Dothan, M. Gell-Mann, and Y. Ne'eman, *Phys. Letters* **17**, 148 (1965).
2. Y. Dothan and Y. Ne'eman, *Proc. 1965 Athens (Ohio) Conf. on Resonant Particles,* p. 17 (1965).
3. Y. Ne'eman, "The Algebraic Description of Hadron Matter and its Observational Implications," in "Topics in Elementary Particle Physics," *Proc. 1965 Pacific Summer School in Physics,* Gordon and Breach, New York, in press.
4. P. Budini and C. Fronsdal, *Phys. Rev. Letters* **14**, 968 (1965).

5. Y. Ne'eman, *Proc. of the Second Coral Gables Conf. on Symmetry Principles at High Energies*, W. H. Freeman Pub., San Francisco, 1965, p. 250 ff.
6. Y. Ne'eman, "Generalized Algebraic Methods in Particle Physics," in *Proc. 1965 Tokyo Summer Institute of Theoretical Physics*, H. Miyazawa and G. Takeda eds., Syokabo and W. A. Benjamin, Inc., Pubs., p. 68 (1966).
7. E. Gotsman and Y. Ne'eman, to be published in *Jour. Math. Phys.*
8. See for example, R. Dalitz, in *High Energy Physics*, Gordon and Breach, N.Y. (1966), p. 253; O. Sinanoglu, *Phys. Rev. Letters* **16**, 207 (1966).
9. S. Goshen and H. J. Lipkin, *Ann. of Phys.* **6**, 301 (1959).
10. Y. Dothan, M. Gell-Mann and Y. Ne'eman, to be published.
11. G. F. Chew and S. C. Frautschi, *Phys. Rev. Letters* **7**, 394 (1961).
12. S. C. Frautschi, M. Gell-Mann, and F. Zachariasen, *Phys. Rev.* **126**, 2204 (1962).
13. E. M. Stein and S. Wainger, *Arkiv for Matematik*, **5**, 553 (1965).
14. P. M. Morse and H. Feshbach, "Methods of Theoretical Physics," McGraw-Hill Pub., New York, 1953 Vol. 2, p. 1662.
15. S. C. Frautschi, "Regge Poles and S-Matrix Theory," W. A. Benjamin, Inc., New York, 1963, Chapter 10.
16. R. Hermann, in "High Energy Physics and Elementary Particles," *Proc. 1965 Trieste seminar, IAEA* (Vienna, 1965), p. 625 ff. discusses this formula of Gell-Mann's.
17. M. A. Naimark, *Uspehi Mat. Nank (N.S.)* **9**, No. 4 (62) 19 (1954), translated in *A., S. Translations*, Series 2, **6** 379 (1957).
18. The hydrogen spectrum corresponds to a representation of SO(2, 4) = SU(2, 2) which had been missed in former studies of the conformal group in spacetime, also an SU(2, 2), New classifications include it; it is the "most highly degenerate" representation in Kihlberg's list ("Comptes Rendus du Colloque International du C.N.R.S.

sur les extensions du groupe de Poincaré,") to be published.

19. H. J. Lipkin, "Lie Groups for Pedestrians," North Holland Pub., Amsterdam, 1965, p. 69.
20. G. Wentzel, *Helv. Phys. Acta* **13**, 269 (1940); **14**, 633 (1941); W. Pauli and S. M. Dancoff, *Phys. Rev.* **62**, 85 (1942); S. Tomonaga, *Prog. Theoret. Phys. (Kyoto)* **1**, 83 (1946); **1**, 109 (1946); **2**, 6 (1947).
21. E. M. Henley and W. Thirring, "Elementary Quantum Field Theory," McGraw-Hill, New York, 1962, p. 153 ff. This book contains an extremely readable review of all above-mentioned strong coupling models; we use in particular the results on pp. 188 and 192-194.
22. The $\Psi(\frac{5}{2}, \frac{5}{2})^+$ may have been observed by T. G. Schumann, *Phys. Rev. Letters* **15**, 531 (1965).
23. F. Gürsey and L. A. Radicati, *Phys. Rev. Letters* **13**, 173 (1964).
24. K. Bardakci, J. M. Cornwall, P. G. O. Freund, and B. W. Lee, *Phys. Rev. Letters* **13**, 698 (1964).
25. M. Gell-Mann, *Phys. Rev. Letters* **14**, 77 (1965).
26. G. Cocho, C. Fronsdal, Harun ar. Rashid and R. White, *Phys. Rev. Letters* **17**, 275 (1966).
27. Y. Ne'eman, in "Comptes Rendus du Col. CNRS sur l'Ext. du Groupe de Poincaré aux Sym. Int." Paris (1966), to be published.
28. J. P. Elliott, *Proc. Roy. Soc. (London)* **A245**, 128 (1958).
29. The states in the array (5) correspond to the **816** representation of SU(18) built upon an $L_q = 1$ quark (R. Hill, private communication).
30. R. W. Griffith, *Phys. Rev.* **147**, 1141 (1966).
31. R. Delbourgo, A. Salam and J. Stathdee, *Proc. Roy. Soc.* **289A**, 177 (1966).
32. S. Meshkov, *Proc. 1966 Third Coral Gables Conf. on Symmetry at High Energy*, p. 151.
33. The situation is rather confusing. The representation **1134** is suggested by an analysis of Y* resonances; see J. J. Coyne, S. Meshkov and G. B. Yodh, *Phys. Rev. Letters* **17**, 666 (1966).

34. R. G. Dashen and M. Gell-Mann, *Proc. 1966 Third Coral Gables Conf. on Symmetry at High Energies*, p. 168.
35. R. G. Dashen and M. Gell-Mann, *Phys. Rev. Letters* **17**, 340 (1966).
36. H. Harari, *Phys. Rev. Letters* **16**, 964 (1966).
37. H. Harari, *Phys. Rev. Letters* **17**, 56 (1966).

11

EPILOGUE

PATTERNS BEFORE STRUCTURE

Let us try and recapitulate and also gain some perspective.

The first factorization of matter into more basic constituents was achieved by chemistry in the nineteenth century. After a thousand years of fruitless experimentation by the alchemists, things really got going with Lavoisier's postulation of the law of conservation of matter (or mass). Dalton introduced his atomic theory, which implied in fact *a separate conservation law* for each one of the thirty-and-some (now 103) supposedly intransmutable elements. This was the absolutely necessary condition for the development of this science. Without conservation laws, there is nothing for the chemist to hang on to. The way was now open for the gradual discovery of the world of chemical elements; every microgram in a chemical reaction should be accountable throughout the entire sequence of combustions, dissolvings, distillations, etc.

One clever physicist, Prout, did however try to guess beyond that stage. He noted that most atomic weights seemed to have integer values when given in terms of the atomic weight of hydrogen. Did not this imply that matter was really of only one kind, with all atoms constructed from hydrogen atoms? We do know that Prout's hypothesis was almost right. Much credit is nowadays given to Prout for this long-range guess; I would like to take the opposite view and stress the dangerous risk presented by such premature and unfounded simplification.

It so happened that a few well-known chemical elements had fractional atomic weights: chlorine (35.5), silver (107.8), and so forth. This is why Prout's hypothesis was never seriously adopted. We now know that this is just because they are uneven isotopic mixtures, where the integer weights of several variants of the same element (35 and 37 for chlorine, 107 and 109 for silver) is averaged out. This is understood now, after several prolonged research efforts. First, the list of chemical elements had to be built up; meanwhile, a variety of new dynamical observables gradually evolved. Valency, ionization, chemical activity, etc.—the quantities which enter into the characterization of a chemical element—were recognized, defined and endowed with appropriate measurement techniques. The chemist learned his trade; he understood better what to search for. By the time the list of chemical elements numbered over 60 entries, enough of their characteristics were known for Mendeleyev and others to begin identifying a pattern. When appropriate weight had been given to the various characteristics, the accumulated list brought out a certain scheme of periodicity. Not the simplest of schemes—indeed Newland's guess at a simple "theory of octaves" was extremely faulty, forcing together such highly dissimilar elements as gold and iodine. Mendeleyev did better in reading out the pattern from the phenomenology, and left it for the next generation to solve the structural riddle originating it.

At the turn of the century, chemistry had indeed reached the structural stage. This was provided by Rutherford, Bohr, and the other atomicists. Atoms were found to resemble solar systems, rather than the Greek's perfect solids. As guessed by Prout, they all contained the same ingredients, with hydrogen offering a sample of two of the simplest bricks.

What would have happened if chlorine and silver on Earth

would have contained only one pure isotope and displayed integer atomic numbers? Imagine the shock to chemists if their assumption of the permanence and separate conservation of the elements would have been put in doubt. If everything is made out of hydrogen, why not transmute elements? If they are all really one single substance, there is indeed room for the alchemists' efforts and there is nothing to hang on to anymore in chemistry. No elements, no characteristics—back to the Middle Ages. We now know that all this is indeed true, transmutation can be achieved, but with reaction energies a million times larger than in the usual chemical reaction. Most elements are intransmutable within certain well-understood energetic limitations. It needed a century of gradual uncovering of the pattern until the structural picture where all this would be encompassed could be worked out.

For a long time the hope was held that everything in particle physics could be computed from first principles: from our understanding of the structure in terms of the apparel of quantum mechanics as it was in the twenties, or in terms of the field theory of the forties, or in terms of the know-all S matrix of the fifties. Presumably, that kind of thinking would have been abandoned by 1962-1963 when the number of hadron states was becoming unmanageable anyhow. Happily the algebraic approach had already started the "quasi-chemical" stage. The identification of conservations laws, exact and approximate, the discovery of the corresponding new dynamical observables characterizing the hadron world, the emergence of patterns—this is where we stand now. Gradually we see more of that pattern, and some semi-structural elements are in too.

Some day we may be able to go beyond this pattern-identification stage. Quarks and their like may yet land us in a world of subparticle physics with a very different set of basic laws; alternatively we shall perhaps really learn to use the bootstrap as a working piece of physics, not just as an idea. In the meantime, a lot more may have to be done at the level of simple matrix kaleidoscopy.

To be more explicit, there is nothing wrong in trying to

work at this stage upon the structure, but much more will probably have to be learned about the pattern before we understand the structure. Bootstraps do give a general feeling of a good basic idea; quarks certainly seem to fit much of what we now see in the pattern. However, it is possible that the final structural theory will bear little resemblance to either of these simple models. Much more will have to be learned about the composition of the hadron spectrum and about the behavior of the hadron Hamiltonian under the various algebra operators, both known and yet to be invented. Had we done it at the SU(3) stage without waiting for SU(6), we would have made baryons from 3 quarks in an antisymmetric juxtaposition, and thereby would never have understood the μ_p/μ_n ratio. This is a point the author emphasized with respect to the bootstrap in the early sixties; had we taken the bootstrap structural model too seriously, we would now be looking for broken SU(4) as the next step.[1] Instead, Gürsey and Radicati just went on to discover the pattern, and got us into more fruitful physics. One should probably be just as careful when dealing with molecular quark models.

THE MATRIX MECHANICS

To understand the pattern, it turned out to be important to inject unitary spin as an extra dynamical observable of hadron matter. Gell-Mann noted that the unitary spin generators are endowed with a material realization through their densities, which appear as currents in the electromagnetic and weak interactions. In fact, the algebra of unitary-spin generators closes under equal-time commutation, with the structure constants of this algebra of generators following the behavior of their densities, best expressed in the form of quark bilinears. This algebra happens at the same time to represent an approximate symmetry of hadron matter. Note that we have here a series of observations, all "structurally" unexplained, but correctly described in algebraic language. It is this method of mapping ever increasing sectors of hadron physics in terms of such operators that we may consider as a successful generalization of the methods of matrix mechanics.

Then came SU(6) and the other static or kinematical symmetries—again with quark-bilinear densities. Some of these densities had been used before, as "chiral" symmetry densities, realizing the axial vector current density components. The most complete system of that nature involved 144 densities and their space integrals; some parts could only represent a transition-operator algebra (and a very useful one), rather than an approximate symmetry.

Early in 1965 we did not know whether this physical algebra was compact or noncompact. The successful results of such calculations as the Dashen - Gell-Mann - Lee and Adler-Weisberger sum rules have since proved unequivocally that it is compact: U(12) and not U(6, 6). A theory in which the generator densities are described by quark-bilinears could still have been a U(6, 6) theory if it were provided with "orbital" expressions for its noncompact generators, their spin parts vanishing as they do in the Lorentz group. However, the above mentioned sum rules leave no room for any further doubt in this respect, as they fix the sign of the structure constants.

Little by little, there emerges a more complete picture of the generators' matrix elements. By working out a variety of sum rules, we observe which operators lead mainly to one-particle nearby states and generate approximate symmetries of the hadron Hilbert space. We also note that others seem to lead strongly out of the set of one-particle states of nearby energies; these are not useful as symmetry generators, they are mainly to be considered as useful transition operators. Finally, we may be able to understand the complete hadron pattern, by identifying its spectrum generating algebra. The systematics themselves may yet have to be "transferred" completely to a relativistic limit $\mathbf{p} \to \infty$.

More recently, we have gained some hope that we may perhaps be nearing a dynamical theory. Again it has emerged out of a pattern—a pattern of slow quasi-quarks which has been reexpressed as yet another piece of matrix dynamics—a theory of strong interaction currents based on the Regge picture of an exchange of trajectories. The theory is much more definite than the quark picture, with far reaching conclusions; let us wish not only that it will develop on its own, but also that its connections with the other algebras will be understood.

PATTERNS AGAIN

To discover the theory of evolution, the animal kingdom had first to be classified. To understand the atom, the chemical elements had first to be organized in the periodic table. To understand the 1/r potential of gravitation, Newton had to follow Kepler and the patterns he registered and systematized. We have certainly gone a long way in pattern identification in the hadron kingdom. All earlier attempts at a structural understanding were premature—whether based upon the know-all S matrix, upon spinning tops, rotators, or even upon known particles as basic constituents. Have we now reached the structural stage? This matrix mechanics method of ours continues the pattern mapping and provides some more insight into the physical interpretation of the classifying tools. There seems room for further continuation along the same line—or should we now let ourselves be carried off by the temptation of building up the hypothetical subparticle world of quarks? Instead, we may find a better understanding of the dynamics of strong interactions by developing the new idea of an algebra of factorized Regge residues. Let us hope that future experiments will enable us to make the wiser decision soon. In the meantime, let us enjoy the aesthetical features of the pattern. Quoting[2] the Swedish poet Harry Martinson in "Aniara," his epos of the space age, seems highly appropriate. Eight thousand immigrants flee radioactive earth to settle on Mars, but an accident makes them head irretrievably into the void (after all we are also living in a spaceship going nowhere). Strange captivating cults—the Yurg—develop in the subsequent period of despair, centered around a fantastic dream machine, the Mima.

"They come in relays. I see them livened
by Yurg and Cult, and cannot but admire

when, Yurg-entranced, they circle between mirrors
reflected eightfold in a mirrored world.
From all directions, swaying in the Yurg,
they seem themselves a dancing heavenly host
in all the glory of eightfold reflection.
Chebeba eight times over, eight times Yaal,
and Gena eight times in an octogonal hall."

REFERENCES

1) D. Neville, *Phys. Rev. Letters* **13**, 118 (1964).
2) H. Martinson, "Aniara," English translation by H. Macdiarmid and E. H. Schubert, publ. by Hutchinson of London (1963), song 36, p. 41.

APPENDIXES

APPENDIX I

Nonzero elements of f_{ijk} and d_{ijk}. The f_{ijk} are odd under permutations of any two indices while the d_{ijk} are even.

ijk	f_{ijk}
123	1
147	$\frac{1}{2}$
156	$-\frac{1}{2}$
246	$\frac{1}{2}$
257	$\frac{1}{2}$
345	$\frac{1}{2}$
367	$-\frac{1}{2}$
458	$\sqrt{3}/2$
678	$\sqrt{3}/2$

ijk	d_{ijk}
118	$1/\sqrt{3}$
146	$\frac{1}{2}$
157	$\frac{1}{2}$
228	$1/\sqrt{3}$
247	$-\frac{1}{2}$
256	$\frac{1}{2}$
338	$1/\sqrt{3}$
344	$\frac{1}{2}$
355	$\frac{1}{2}$
366	$-\frac{1}{2}$
377	$-\frac{1}{2}$
448	$-1/(2\sqrt{3})$
558	$-1/(2\sqrt{3})$
668	$-1/(2\sqrt{3})$
778	$-1/(2\sqrt{3})$
888	$-1/\sqrt{3}$

APPENDIX II

THE 8x8 PRODUCT†

Table II-1
The Crossing Matrix for the Octet Product

	{ee}	{f f}	{f d}	{d f}	{dd}	$\{\bar{b}b\}$	$\{b\bar{b}\}$	{aa}
{ee}	$\frac{1}{8}$	$-\frac{1}{8}$	0	0	$\frac{1}{8}$	$-\frac{1}{8}$	$-\frac{1}{8}$	$\frac{1}{8}$
{f f}	-1	$\frac{1}{2}$	0	0	$-\frac{1}{2}$	0	0	$\frac{1}{3}$
{f d}	0	0	$-\frac{1}{2}$	$\frac{1}{2}$	0	$\frac{1}{\sqrt{5}}$	$-\frac{1}{\sqrt{5}}$	0
{d f}	0	0	$\frac{1}{2}$	$-\frac{1}{2}$	0	$\frac{1}{\sqrt{5}}$	$-\frac{1}{\sqrt{5}}$	0
{dd}	1	$-\frac{1}{2}$	0	0	$-\frac{3}{10}$	$\frac{2}{5}$	$\frac{2}{5}$	$\frac{1}{5}$
$\{\bar{b}b\}$	$-\frac{5}{4}$	0	$\frac{\sqrt{5}}{4}$	$\frac{\sqrt{5}}{4}$	$\frac{1}{2}$	$\frac{1}{4}$	$\frac{1}{4}$	$\frac{1}{12}$
$\{b\bar{b}\}$	$-\frac{5}{4}$	0	$-\frac{\sqrt{5}}{4}$	$-\frac{\sqrt{5}}{4}$	$\frac{1}{2}$	$\frac{1}{4}$	$\frac{1}{4}$	$\frac{1}{12}$
{aa}	$\frac{27}{8}$	$\frac{9}{8}$	0	0	$\frac{27}{40}$	$\frac{9}{40}$	$\frac{9}{40}$	$\frac{7}{40}$

(Notation for the Table appears on next page.)

---

*Reprinted from H. Goldberg, "The Crossing Matrix in the Gell-Mann–Ne'eman Model," Israel Atomic Energy Commission report 1A-834, 1963.

†Phase conventions differ among authors. Proper care should

The following notation was used:

$\{aa\}$ is the scalar appearing in (22) × (22)
$\{b\bar{b}\}$ is the scalar appearing in (30) × (03)
$\{\bar{b}b\}$ is the scalar appearing in (03) × (30)
$\{dd\}$ is the scalar appearing in $(11)^+ \times (11)^+$
$\{df\}$ is the scalar appearing in $(11)^+ \times (11)^-$
$\{fd\}$ is the scalar appearing in $(11)^- \times (11)^+$
$\{ff\}$ is the scalar appearing in $(11)^- \times (11)^-$
$\{ee\}$ is the scalar appearing in (00) × (00)

Table II-2
Correspondance of Octet-Vectors and Particles

Vector	Y	T	T_z	Baryons	Anti-Baryons	Mesons	Vector-Mesons
1	1	$\frac{1}{2}$	$\frac{1}{2}$	p	$\overline{\Xi^-}$	K^+	K^{*+}
2	1	$\frac{1}{2}$	$-\frac{1}{2}$	n	$\overline{\Xi^0}$	K^0	K^{*0}
3	0	1	1	Σ^+	$\overline{\Sigma^-}$	Π^+	ρ^+
4	0	0	0	Λ	$\overline{\Lambda}$	η^0	$\frac{1}{\sqrt{3}}(\omega\sqrt{2}-\phi)$
5	0	1	0	Σ^0	$\overline{\Sigma^0}$	Π^0	ρ^0
6	0	1	-1	Σ^-	$\overline{\Sigma^+}$	Π^-	ρ^-
7	-1	$\frac{1}{2}$	$\frac{1}{2}$	Ξ^0	$\overline{n}$	$\overline{K^0}$	$\overline{K^{*0}}$
8	-1	$\frac{1}{2}$	$-\frac{1}{2}$	Ξ^-	$\overline{p}$	K^-	K^{*-}

be taken in using these tables, mainly when comparing with results computed from different ones.

Table II-3
Reduction of the Basis of (11) × (11)
(ab) = ab + ba; (aa) = 2aa; [ab] = ab − ba

Vector	Weight			Y	T	T_z	
							(a) The basis of (22), i.e., **27**
x(1)	2	0	−2	2	1	1	$\frac{1}{2}(11)$
x(2)	2	−1	−1	2	1	0	$\sqrt{\frac{1}{2}}\,(12)$
x(3)	2	−2	0	2	1	−1	$\frac{1}{2}(22)$
x(4)	1	1	−2	1	$\frac{3}{2}$	$\frac{3}{2}$	$\sqrt{\frac{1}{2}}\,(13)$
x(5)	1	0	−1	1	$\frac{1}{2}$	$\frac{1}{2}$	$\sqrt{\frac{1}{30}}\,\{3\sqrt{\frac{3}{2}}\,(14) + \sqrt{\frac{1}{2}}\,(15) + (23)\}$
x(6)	1	0	−1	1	$\frac{3}{2}$	$\frac{1}{2}$	$\sqrt{\frac{1}{6}}\,\{-(23) + \sqrt{2}\,(15)\}$
x(7)	1	−1	0	1	$\frac{1}{2}$	$-\frac{1}{2}$	$\sqrt{\frac{1}{30}}\,\{(16) + 3\sqrt{\frac{3}{2}}\,(24) - \sqrt{\frac{1}{2}}\,(25)\}$
x(8)	1	−1	0	1	$\frac{3}{2}$	$-\frac{1}{2}$	$\sqrt{\frac{1}{6}}\,\{(16) + \sqrt{2}\,(25)\}$
x(9)	1	−2	1	1	$\frac{3}{2}$	$-\frac{3}{2}$	$\sqrt{\frac{1}{2}}\,(26)$
x(10)	0	2	−2	0	2	2	$\frac{1}{2}(33)$
x(11)	0	1	−1	0	1	1	$\sqrt{\frac{1}{5}}\,\{(17) - \sqrt{\frac{3}{2}}\,(34)\}$
x(12)	0	1	−1	0	2	1	$\sqrt{\frac{1}{2}}\,(35)$

x(13)	0	0	0	0	0	0	$\frac{1}{2}\sqrt{\frac{1}{30}}\{3(18) + 3(27) - (36) - \frac{9}{2}(44) - \frac{1}{2}(55)\}$
x(14)	0	0	0	0	1	0	$\sqrt{\frac{1}{10}}\{(18) - (27) - \sqrt{3}\ (45)\}$
x(15)	0	0	0	0	2	0	$\sqrt{\frac{1}{6}}\{(36) - (55)\}$
x(16)	0	−1	1	0	1	−1	$\sqrt{\frac{1}{5}}\{(28) - \sqrt{\frac{3}{2}}\,(46)\}$
x(17)	0	−1	1	0	2	−1	$\sqrt{\frac{1}{2}}\,(56)$
x(18)	0	−2	2	0	2	−2	$\frac{1}{2}(66)$
x(19)	−1	2	−1	−1	$\frac{3}{2}$	$\frac{3}{2}$	$\sqrt{\frac{1}{2}}\,(37)$
x(20)	−1	1	0	−1	$\frac{1}{2}$	$\frac{1}{2}$	$\sqrt{\frac{1}{30}}\{(38) + 3\sqrt{\frac{3}{2}}(47) - \sqrt{\frac{1}{2}}\,(57)\}$
x(21)	−1	1	0	−1	$\frac{3}{2}$	$\frac{1}{2}$	$\sqrt{\frac{1}{6}}\{(38) + \sqrt{2}\,(57)\}$
x(22)	−1	0	1	−1	$\frac{1}{2}$	$-\frac{1}{2}$	$\sqrt{\frac{1}{30}}\{3\sqrt{\frac{3}{2}}(48) + \sqrt{\frac{1}{2}}\,(58) + (67)\}$
x(23)	−1	0	1	−1	$\frac{3}{2}$	$-\frac{1}{2}$	$\sqrt{\frac{1}{6}}\{\sqrt{2}\,(58) - (67)\}$
x(24)	−1	−1	2	−1	$\frac{3}{2}$	$-\frac{3}{2}$	$\sqrt{\frac{1}{2}}\,(68)$
x(25)	−2	2	0	−2	1	1	$\frac{1}{2}(77)$
x(26)	−2	1	1	−2	1	0	$\sqrt{\frac{1}{2}}\,(78)$
x(27)	−2	0	2	−2	1	−1	$\frac{1}{2}(88)$

(continued)

Table II-3 (continued)

Vector	Weight			Y	T	T_z	
							(b) The basis of $(11)^{+}$, i.e., 8^{D}
y(1)	1	0	−1	1	$\frac{1}{2}$	$\frac{1}{2}$	$\sqrt{\frac{3}{10}}\{-\sqrt{\frac{1}{6}}(14)+\sqrt{\frac{1}{2}}(15)+(23)\}$
y(2)	1	−1	0	1	$\frac{1}{2}$	$-\frac{1}{2}$	$\sqrt{\frac{3}{10}}\{(16)-\sqrt{\frac{1}{6}}(24)-\sqrt{\frac{1}{2}}(25)\}$
y(3)	0	1	−1	0	1	1	$\sqrt{\frac{1}{5}}\{\sqrt{\frac{3}{2}}(17)+(34)\}$
y(4)	0	0	0	0	0	0	$-\sqrt{\frac{1}{20}}\{(18)+(27)-2(36)+(44)-(55)\}$
y(5)	0	0	0	0	1	0	$\sqrt{\frac{3}{20}}\{(18)-(27)+2\sqrt{\frac{1}{3}}(45)\}$
y(6)	0	−1	1	0	1	−1	$\sqrt{\frac{1}{5}}\{\sqrt{\frac{3}{2}}(28)+(46)\}$
y(7)	−1	1	0	−1	$\frac{1}{2}$	$\frac{1}{2}$	$\sqrt{\frac{3}{10}}\{(38)-\sqrt{\frac{1}{6}}(47)-\sqrt{\frac{1}{2}}(57)\}$
y(8)	−1	0	1	−1	$\frac{1}{2}$	$-\frac{1}{2}$	$\sqrt{\frac{3}{10}}\{(67)-\sqrt{\frac{1}{6}}(48)+\sqrt{\frac{1}{2}}(58)\}$

To recover Gell-Mann's normalization for d^{ijk}, multiply by $\sqrt{\frac{5}{3}}$

(c) The basis of (00), i.e., **1**

w(1)	0	0	0	0	0	0	$\frac{1}{2}\sqrt{\frac{1}{2}}\,\{(18) + (27) + (36) + \frac{1}{2}(44) + \frac{1}{2}(55)\}$

(d) The basis of (30), i.e., **10***

u(1)	2	−1	−1	2	0	0	$\sqrt{\frac{1}{2}}\,[12]$
u(2)	1	0	−1	1	$\frac{1}{2}$	$\frac{1}{2}$	$\sqrt{\frac{1}{6}}\,\{\sqrt{\frac{3}{2}}\,[14] - \sqrt{\frac{1}{2}}\,[15] - [23]\}$
u(3)	1	−1	0	1	$\frac{1}{2}$	$-\frac{1}{2}$	$\sqrt{\frac{1}{6}}\,\{-[16] + \sqrt{\frac{3}{2}}\,[24] + \sqrt{\frac{1}{2}}\,[25]\}$
u(4)	0	1	−1	0	1	1	$\sqrt{\frac{1}{6}}\,\{[17] - \sqrt{\frac{3}{2}}\,[34] + \sqrt{\frac{1}{2}}\,[35]\}$
u(5)	0	0	0	0	1	0	$\frac{1}{2}\sqrt{\frac{1}{3}}\,\{-[18] + [27] + [36] - \sqrt{3}\,[45]\}$
u(6)	0	−1	1	0	1	−1	$\sqrt{\frac{1}{6}}\,\{[28] + \sqrt{\frac{3}{2}}\,[46] + \sqrt{\frac{1}{2}}\,[56]\}$
u(7)	−1	2	−1	−1	$\frac{3}{2}$	$\frac{3}{2}$	$\sqrt{\frac{1}{2}}\,[37]$
u(8)	−1	1	0	−1	$\frac{3}{2}$	$\frac{1}{2}$	$\sqrt{\frac{1}{6}}\,\{[38] + \sqrt{2}\,[57]\}$
u(9)	−1	0	1	−1	$\frac{3}{2}$	$-\frac{1}{2}$	$\sqrt{\frac{1}{6}}\,\{-[67] + \sqrt{2}\,[58]\}$
u(10)	−1	−1	2	−1	$\frac{3}{2}$	$-\frac{3}{2}$	$\sqrt{\frac{1}{2}}\,[68]$

(continued)

Table II-3 (continued)

Vector	Weight			Y	T	T_z	
					(e) The basis of (03), i.e., **10**		
v(1)	1	1	−2	1	$\frac{3}{2}$	$\frac{3}{2}$	$\sqrt{\frac{1}{2}}\,[13]$
v(2)	1	0	−1	1	$\frac{3}{2}$	$\frac{1}{2}$	$\sqrt{\frac{1}{6}}\,\{\sqrt{2}\,[15] - [23]\}$
v(3)	1	−1	0	1	$\frac{3}{2}$	$-\frac{1}{2}$	$\sqrt{\frac{1}{6}}\,\{[16] + \sqrt{2}\,[25]\}$
v(4)	1	−2	1	1	$\frac{3}{2}$	$-\frac{3}{2}$	$\sqrt{\frac{1}{2}}\,[26]$
v(5)	0	1	−1	0	1	1	$\sqrt{\frac{1}{6}}\,\{[17] + \sqrt{\frac{3}{2}}\,[34] + \sqrt{\frac{1}{2}}\,[35]\}$
v(6)	0	0	0	0	1	0	$\frac{1}{2}\sqrt{\frac{1}{3}}\,\{-[18] + [27] + [36] + \sqrt{3}\,[45]\}$
v(7)	0	−1	1	0	1	−1	$\sqrt{\frac{1}{6}}\,\{-\sqrt{\frac{3}{2}}\,[46] + \sqrt{\frac{1}{2}}\,[56] + [28]\}$
v(8)	−1	1	0	−1	$\frac{1}{2}$	$\frac{1}{2}$	$\sqrt{\frac{1}{6}}\,\{-[38] + \sqrt{\frac{3}{2}}\,[47] + \sqrt{\frac{1}{2}}\,[57]\}$
v(9)	−1	0	1	−1	$\frac{1}{2}$	$-\frac{1}{2}$	$\sqrt{\frac{1}{6}}\,\{\sqrt{\frac{3}{2}}\,[48] - \sqrt{\frac{1}{2}}\,[58] - [67]\}$
v(10)	−2	1	1	−2	0	0	$\sqrt{\frac{1}{2}}\,[78]$

(f) The basis of $(11)^-$, i.e., $\mathbf{8}^F$

z(1)	1	0	1	1	$\frac{1}{2}$	$\frac{1}{2}$	$\sqrt{\frac{1}{6}}\{\sqrt{\frac{3}{2}}[14] + \sqrt{\frac{1}{2}}[15] + [23]\}$
z(2)	1	−1	0	1	$\frac{1}{2}$	$-\frac{1}{2}$	$\sqrt{\frac{1}{6}}\{[16] + \sqrt{\frac{3}{2}}[24] - \sqrt{\frac{1}{2}}[25]\}$
z(3)	0	1	−1	0	1	1	$\sqrt{\frac{1}{6}}\{-[17] + \sqrt{2}[35]\}$
z(4)	0	0	0	0	0	0	$-\frac{1}{2}\{[18] + [27]\}$
z(5)	0	0	0	0	1	0	$-\frac{1}{2}\sqrt{\frac{1}{3}}\{[18] - [27] + 2[36]\}$
z(6)	0	−1	1	0	1	−1	$\sqrt{\frac{1}{6}}\{-[28] + \sqrt{2}[56]\}$
z(7)	−1	0	1	−1	$\frac{1}{2}$	$\frac{1}{2}$	$\sqrt{\frac{1}{6}}\{[38] + \sqrt{\frac{3}{2}}[47] - \sqrt{\frac{1}{2}}[57]\}$
z(8)	−1	0	1	−1	$\frac{1}{2}$	$-\frac{1}{2}$	$\sqrt{\frac{1}{6}}\{\sqrt{\frac{3}{2}}[48] + \sqrt{\frac{1}{2}}[58] + [67]\}$

To recover Gell-Mann's normalization for f^{ijk}, multiply by $\sqrt{3}$.

To find quantum numbers:

$$i_z = \sqrt{3}\, z(5)$$

$$y = 2z(4)$$

$$Q/e = \sqrt{3}\, z(5) + z(4)$$

d-type electric form factor: $[\sqrt{3}\, y(5) + y(4)]\,\frac{\sqrt{5}}{3}$

Example: z(6) for $\overline{B}B$ would be

$$\sqrt{\tfrac{1}{6}}\{-(\overline{\Xi}^0\Xi^- - \bar{p}n) + \sqrt{2}\,(\overline{\Sigma}^0\Sigma^- - \overline{\Sigma}^+\Sigma^0)\}$$

Table II-4
The Scalars Which Appear in the Basis
of (11) × (11) × (11) × (11)

$$\{ee\} = w(1)\overline{w(1)}$$

$$\{f\,f\} = z(1)\overline{z(8)} + z(2)\overline{z(7)} + z(3)\overline{z(6)} + z(4)\overline{z(4)} + z(5)\overline{z(5)}$$
$$+ z(6)\overline{z(3)} + z(7)\overline{z(2)} + z(8)\overline{z(1)}$$

$$\{f\,d\} = z(1)\overline{y(8)} + z(2)\overline{y(7)} + z(3)\overline{y(6)} + z(4)\overline{y(4)} + z(5)\overline{y(5)}$$
$$+ z(6)\overline{y(3)} + z(7)\overline{y(2)} + z(8)\overline{y(1)}$$

$$\{d\,f\} = y(1)\overline{z(8)} + y(2)\overline{z(7)} + y(3)\overline{z(6)} + y(4)\overline{z(4)} + y(5)\overline{z(5)}$$
$$+ y(6)\overline{z(3)} + y(7)\overline{z(2)} + y(8)\overline{z(1)}$$

$$\{dd\} \quad y(1)\overline{y(8)} + y(2)\overline{y(7)} + y(3)\overline{y(6)} + y(4)\overline{y(4)} + y(5)\overline{y(5)}$$
$$+ y(6)\overline{y(3)} + y(7)\overline{y(2)} + y(8)\overline{y(1)}$$

$$\{\bar{b}b\} = v(1)\overline{u(10)} + v(2)\overline{u(9)} + v(3)\overline{u(8)} + v(4)\overline{u(7)} + v(5)\overline{u(6)}$$
$$+ v(6)\overline{u(5)} + v(7)\overline{u(4)} + v(8)\overline{u(3)} + v(9)\overline{u(2)} + v(10)\overline{u(1)}$$

$$\{b\bar{b}\} = u(1)\overline{v(10)} + u(2)\overline{v(9)} + u(3)\overline{v(8)} + u(4)\overline{v(7)} + u(5)\overline{v(6)}$$
$$+ u(6)\overline{v(5)} + u(7)\overline{v(4)} + u(8)\overline{v(3)} + u(9)\overline{v(2)} + u(10)\overline{v(1)}$$

$$\{aa\} = x(1)\overline{x(27)} + x(2)\overline{x(26)} + x(3)\overline{x(25)} + x(4)\overline{x(24)}$$
$$+ x(5)\overline{x(22)} + x(6)\overline{x(23)} + x(7)\overline{x(20)} + x(8)\overline{x(21)}$$
$$+ x(9)\overline{x(19)} + x(10)\overline{x(18)} + x(11)\overline{x(16)} + x(12)\overline{x(17)}$$
$$+ x(13)\overline{x(13)} + x(14)\overline{x(14)} + x(15)\overline{x(15)}$$

(The unbarred factor in each summand is a tensor built out of vectors of the first and second bases of (11); the barred factor is a tensor built out of vectors of the third and fourth bases.)

Table II-5
The Representation (11) or **8**

E_3^1 $x(4) \rightarrow -\sqrt{\frac{3}{2}}x(1)$	E_3^2 $x(3) \rightarrow -x(1)$	E_2^1 $x(2) \rightarrow x(1)$
$x(5) \rightarrow -\sqrt{\frac{1}{2}}x(1)$	$x(4) \rightarrow -\sqrt{\frac{3}{2}}x(2)$	$x(5) \rightarrow -\sqrt{2}x(3)$
$x(6) \rightarrow -x(2)$	$x(5) \rightarrow \sqrt{\frac{1}{2}}x(2)$	$x(6) \rightarrow \sqrt{2}x(6)$
$x(7) \rightarrow x(3)$	$x(7) \rightarrow \sqrt{\frac{3}{2}}x(4) - \sqrt{\frac{1}{2}}x(5)$	$x(8) \rightarrow -x(7)$
$x(8) \rightarrow \sqrt{\frac{3}{2}}x(4) + \sqrt{\frac{1}{2}}x(5)$	$x(8) \rightarrow x(6)$	
E_1^3 $x(1) \rightarrow -\sqrt{\frac{3}{2}}x(4) - \sqrt{\frac{1}{2}}x(5)$	E_2^3 $x(1) \rightarrow -x(3)$	E_1^2 $x(1) \rightarrow x(2)$
$x(2) \rightarrow -x(6)$	$x(2) \rightarrow -\sqrt{\frac{3}{2}}x(4) + \sqrt{\frac{1}{2}}x(5)$	$x(3) \rightarrow -\sqrt{2}x(5)$
$x(3) \rightarrow x(7)$	$x(4) \rightarrow \sqrt{\frac{3}{2}}x(7)$	$x(5) \rightarrow \sqrt{2}x(6)$
$x(4) \rightarrow \sqrt{\frac{3}{2}}x(8)$	$x(5) \rightarrow -\sqrt{\frac{1}{2}}x(7)$	$x(7) \rightarrow -x(8)$
$x(5) \rightarrow \sqrt{\frac{1}{2}}x(8)$	$x(6) \rightarrow x(8)$	

Table II-6
The Representation (03) or **10**

E_3^1	$x(5) \to \sqrt{3}\,x(1)$		E_3^2	$x(5) \to -\,x(2)$		E_2^1	$x(2) \to -\sqrt{3}\,x(1)$	
	$x(6) \to \sqrt{2}\,x(2)$			$x(6) \to -\,\sqrt{2}\,x(3)$			$x(3) \to 2x(2)$	
	$x(7) \to x(3)$			$x(7) \to \sqrt{3}\,x(4)$			$x(4) \to \sqrt{3}\,x(3)$	
	$x(8) \to -2x(5)$			$x(8) \to -\sqrt{2}\,x(6)$			$x(6) \to \sqrt{2}\,x(5)$	
	$x(9) \to \sqrt{2}\,x(6)$			$x(9) \to -2x(7)$			$x(7) \to -\,\sqrt{2}\,x(6)$	
	$x(10) \to \sqrt{3}\,x(8)$			$x(10) \to \sqrt{3}\,x(9)$			$x(9) \to -\,x(8)$	
E_1^3	$x(1) \to \sqrt{3}\,x(5)$		E_2^3	$x(2) \to -x(5)$		E_1^2	$x(1) \to -\sqrt{3}\,x(2)$	
	$x(2) \to -\sqrt{2}\,x(6)$			$x(3) \to -\sqrt{2}\,x(6)$			$x(2) \to 2x(3)$	
	$x(3) \to x(7)$			$x(4) \to \sqrt{3}\,x(7)$			$x(3) \to \sqrt{3}\,x(4)$	
	$x(5) \to -2x(8)$			$x(6) \to -\sqrt{2}\,x(8)$			$x(5) \to \sqrt{2}\,x(6)$	
	$x(6) \to \sqrt{2}\,x(9)$			$x(7) \to -2x(9)$			$x(6) \to -\sqrt{2}\,x(7)$	
	$x(8) \to -\sqrt{3}\,x(10)$			$x(9) \to \sqrt{3}\,x(10)$			$x(8) \to -x(9)$	

Table II-7
The Representation (30) or **10***

E_3^1	$x(3) \to \sqrt{3}\,x(1)$	E_3^2	$x(2) \to -\sqrt{3}\,x(1)$	E_2^1	$x(3) \to x(2)$
	$x(5) \to -\sqrt{2}\,x(2)$		$x(4) \to 2x(2)$		$x(5) \to \sqrt{2}\,x(4)$
	$x(6) \to 2x(3)$		$x(5) \to \sqrt{2}\,x(3)$		$x(6) \to -\sqrt{2}\,x(5)$
	$x(8) \to -x(4)$		$x(7) \to -\sqrt{3}\,x(4)$		$x(8) \to -\sqrt{3}\,x(7)$
	$x(9) \to \sqrt{2}\,x(5)$		$x(8) \to \sqrt{2}\,x(5)$		$x(9) \to -2x(8)$
	$x(10) \to -\sqrt{3}\,x(6)$		$x(9) \to x(6)$		$x(10) \to \sqrt{3}\,x(9)$
E_1^3	$x(1) \to \sqrt{3}\,x(3)$	E_2^3	$x(1) \to -\sqrt{3}\,x(2)$	E_1^2	$x(2) \to x(3)$
	$x(2) \to -\sqrt{2}\,x(5)$		$x(2) \to 2x(4)$		$x(4) \to \sqrt{2}\,x(5)$
	$x(3) \to 2x(6)$		$x(3) \to +\sqrt{2}\,x(5)$		$x(5) \to -\sqrt{2}\,x(6)$
	$x(4) \to -x(8)$		$x(4) \to -\sqrt{3}\,x(7)$		$x(7) \to -\sqrt{3}\,x(8)$
	$x(5) \to \sqrt{2}\,x(9)$		$x(5) \to \sqrt{2}\,x(8)$		$x(8) \to -2x(9)$
	$x(6) \to -\sqrt{3}\,x(10)$		$x(6) \to x(9)$		$x(9) \to \sqrt{3}\,x(10)$

Table II-8
The Representation (22) or **27**

E_3^1	E_3^2	E_2^1
$x(5) \to -\sqrt{\frac{10}{3}}\, x(1)$	$x(4) \to -\sqrt{2}\, x(1)$	$x(2) \to \sqrt{2}\, x(1)$
$x(6) \to -\sqrt{\frac{2}{3}}\, x(1)$	$x(5) \to -\sqrt{\frac{5}{3}}\, x(2)$	$x(3) \to \sqrt{2}\, x(2)$
$x(7) \to -\sqrt{\frac{5}{3}}\, x(2)$	$x(6) \to \frac{2}{\sqrt{3}}\, x(2)$	$x(6) \to -\sqrt{3}\, x(4)$
$x(8) \to -\frac{2}{\sqrt{3}}\, x(2)$	$x(7) \to -\sqrt{\frac{10}{3}}\, x(3)$	$x(7) \to x(5)$
$x(9) \to -\sqrt{2}\, x(3)$	$x(8) \to \sqrt{\frac{2}{3}}\, x(3)$	$x(8) \to 2x(6)$
$x(11) \to \sqrt{\frac{5}{2}}\, x(4)$	$x(10) \to -\sqrt{2}\, x(4)$	$x(9) \to \sqrt{3}\, x(8)$
$x(12) \to -\sqrt{\frac{1}{2}}\, x(4)$	$x(11) \to \sqrt{\frac{8}{3}}\, x(5) - \sqrt{\frac{5}{6}}\, x(6)$	$x(12) \to -2x(10)$
$x(13) \to 2x(5)$	$x(12) \to -\sqrt{\frac{3}{2}}\, x(6)$	$x(14) \to -\sqrt{2}\, x(11)$
$x(14) \to \frac{2}{\sqrt{3}}\, x(5) + \sqrt{\frac{5}{3}}\, x(6)$	$x(13) \to 2x(7)$	$x(15) \to \sqrt{6}\, x(12)$
$x(15) \to x(6)$	$x(14) \to -\frac{2}{\sqrt{3}}\, x(7) + \sqrt{\frac{5}{3}}\, x(8)$	$x(16) \to \sqrt{2}\, x(14)$
$x(16) \to 2\sqrt{\frac{2}{3}}\, x(7) + \sqrt{\frac{5}{6}}\, x(8)$	$x(15) \to -x(8)$	$x(17) \to -\sqrt{6}\, x(15)$

$x(17) \rightarrow -\sqrt{\tfrac{3}{2}}\, x(8)$

$x(18) \rightarrow -\sqrt{2}\, x(9)$

$x(19) \rightarrow \sqrt{2}\, x(10)$

$x(20) \rightarrow -2\sqrt{\tfrac{2}{3}}\, x(11)$

$x(21) \rightarrow -\sqrt{\tfrac{5}{6}}\, x(11) + \sqrt{\tfrac{3}{2}}\, x(12)$

$x(22) \rightarrow -2x(13) - \frac{2}{\sqrt{3}}\, x(14)$

$x(23) \rightarrow -\sqrt{\tfrac{5}{3}}\, x(14) - x(15)$

$x(24) \rightarrow -\sqrt{\tfrac{5}{2}}\, x(16) + \sqrt{\tfrac{1}{2}}\, x(17)$

$x(25) \rightarrow \sqrt{2}\, x(19)$

$x(26) \rightarrow \sqrt{\tfrac{5}{3}}\, x(20) + \frac{2}{\sqrt{3}}\, x(21)$

$x(27) \rightarrow \sqrt{\tfrac{10}{3}}\, x(22) + \sqrt{\tfrac{2}{3}}\, x(23)$

$x(16) \rightarrow \sqrt{\tfrac{5}{2}}\, x(9)$

$x(17) \rightarrow \sqrt{\tfrac{1}{2}}\, x(9)$

$x(19) \rightarrow -\sqrt{\tfrac{5}{2}}\, x(11) - \sqrt{\tfrac{1}{2}}\, x(12)$

$x(20) \rightarrow -2x(13) + \frac{2}{\sqrt{3}}\, x(14)$

$x(21) \rightarrow -\sqrt{\tfrac{5}{3}}\, x(14) + x(15)$

$x(22) \rightarrow -2\sqrt{\tfrac{2}{3}}\, x(16)$

$x(23) \rightarrow \sqrt{\tfrac{5}{6}}\, x(16) + \sqrt{\tfrac{3}{2}}\, x(17)$

$x(24) \rightarrow \sqrt{2}\, x(18)$

$x(25) \rightarrow \sqrt{\tfrac{10}{3}}\, x(20) - \sqrt{\tfrac{2}{3}}\, x(21)$

$x(26) \rightarrow \sqrt{\tfrac{5}{3}}\, x(22) - 2\sqrt{\tfrac{1}{3}}\, x(23)$

$x(27) \rightarrow \sqrt{2}\, x(24)$

$x(18) \rightarrow 2x(17)$

$x(21) \rightarrow -\sqrt{3}\, x(19)$

$x(22) \rightarrow -x(20)$

$x(23) \rightarrow -2x(21)$

$x(24) \rightarrow \sqrt{3}\, x(23)$

$x(26) \rightarrow -\sqrt{2}\, x(25)$

$x(27) \rightarrow -\sqrt{2}\, x(26)$

(continued)

Table II-8 (continued)

E_1^3	x(1)	$\rightarrow -\sqrt{\frac{10}{3}}\,x(5) - \sqrt{\frac{2}{3}}\,x(6)$
	x(2)	$\rightarrow -\sqrt{\frac{5}{3}}\,x(7) - \frac{2}{\sqrt{3}}\,x(8)$
	x(3)	$\rightarrow -\sqrt{2}\,x(9)$
	x(4)	$\rightarrow \sqrt{\frac{5}{2}}\,x(11) - \sqrt{\frac{1}{2}}\,x(12)$
	x(5)	$\rightarrow 2x(13) + \frac{2}{\sqrt{3}}\,x(14)$
	x(6)	$\rightarrow \sqrt{\frac{5}{3}}\,x(14) + x(15)$
	x(7)	$\rightarrow 2\sqrt{\frac{2}{3}}\,x(16)$
	x(8)	$\rightarrow \sqrt{\frac{5}{6}}\,x(16) - \sqrt{\frac{3}{2}}\,x(17)$
	x(9)	$\rightarrow -\sqrt{2}\,x(18)$
	x(10)	$\rightarrow \sqrt{2}\,x(19)$
	x(11)	$\rightarrow -2\sqrt{\frac{2}{3}}\,x(20) - \sqrt{\frac{5}{6}}\,x(21)$

E_2^3	x(1)	$\rightarrow -\sqrt{2}\,x(4)$
	x(2)	$\rightarrow -\sqrt{\frac{5}{3}}\,x(5) + \frac{2}{\sqrt{3}}\,x(6)$
	x(3)	$\rightarrow -\sqrt{\frac{10}{3}}\,x(7) + \sqrt{\frac{2}{3}}\,x(8)$
	x(4)	$\rightarrow -\sqrt{2}\,x(10)$
	x(5)	$\rightarrow 2\sqrt{\frac{2}{3}}\,x(11)$
	x(6)	$\rightarrow -\sqrt{\frac{5}{6}}\,x(11) - \sqrt{\frac{3}{2}}\,x(12)$
	x(7)	$\rightarrow 2x(13) - \frac{2}{\sqrt{3}}\,x(14)$
	x(8)	$\rightarrow \sqrt{\frac{5}{3}}\,x(14) - x(15)$
	x(9)	$\rightarrow \sqrt{\frac{5}{2}}\,x(16) + \sqrt{\frac{1}{2}}\,x(17)$
	x(11)	$\rightarrow -\sqrt{\frac{5}{2}}\,x(19)$
	x(12)	$\rightarrow -\sqrt{\frac{1}{2}}\,x(19)$

E_1^2	x(1)	$\rightarrow \sqrt{2}\,x(2)$
	x(2)	$\rightarrow \sqrt{2}\,x(3)$
	x(4)	$\rightarrow -\sqrt{3}\,x(6)$
	x(5)	$\rightarrow x(7)$
	x(6)	$\rightarrow 2x(8)$
	x(8)	$\rightarrow \sqrt{3}\,x(9)$
	x(10)	$\rightarrow -2x(12)$
	x(11)	$\rightarrow -\sqrt{2}\,x(14)$
	x(12)	$\rightarrow \sqrt{6}\,x(15)$
	x(14)	$\rightarrow \sqrt{2}\,x(16)$
	x(15)	$\rightarrow -\sqrt{6}\,x(17)$

$x(12) \to \sqrt{\tfrac{3}{2}}\, x(21)$

$x(13) \to -2x(22)$

$x(14) \to -\dfrac{2}{\sqrt{3}}\, x(22) - \sqrt{\tfrac{5}{3}}\, x(23)$

$x(15) \to -x(23)$

$x(16) \to -\sqrt{\tfrac{5}{2}}\, x(24)$

$x(17) \to \sqrt{\tfrac{1}{2}}\, x(24)$

$x(19) \to \sqrt{2}\, x(25)$

$x(20) \to \sqrt{\tfrac{5}{3}}\, x(26)$

$x(21) \to \dfrac{2}{\sqrt{3}}\, x(26)$

$x(22) \to \sqrt{\tfrac{10}{3}}\, x(27)$

$x(23) \to \sqrt{\tfrac{2}{3}}\, x(27)$

$x(13) \to -2x(20)$

$x(14) \to \dfrac{2}{\sqrt{3}}\, x(20) - \sqrt{\tfrac{5}{3}}\, x(21)$

$x(15) \to x(21)$

$x(16) \to -2\sqrt{\tfrac{2}{3}}\, x(22) + \sqrt{\tfrac{5}{6}}\, x(23)$

$x(17) \to \sqrt{\tfrac{3}{2}}\, x(23)$

$x(18) \to \sqrt{2}\, x(24)$

$x(20) \to \sqrt{\tfrac{10}{3}}\, x(25)$

$x(21) \to -\sqrt{\tfrac{2}{3}}\, x(25)$

$x(22) \to \sqrt{\tfrac{5}{3}}\, x(26)$

$x(23) \to -2\sqrt{\tfrac{1}{3}}\, x(26)$

$x(24) \to \sqrt{2}\, x(27)$

$x(17) \to 2x(18)$

$x(19) \to -\sqrt{3}\, x(21)$

$x(20) \to -x(22)$

$x(21) \to -2x(23)$

$x(23) \to \sqrt{3}\, x(24)$

$x(25) \to -\sqrt{2}\, x(26)$

$x(26) \to -\sqrt{2}\, x(27)$

APPENDIX III

THE KILLING-CARTAN CLASSIFICATION OF LIE ALGEBRAS OVER THE COMPLEX NUMBERS

There are four infinite series termed "classical,"

A_r – the algebras of traceless $(r + 1)$ – dimensional matrices, with p (number of parameters) = $(r + 1)^2 - 1$

B_r – the algebras of orthogonal matrices in $(2r + 1)$ dimensions, with $p = r(2r + 1)$

C_r – the algebras of symplectic orthogonal matrices in 2r dimensions, $p = r(2r + 1)$

(These are orthogonal matrices leaving invariant an anti-symmetric scalar product)

D_r – the algebras of orthogonal matrices in 2r dimensions, $p = r(2r - 1)$

and five "isolated" (or "exceptional") algebras G_2, F_4, E_6, E_7, E_8; $p(G_2) = 14$, $p(F_4) = 52$, $p(E_6) = 78$, $p(E_7) = 133$, $p(E_8) = 248$.

Following are the π-schemata. These represent instructions for the construction of a root diagram, with one set of linearly independent raising operators as a basis. Each circle is one such raising operator; a single line 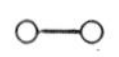 implies an angle of 120° (such as between I^+ and U^+ in A_2, the algebra of SU(3)). A double line  indicates an angle of 135°; and a triple line  represents 150°. Two circles without a direct linking by one of these three are at 90° to each other. The letter under the circle represents a scale for the square of the length; the number shows the order of appearance of additional raising operators with increasing dimensionality; e.g., for D_2 we take 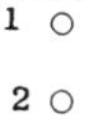, for D_3 it is 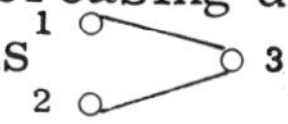, etc.

A_r

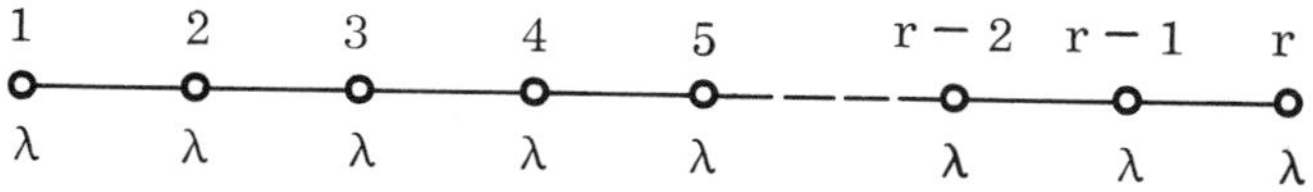

B_r

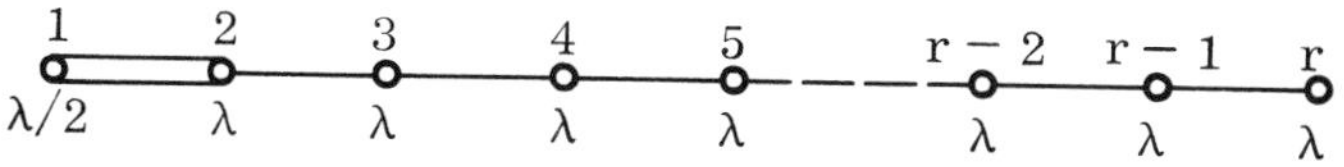

C_r

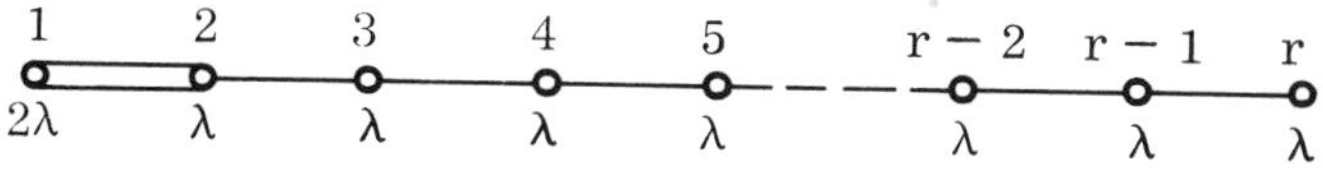

D_r

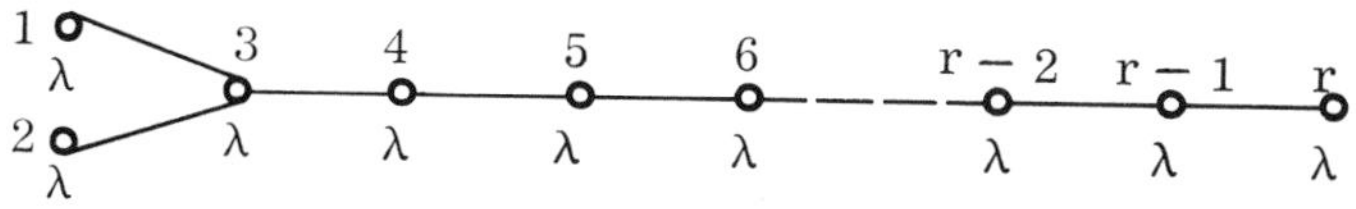

G_2

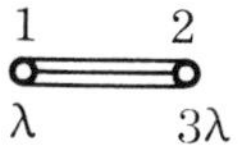

F_4

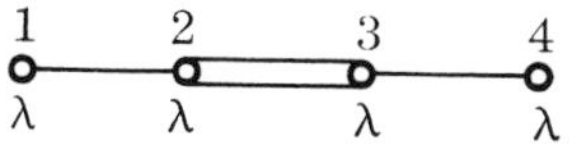

E_6

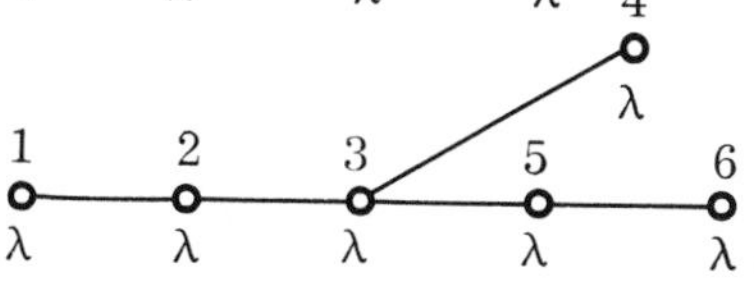

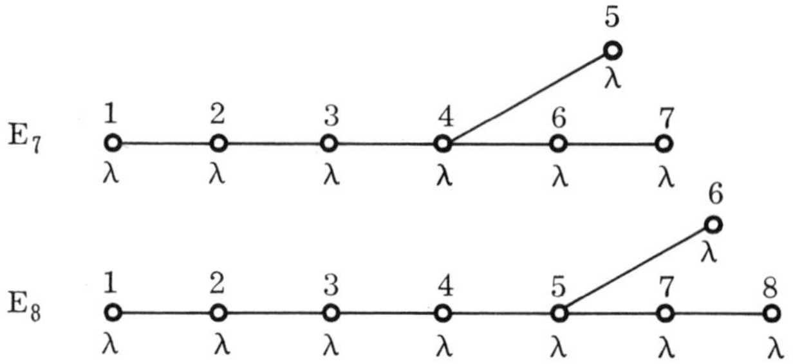

After construction of the basis from these instructions, one has to complete the root diagram by taking all combinations of the form ($\mathbf{a}$, $\mathbf{b}$ are roots which are already known, i.e., first the basis vectors and then all others),

$$\mathbf{a} + \ell_{ab}\mathbf{b}, \quad q_{ab} \leq \ell_{ab} \leq q^1_{ab}, \quad \ell \text{ an integer}$$

such that

$$\frac{2(\mathbf{a}, \mathbf{b})}{(\mathbf{a}, \mathbf{a})} = -(q_{ab} + q^1_{ab}); \quad q \leq 0, \; q^1 \geq 0.$$

where $(\mathbf{a}, \mathbf{b})$ is the scalar product.

The A_r generate by exponentiation the compact SU(r + 1), U(r + 1), SU(r + 1)/Z(r + 1) and the noncompact GL(r + 1), SL(r + 1, C), SL(r + 1, R), $SU(n, m)_{n+m=r+1}$

The B_r generate the compact SO(2r + 1, R) and the noncompact 0(2r + 1) or SO(2r + 1, C) and $SO(n, m)_{n+m=2r+1}$, i.e., the various Lorentz groups.

The C_r generate the compact USp(2r) and the noncompact Sp(2r, C) or Sp(2r, R), etc.

For D_r, replace 2r + 1 by 2r in B_r.

U stands for "unitary," L represents unimodularity (det = 1), GL is general linear, R is real, C is complex.

To study the representation theory, see H. Boerner, "Representations of Groups," North-Holland Pub. Co., Amsterdam, 1963.

E. B. Dynkin, *American Math. Soc. Translations*, Series 1, **9**, 328 (revised 1962); Series 2, **6**, 111 and 245 (1960).

G. Racah, *Springer Tracts in Modern Physics*, **37** (1964).

For the non-compact groups, use

I. M. Gel'fand and M. A. Naĭmark, "Unitäre Darstellungen der Klassischen Gruppen," Akademie-Verlag, Berlin (East), 1957.

S. Helgason, "Differential Geometry and Symmetric Spaces," Academic Press, New York, 1962.

INDEX